MIND OVER MATTER

How To Build The
Ultimate Dieting Mindset

Daniel Harrod

Mind Over Matter: How To Build The Ultimate Dieting Mindset by Daniel Harrod

Published by Daniel Harrod

www.danielharrod.com

Print ISBN: 978-1-7392297-0-2
eBook ISBN: 978-1-7392297-1-9

Printed in United Kingdom

1st Edition

CONTENTS

INTRODUCTION

Imagine for a moment – for no other reason than because I'm a nice guy – that I give you a free milkshake. It tastes delicious. Labelled '*Indulgence*', its thick, frosty blend is irresistibly gratifying. The fact I inform you that it contains 620 calories does little to assuage its decadent taste – although you are slightly troubled it doesn't align with your latest New Year's resolution. You leave feeling rather full and satisfied, all the same.

A week later, I give you another free milkshake. This one is labelled '*Sensi-Shake*', described as a low-fat option containing only 140 calories. This time, I'm not so nice, apparently. The second, 'light and healthy' milkshake isn't terrible but doesn't leave you feeling half as full, or satisfied. You do leave, however, content in the knowledge that you've extorted me for two free milkshakes.

The following day, I give you a call, informing you that – having measured your physiological responses to consuming each beverage – the 620-calorie, indulgent shake reduced your appetite. Your body said, "Hey, let's stop; you're stuffed". You're not surprised; it was delicious *and* filling.

I also reveal, on the other hand, that your satiety levels were *markedly lower* after consuming the 140-calorie, sensible shake. You weren't as physiologically satisfied on finishing the lighter, 'healthier' drink. You're not surprised, either. You're convinced that anything nutritious, containing fewer calories will inevitably leave you more famished. It makes sense.

Now, here's the kicker. I then explain that each milkshake actually contained exactly the *same* number of calories – 380 to be precise. There was no glaring difference in each milkshake's energy supply. You're shocked – confused, even. And don't feel quite as overjoyed, now, with having fleeced me for two free milkshakes.

I can only apologise for my unwarranted act of deception.

Your chagrin quickly gets the better of you, despite my compelling apology. You have questions. Why is it you would feel more satiated with one of the milkshakes, despite both containing the same number of calories? Why would drinking an 'indulgent' shake create more physiological differences in you than a 'healthy' shake? Why would your mind play such devilish tricks?

This is exactly what researchers at Yale and Arizona State University in America discovered when they performed this study on a group of milkshake-loving participants.[1] Ghrelin levels (ghrelin being a hormone that increases appetite) were found to be as much as three times *lower* in those who consumed – or at least they thought they had consumed – the shake loaded with sugar, fat, and calories. In other words, they felt more satiated due to the perception that the 'indulgent' shake would fill them up. When participants drank the 0-per cent fat, 0-added sugar, 'sensible' shake, they were, however, still left feeling hungry. It was each subject's perception of whether the shake was healthy or not, calorific or not, and guilt-free or not that regulated their response to what they were consuming. They ended up feeling more satiated when they *believed* they were drinking a higher calorie beverage.

Simply put, what subjects were told – and what they subsequently believed – determined both psychological and physiological outcomes. Their perceptions, assumptions, and judgements altered their body's behaviour, in that they felt full or not so full. No longer was their entire disposition shaped only by their actions and environment, but, also, by their mind. Wherever they placed their thoughts and attention, their body then followed. It appears that their mindset influenced reality.

Mind Over Matter

It's no secret that the health and fitness industry is littered with timeworn clichés and overused motivational quotes. Rather like an infectious disease, these can permeate the minds and beliefs of you, me, and anyone else who enjoys a free milkshake. Internet articles, memes, and social media posts can alter how we view well-being, exercise, and nutrition. We can't easily escape them. Unfortunately, many of these statements are worthless – and at worse, harmful. From *"No pain, no gain"*, to *"Sweat is your fat crying"*, and *"Nothing tastes as good as skinny feels"*, such hackneyed expressions can cripple people's expectations and actions. If we indulge in what may amount only to fashionable foolishness, it can eventually lead us down a path of hope, despair, and – ultimately – failure.

There is one deep-rooted maxim, however, that's always piqued my interest. One that perhaps holds more relevance and purpose than all the others combined:

"Mind over matter"

Uttered everywhere – from the gym to extreme sports, and from a work setting to offering the courage to force down a spoonful of cottage cheese – those three words have always intrigued me. Can the way we view a situation really dictate reality? Can discreet nudges from our brain change our existence? Do our thoughts, beliefs, and expectations influence psychological, behavioural, and physiological outcomes? Is it really mind over matter?

Research would say, "Yes". It's why the study participants' hunger levels dropped and metabolism increased when they perceived their indulgent milkshake to contain more sugar, fat, and calories than it actually did. It's why students who believe they can change their IQ score better on test results.[2] It's why cyclists record quicker race times when they believe they're racing an imaginary, faster version of themselves.[3] It's why individuals prefer the taste of Coca-Cola when it's consumed from a brand-labelled cup.[4] And it's why older people who hold more positive perceptions of ageing live longer.[5] The mind's ubiquitous impact is more telling than we ever thought. Our mindset truly matters.

It is the mental frame that we use to define certain situations that allows us to make sense of the world.[6] This enables us to understand a particular experience and respond accordingly – it's the foundation of everything we do. Will we throw the towel in, or persevere, when we fail at a task? Will the beliefs we've crafted from an early age influence our actions later in life? Will our attitude towards a situation take us closer to – or further away from – any goals we have? Will we eat that cottage cheese, or not? It's clear that the type of mindset we adopt towards a given situation will influence our behaviours and reactions.

There is an argument to say that sustainable transformation happens from the inside out. That is, by increasing awareness of our beliefs, attitudes, values, and reactions, we can change how we lead our lives. This is not just concerning our physical behaviours, habits, and actions. Enabling ourselves to champion the right 'frame of mind' allows us to succeed in numerous aspects of our lives. As it's evident our psychological – and not just physiological – limits could be the deciding factor in breaking through resolute performance ceilings, those who ignore their 'mindset' perhaps sidestep mastery, sustained effort, and goal achievement – along with the opportunity to experience greater accomplishments, overall.

We know our mindset plays a prominent role in business, academia, sport, and relationships.[7] Those with superior mentalities in their fields experience improved outcomes. They possess greater motivation and implement behavioural changes swiftly and with ease. They are proficient at dealing with failure, whilst often reaching their goals with fewer distractions. A prevailing mindset is a powerful cog in the achievement machine. It's why we respect those who display qualities such as resilience, optimism, passion, and ownership. We admire entrepreneurs who have turned businesses around, athletes who've reached the pinnacle of their sport having surfaced from nothing, and our friend who meets the love of their life having always struggled to find the right partner. We laud those who display superior mental – not just physical – competence.

It's time, therefore, to turn our attention away from these celebrated disciplines of business, sport, and love and focus on one that holds even more significance for many. One that we've all likely tried – and likely failed with – at some point. One we all wish we'd eventually triumph over.

The elusive – and often demanding – art of dieting.

If we're able to cultivate such a celebrated mindset in other aspects of our lives, then it's time to ask if we can implement this line of thinking in the world of dieting as well. Is it a case of mind over matter with eating well? With exercise? With weight loss? Do our thoughts, beliefs, and expectations influence the outcomes of a successful fat loss journey? Do factors like our ability to deal with failure, our values, or even our success dictate our destination? We possess the knowledge to assemble the ultimate mindset in other domains; can we craft the ultimate dieting mindset, too?

The Problem: You Know What To Do, So Why Aren't You Doing It?

The chances are you know what to eat more of. You know what to eat less of. You are aware that fruit, vegetables, and protein-rich dishes should be encouraged, and highly processed, calorie-loaded takeaways should be minimised. You also know that devouring sweet-smelling chocolate cookies for breakfast isn't going to cut it; that you should probably prioritise nutrient-rich foods at every meal, instead. You likely *know* all of this. And yet, I'm assuming you start every fat loss journey with unrivalled enthusiasm and vigour but wind up a week later with your arms elbow-deep in the biscuit tin and your fingers frantically tapping their way through food delivery apps.

You know that hitting the gym is going to be to your benefit. And that being as active as possible will help craft a leaner physique, whilst staying sedentary can only harm your chances of halting that ever-expanding waistline. You *know* this. And yet, I'll take a guess you still find yourself on the sofa, gawking at another episode on Netflix – not to mention continually taking the lift, instead of the stairs.

You still favour the 'I'll do it tomorrow' approach, over the 'Let's start now' attitude. You still sit back at the end of each day, fed up, and think, 'I guess I'll have to start again'. You still manage, nonetheless, to stumble upon another neatly packaged – and overpriced – diet and think, 'This looks exciting; maybe I'll give it a go'. You know you shouldn't chase perfection, you know you shouldn't succumb to feelings of failure, and you know the number on the scales shouldn't influence your emotions. And yet, you're still cemented in this ceaseless state of mind. You just can't sustain that grip on your nutrition, exercise, and lifestyle. On the off chance you do succeed, that progress made feels no more than a fleeting moment of triumph. But, why? Why is it so hard? Why do you know what to do yet can't seem to actually do it?

Because we're looking down the wrong path.

Instead of fretting over macronutrient targets, and when to consume your first and last meal of the day; as well as what gym programme to follow, and whether or not quinoa and kale burgers are a good protein source, it's time to dig deeper. It's time to accept that we do know what we *should* be doing but need to figure out *how* to do it effectively, instead. It's time to ignore the physical, and to focus on the mental. It's time to swallow our pride and admit that all we've been doing before hasn't worked. If it had, we wouldn't still be having the same discussion, over and over again. Perhaps it's not just a case of 'eating less and moving more', but, instead, 'hoping less and thinking better'.

Having coached people through numerous, challenging weight loss journeys, having plunged deep into the dieting research, and, above all, listened to people just like you, it's evident there's a big, bright component of the weight loss adventure that we're overlooking. A component that holds more prestige than we like to give it; something that wields more power than banishing carbs, cajoling our ketones, or spending our hard-earned money on apple cider vinegar.

Our mindset.

We need to supplement the physiology with the psychology. It's time to unearth and reassemble the shattered fragments of our current dieting mentality and champion a fresh, results-driven approach to weight loss. When you've learned to take control of your mindset, you'll open up a new world of possibilities as to how you view your dieting venture. You'll change how you view your relationship with food, with your body, and with exercise. You'll craft new perceptions and expectations surrounding your ability to lose weight. You'll understand what it's like to fail and still come out on top, along with how to use the perils of social comparison to your benefit – and how to exhibit greater acceptance and control over your decision-making. Finally, you'll learn how to experience true, long-lasting change.

This book has collated the struggles, toils, and mental battles of those wanting to lose weight and constructed a proven blueprint to overcome them. The following pages will not only explain how your current cognitive processes have been affecting your ability to succeed, but also provide you with the solutions to combat such familiar problems. I'll set you up with the necessary tools to abandon the traditional dieting frame of mind and enable you to craft a fresh, resilient, and improved one.

Together, we'll discover what footballer Cristiano Ronaldo can teach us about our current mindset, why the lessons learnt from a 1792-mile swim around Great Britain hold more significance than we realise, why hailing a taxi on a rainy day mirrors our flawed goal setting approach, and why the mentality of a promising young actor who completely lost his sight will teach us more than any 30-day detox could. We'll examine everything from identities, to motivation, to willpower, to failure, to goal setting, to the art of control and acceptance. We'll overhaul everything we currently know about the weight loss world, exploring it all from a different perspective. From the very outset, we'll recognise that our mindset is the key to unlocking the essential mechanisms of behaviour change. We'll realise that it really is, "Mind over matter".

Who Am I To Help You?

I've never been fat. I've never been on a diet, nor had to start that same diet again on a Monday. I've never decided to lose weight, nor had to drop a jean size (or four). Damn, the closest I've ever come to losing weight was ditching a pair of shoes from my suitcase when they failed to meet the airline baggage allowance, on a trip to Thailand.

What am I doing then, writing a book on crafting the ultimate dieting mindset? How can a guy like me, whose only struggles with food have been deciding whether to order a burger or pizza (and not worry about putting on a pound, let alone ten) teach anyone else how to conquer their dieting demons? How can someone like me, whose biggest struggle in the gym has been navigating a packed weight room (let alone actually getting to the gym), demonstrate how to establish an unequalled and untouchable mindset? How can I, of all people, tell you what to do?

Because I get it.

Having helped thousands of clients, in my line of work as a personal trainer and online coach, I know. I have voluntarily surrounded myself with an endless stream of people who are constantly struggling with their eating, exercise, and bodies. I have dedicated my career to helping, understanding, and guiding those very same people.

I am mindful of the prevalent cycle of ambitions, frustrations, and struggles people endure. The burning desire to succeed whilst never being quite able to reach the podium. The longing to prove to yourself you can do it, yet never quite prevailing. The taking of two steps forward, whilst swiftly experiencing the debilitating, self-sabotage whenever things do somehow start to lean in the right direction. The persistent troubles with staying on track long enough to notice – and hold onto – results. And the inexplicable reason you always choose the 'Cinnabon Frosting-Filled Cinnapastry', instead of the simple, humble – but nutritionally impeccable – banana.

While I may be fortunate to never experience what it's like to face the loathsome, dieting demons many of you will encounter, you can trust me to provide you with the pertinent information and a plan to craft the ultimate dieting mindset. As part of this, I'll use experiences from clients who've shared the same frustrations as you. Evidence from robust scientific research. Lessons from stories all over the world. I have had the privilege to listen to the avalanche of difficulties, barriers, and psychological conflicts that a host of dieters have approached me with. While I've never had to diet, personally – although I, too, have admittedly found myself devouring my thirteenth biscuit-in-quick-succession and become imbued with the persuasive inclination to miss the gym on occasion – I'll continue to do my best to appreciate what it's like for people just like you.

This *Is* A Dieting Book

There's been great furore surrounding the diet industry in recent years. The notion that 'Diets don't work',[8] and you can, indeed, be 'Healthy at every size'. While that pendulum continues to oscillate from one side to the other – suggesting benefits to both sides of the argument – this book *is* aimed at people wanting to lose weight. It's targeted at those who want to lose body fat, get leaner, and cultivate increased body satisfaction with how they look. This *is* a dieting book.

Dieting interventions *do* work.[9,10] It's clear, however, that the way society views – and enacts – weight loss needs upgrading. For most, it's a damaged endeavour that has led to years of yo-yo dieting, unhappy relationships with food and bodies, and – ultimately – misery.[11] When people diet with a rigid, quick-fix, goal-driven mentality, then failure will inevitably surface. Some even end up gaining more weight.[12] I suspect you've experienced it yourself or, at least, witnessed it happen to others.

It's not my intention to criticise anyone for their previous dieting attempts. My interest solely lies in upgrading your mindset to avoid the problems those uncompromising diets lead to. We'll bypass the host of troubles conventional dieting presents and take on a new, powerful approach to losing weight successfully. I believe there's room for intuitive eating[13] and mindful decision-making, just like there's room for flexible dieting[14] and adopting a skills-based eating approach. It's not necessarily how you get there; it's about getting and ensuring you *stay* there in the first place. We need to stop fighting a battle that only heightens the confusion.

While the industry as a whole requires remodelling, we can't escape the fact that weight loss can not only significantly improve a variety of health markers[15,16,17] but, when executed in the right manner, also leads to improved confidence, sharpened resilience, upgraded patience, and empowers a greater foundation for tackling life's problems. While, admittedly, weight loss isn't *always* synonymous with 'health', I believe there's nothing wrong with wanting to diet. The endeavour – when executed correctly, at the right time, and for the right reasons – cultivates helpful character traits and brings valuable experiences. Weight loss *can* change lives. If you want abs, I believe you should set out to get them. If you want to feel self-assured flaunting a bikini, I encourage you to reach that position of confidence. If you want to diet, I believe you should undertake such an endeavour with a sense of freedom and enthusiasm.

To achieve this, however, we need to ditch the archaic methods that have plagued the industry for years – the crash diets, the cleanses, the rebounds – and build a foundation from which we can succeed. No longer should we slash calories, pound the treadmill, and assume everyone requires the same eating guidelines, as we attempt to white-knuckle the fat off. Nor should we trouble ourselves with feelings of embarrassment, guilt, or shame, in order to drop a pound or two. Those are flawed approaches. We need something new.

The physiological components of losing body fat still matter – and shouldn't be ignored – but setting up an indomitable mindset will add another tool to your dieting arsenal. Whilst changing your mindset is, of course, not a panacea, correctly shaping it will allow you to succeed for years to come – and not just for six weeks of the year. By positioning your frame of mind in an optimal place to start losing weight – and continue to do so – you'll beat the notion that diets don't work. We won't delve into the complexities of calories, macronutrients, and specific dieting interventions, but everything we shall pore over will enable you to flick a switch inside, and view losing weight in a completely different way. This is a book about your mindset. This is a dieting book.

A Note On The Words I Use

In this book, I'll talk about being 'fat'. About being 'thinner', or 'leaner', or 'healthier'. Plus, 'successful' physiques and potentially looking 'better'. This will risk causing offence, no doubt – for which I apologise. I am all too aware of the harmful, and often unwarranted stigma, surrounding dieting, obesity, and individuals carrying high levels of fat on their bodies.[18] I am also cognisant, however, of the evidence to show that having a body that's carrying extra fat shouldn't always be viewed as a negative. I discuss these terms and situations in this book only from the position that our aim *is* to lose weight.

None of the words I use are intended to add to any insinuations about what individual weight gain means. I would never set out with the purpose of disgracing anyone in this context, or judging that they should somehow be changed for the betterment of the world. If you've picked up this book, I believe it's because you *want* to lose weight, and arrive from an already steady footing of satisfaction and health with food, exercise, and your body. My advice will be provided in that context. Similarly, I don't mean to compound any detrimental classification of 'overweight' or 'obese' bodies. The size or shape of a body has no bearing on who someone is as a person. I don't think that thin people are in any way 'better', or 'more deserving', nor 'more disciplined'. I also don't believe there's a physical, societal standard or norm that we should all strive for. While I'm mindful of the argument against promoting weight loss – and simultaneously taking a stance against weight stigma – my job here is merely to unfold the inner workings of that ultimate, dieting mindset.

In this book, I'll also intimate that salads, healthy meals, and going to the gym lead to weight loss, whilst implying that cookies, burgers, and avoiding the gym contribute to weight gain. This, again, is all done in the context of the book. I don't believe that consistently favouring one over the other is the solution to conquering any obesity epidemic, nor the inherent reasons that people struggle with their weight. Such dichotomous, 'good or bad', 'clean or dirty', thinking has been found to lead to weight regain, decreased well-being, and eating disorders, after all.[19] I'm aware that my using this vocabulary could risk intensifying these thoughts, but only include them to demonstrate points and aid the book's flow and understanding. They should not be allowed to shape your views around what might exclusively lead to fat loss or fat gain. Believe it or not, eating a cookie *won't* make you fat.

As you read on, you'll see that I use the phrases, 'fat loss' and 'weight loss'. They'll be used interchangeably. While I appreciate they are explicitly defined as different things – with the real goal, for most, of fat loss instead of weight loss – they are referred to similarly, in this book, for ease of reading. Most people's goal, when dieting, should be reducing the amount of body fat they hold while preserving muscle mass, not hacking away at the number glaring back at them on the scales. To me, the term 'weight loss' implies 'fat loss'. Language is important – especially in the world of dieting and weight loss – and, while I'm aware how I use it in the following chapters doesn't always aid our cause, it would be confusing to change it completely.

It would also be remiss of me if I didn't mention the range of underlying factors that create a volatile and sometimes insurmountable environment to lose weight successfully. While the 'try harder' and, 'you don't want it enough' brigades may continue to spout baseless clichés, in return for instant dopamine hits on their social media platforms, they possibly disregard the multitude of factors at play surrounding weight loss. Genetics, inequality, poverty, eating disorders, trauma, mental health, the environment, fat-shaming, and stigma, amongst others, all create lofty and intimidating obstacles. For many individuals, it really *is* that hard.

As Anthony Warner, in his book, *The Truth About Fat,* says, "Certainly the factors that create an obesogenic environment are many and varied, and not always a matter of personal choice. They are interconnected, pushing and pulling at each other in different ways, perhaps only having a noticeable effect in combination."[20] Shoving someone onto a cookie-cutter, low-calorie diet, and berating them for succumbing to the occasional chocolate bar is detrimental to the industry as a whole. Seldom do the common, 'knuckle-down' endeavours we're accustomed to actually succeed; which isn't quite the same as saying it *isn't possible* to succeed with them.

Simply acknowledging the host of concealed circumstances at play will place you in a better position to triumph – instead of blaming yourself when you fail. Some people may have limited opportunities, wealth, or freedom to diet, but they can still experience positive, bodily change. No matter these kinds of circumstances, your mindset continues to matter. Even if just to make marginal improvements in your physique, this book will provide guidance on how to conquer an unhealthy and injurious mindset, whilst simultaneously acknowledging any potential obstacles. As we've established, your perception of a situation can matter more than the situation itself.

It's worth adding that in avoiding the 'just try harder' mindset, I'm not overlooking the necessity to work hard, period. The cliché of 'nothing worth having comes easy' still holds strong. Expecting a new physique, or abs, to just fall into your lap – or stomach – won't earn you the results you deserve. Solely playing the 'blame game', because the introduction of a dieting book said your genetics and socioeconomic background will hurt your chances of even making a one-per cent improvement in your physique and health, is just as detrimental as not trying at all.

In this book, I will talk about taking responsibility for your actions – and taking control of situations. I'll describe how you can charm your own discipline, and how we possess the power to change. It's important to remember, however, that these are all discussed with the understanding that not every part of people's weight loss journey automatically leans in their favour.

Mind Over Matter: How To Build The Ultimate Dieting Mindset

Legend has it that the American Psychological Association once invited revered psychologist and philosopher, William James, to give a talk on the first 50 years of psychology research. James, upon arriving, got up, looked out into the audience, and said, *"People by and large become what they think of themselves."*

Then he left.

I firmly believe that, by conquering our state of mind, we'll be at least one small step closer to successfully changing our bodies for good. I'm not talking about healing cancer, nor helping people jump out of wheelchairs; but we'll enhance our chances of success by reshaping our thoughts and transforming any obsolete views on dieting. We will become what we think of ourselves.

Crafting the ultimate dieting mindset will dictate how we view our bodies, as well as our relationship with food, and our weight loss journey. This, in turn, will influence our actions. By appreciating how everything – from our identity, to our view on procrastination, to a growth mindset, to our perception of self-control – affects our ability to succeed, we'll be able to chip away at an endeavour that has frequently caused us countless difficulties. We'll choose how to interpret reality. We'll determine what different circumstances mean to us. We'll appreciate how different narratives hold varying powers. And we'll, subsequently, find losing weight a whole lot easier.

Whilst I don't, unfortunately, hold all the answers, funnily enough, neither does 'Big Biceps Dave' at the gym, or 'Superfood Sarah' from the office. Anyone who says they do is lying. Pointing the finger solely at carbs, sugar, insulin, genetics, money, or that extra 'Pumpkin Spice Latte' you snuck in at lunch, is never going to work. There is no *one* solution. But stepping back, ignoring these delicate rationalisations, and focusing on your mindset, will place you in a better position from the outset.

When it comes to dieting, people tend to crave rules. They usually want to know what 'fat' foods to avoid and what 'fat-burning' foods to eat. What exercise programmes to follow and what exercise classes to avoid. What supplements to take, and what hacks they can implement. These are all absolute and actionable strategies. Yet, as we know, are only setting us up for failure. By contrast, changing our mindset assumes a more enigmatic approach. There are no hard or fast rules. Things are less defined. You must do the work yourself, discovering what does and doesn't work for you. It is imperative you take the time to practice changing your thoughts, beliefs, and perceptions. It's not nearly as straightforward as copying a food regime you swiped from a health magazine. Yet, it is more beneficial than you could ever imagine.

The pages that follow will not afford you a meal plan, nor any step-by-step instructions on the physiology behind dropping weight. They will, however, illuminate a previously concealed landscape on which you can execute your own course of action, as per your personal needs.

I implore you to use this book wisely. Take every piece of information provided and – crucially – apply it to your life. Plenty of reading, nodding, and smiling will get you nowhere without following up with definite action. Take notes as you read. Create space to think. Journal thoughts, memories, and reactions. Allocate time to answer the questions at the end of each chapter, and to practice what you've gleaned from the preceding pages. If reading without implementing is what you've always done, why would you assume you'll make changes this time?

The swathe of books that sit, currently, in the dieting world are lacking something. If the tactics of 28-day juice cleanses and low-carb meal plans worked long-term, everyone at work wouldn't be undertaking their seventh diet of the year come May – again. It is vital, therefore, that we pore over the assembly of a successful diet from a fresh, psychological angle. How can we construct an innovative method of dieting that's resilient and resourceful enough to combat all the obstacles thrown its way? How can we ensure we successfully lose weight *without* worrying about the type of foods we eat? This book argues that the answers arrive by understanding our psychological selves and – subsequently – building the ultimate dieting mindset.

CHAPTER 1
Who Are You:
How To Build A New Identity

During my time at university, I had a friend who was on more diets than I had hangovers. Every semester, a new diet-book was plonked onto our living room table, accompanied with an army of rules and – often – a novel, kitchen utensil. We'd often hear her say:

"Please don't eat pasta in front of me; I'm not allowed carbs."

"I won't be eating with you today; I'm on the 'two' of my 'five : two'."

"Damn, I couldn't get my seaweed-and-tempeh-infused sauerkraut in the shop this week."

These requests may well have aided my propensity for the perennial hangover.

Don't get me wrong, though; my friend did lose weight. Sometimes a lot of weight. To which she would often be greeted with a flurry of Facebook 'likes' and a new dress to grace the student nightclubs. For every successful dieting endeavour that took place, however, the inevitable crash would then follow – with an almighty bang. A new term would start, and a new figure would appear, often larger than the one that preceded it. No matter how hard she tried – no matter how much energy and time she invested in the cause – she couldn't shift that weight for longer than a few months.

Knowing what I know now, I understand how these quick-fix, unsustainable diets were never going to work. Failing to account for my friend's desire for the occasional pizza, along with her hectic, university work schedule, and her student-like activity levels, each diet brought her more problems than solutions. Who knew that forcing down daikon and kombucha smoothies wouldn't quite cut it? These blanket diets failed my friend. And they are likely to continue to fail others, too.

Granted the use of a time machine, I'd use it to return to my university days and set about changing everything surrounding my friend's dieting efforts. From her long-held, 'Carbs are bad for you' beliefs, to her abstruse and harmful methods of creating an energy deficit, her sporadic approaches to losing weight were flawed. She needed help. There's one aspect of her venture, however, that I would reshape before anything else. Before the calorie and macronutrient targets and the food preferences; before the eating skills, activity levels, specific habits, and overarching goals. It didn't matter to me at the time but, looking back, my friend had one protuberant trait that surfaced daily: her habit of uttering negative affirmations.

"God, I look so fat in this dress."

"I don't have the discipline to say 'no' to the snacks, like you do."

"Ugh, I've always hated exercising."

"Sure, pick on the fat one."

Those assertions would surreptitiously seep into our conversations almost every day. It was those prominent narratives my friend consigned herself to that were more damaging than any low-carb, macrobiotic, crash-diet she ever attempted. The stories she soaked herself in formed a belief system that was more formidable than any attempt at yet another futile, dieting technique. Those reflections, stories, and comments slotted together perfectly – like a children's puzzle – to form her *identity.* And it's this – your identity – that bears the weight of any successful transformation. *Who* you are matters.

The type of person you want to become, and imagine you can become, is more influential than any diet would have you believe. Your identity holds the golden key to behaviour change. Unearthing, and understanding that individual identity is, therefore, the first task anyone must face and work with, to build a successful dieting mindset. It's where we'll start our journey.

What Is Your Identity?

Identities are the traits, characteristics, social relationships, goals, and values that define who we are.[1] They steer us to make certain choices, providing an interpretative lens in which we can make sense of situations, and act accordingly. With this approach, you're impelled to work towards a future you believe you can attain. You're motivated to act in ways that feel *identity congruent.*[2] Play football and tennis every week and you'll perceive yourself as 'athletic'. Go out clubbing every weekend and you'll view yourself as a 'party-goer'. Wake up before everyone else every day and you'll see yourself as an 'early riser'. Regularly tell yourself you're the 'fat one,' and – guess what – you'll perceive yourself as 'fat'.

Your identity is a core part of your life. It forms a viscous lava around your personality and determines the knowledge and understanding you possess about yourself. It distinguishes you from others and dictates what you find important in your life. You transport these narratives around with you, just like the phone in your pocket, and define yourself by them – much like the hairstyle you display. Repeat these loquacious concepts to yourself – again and again – and you will find ways to embody what they represent. This is why people who believe they hold the identity of an 'exerciser' are more likely to increase exercise frequency in the future,[3] and why individuals who undertake a process of 'reinvention' – an identity shift – are more likely to sustain their weight loss.[4]

It's no coincidence that my friend – the one who declared she looked fat in whatever she wore, and who frequently stated she'd always hated exercise – simply couldn't obtain, and keep hold of, that slimmer physique she wanted. She didn't possess the identity of someone who could live a life with the body that she desired.

How have we arrived at a current identity, then? This is accomplished through your beliefs, thoughts, words, and emotions, all conspiring to form an almighty, all-conquering team. If you choose to take on the task of reinventing your identity, that same process occurs, but in a way that lets you steer yourself, consciously, along a more positive and empowered course.

When these aspects unite and work together, from this new identity, you form an immovable mindset, along with a daily existence that guides you closer to who you want to be. This might include living a healthy lifestyle and showcasing the physique you want, for example. On the opposite side, persisting with an identity that may be unconsciously driving negative narratives means those facets unite to work *against* you. You're escorted to undesirable situations – living an unhealthy lifestyle and revealing a physique you don't want, for example. Previous experiences and your perception of those moments tend to entwine to form your character, too.

Despite your sense of self potentially working *for* or *against* you, this all still equates to promising news. It means that you're able to change your beliefs, thoughts, words, and emotions, to support long-term ambitions. While difficult – the longer you attach yourself to a perceived existence, the more you accept it as fact – it is possible to elevate and reshape who you are. You have the facility to uproot any components of yourself that don't support your aspirations, and reshape them to reinforce the type of person you wish to be.

Author, Jen Sincero, compares our identity to that of a bus journey.[5] Your beliefs are the bus. Once seated, these beliefs – the acceptance that something is true – take you to where you're going, whether you like it or not. Your internal model of the world steers you towards achieving certain goals.[6] As most of us don't like feeling we are wrong, we will seek out information that's relevant to our own interests, goals, and desires. This is why your mind will twist experiences, to align with how you process and interpret new information. The beliefs you hold are a source of value in and of themselves, such that you're motivated to hold particular conclusions, regardless of whether those theories are true or false.[7]

You aren't born with assumptions about being overweight; you learn those from the environment around you, through the messages received from others, and the experiences you undergo. You might learn that being overweight is associated with laziness; that it's an unattractive trait, rather than a desirable one. Or perhaps you hear that *you're* lazy and unattractive. You then also discover, quite quickly, that dieting is meant to be a painful experience, only achieved through punishment and hardship. And that slaving away at the gym and starving your body equates to an acclaimed physique; that people receive nice compliments when they've lost a couple of pounds. You may, unfortunately, lack access to additional life experiences to support other hypotheses; in which case you sometimes let those detrimental beliefs – that 'bus' – dictate your weight loss journey.

Whether any of the overhead ideas are true or not, you absorb that information and there it remains in your subconscious, prodding at your belief system with every decision you make. You now believe dieting is reserved for those with unrivalled motivation; you, subsequently, blame yourself for giving in to the odd biscuit.[8] You may also believe that dieting is associated with beauty and, consequently, assume that you're not a 'beautiful' person if you're not losing weight.[9] While some beliefs you possess can propel you towards any weight loss goals you have, other limiting ideas will curb your progress. Understanding the difference between the two will, however, enable you to disregard self-limiting beliefs and cultivate a favourable belief system – and related identity – instead.

Your thoughts are the bus driver. A strong and forceful person, who's able to slow down, speed up, and change direction with the turn of a hand or push of a foot. The driver is able to transport you to where you want to go, but equally able to steer you off course, too. The long-held beliefs you possess about weight loss transpire into thoughts. These mental cognitions are powerful and bring perspective to a situation or experience that colours your point of view. They're what you're used to. If you believe you're fat, you *think* it's impossible to lose weight. If you believe you're lazy, you *think* a leaner physique isn't intended for people like you. If you believe junk food equates to fat gain, you *think* you enjoy food too much to warrant a slimmer frame. Your thoughts dictate the direction you're going.

Unfortunately, the majority of these thoughts are so deeply ingrained in your psyche that they arrive at your brain's consciousness on autopilot. This is why, no matter how much weight you may have lost, you may have tended to always think of yourself as too fat, overweight, or unattractive. It would also be the root cause as to why, no matter how much motivation you believed you possessed, you would perhaps experience temptations and cravings. Those viewpoints would be continually whirring inside your mind, convincing you of things that often didn't add up.

Your words are the ticket inspector. This individual assists the bus driver. The words you charge yourself with will support your thoughts, awarding them a voice and underlining their significance. They help to lodge your identity deep inside you, meaning it becomes incredibly hard to remove, and change it. Every time you tell yourself you're 'lazy' for missing the gym, you reinforce that judgement. Every time you outwardly chastise yourself for lacking motivation, you become the person who lacks motivation. On each occasion you call yourself a 'moron' for choosing the cake over the fruit, you believe you're a moron. Words are influential and persuasive. Although you may not realise it, everything you tell yourself – and others about yourself – embeds itself deeper into the person you believe you are. Unless utilised effectively, that inner voice – complete with its 'ticket inspector' chatter – will lead to doubt, uncertainty, and failure.

Your emotions are the petrol that keeps the bus moving. You can't see it; you just know it's there. Our emotions are incredibly effective, often guiding our identity without us being aware of that identity's existence. Notice how, when you're feeling sad, you suddenly find yourself next to an empty pack of Jaffa Cakes without quite understanding how such an incident happened? Or your friend annoys you and you take your frustrations out on the cheesecake that's sitting in the fridge? Your emotions fuel actions. They bulldoze their way through your mind and compel you to enact weird and wonderful decisions.

These emotions are controlled by your beliefs, thoughts, and words. They create an identity that, at times, doesn't make sense. You want to lose weight, yet have a hard time making good choices when you're stressed or tired. On the occasions when you feel upbeat, those same decisions become a lot easier to make. Your emotions are patiently waiting to materialise but can only do so when given the green light from other members of the team.

Finally, your actions are the road that the bus travels on. They're already mapped out, but accessibility to them depends on where you want to go. When the bus, its driver, the ticket inspector, and the bus's fuel cooperate, the route is a smooth one. Your actions take you where you want to go. You go to the gym, you choose the salad at lunch, and say 'no' to a post-dinner drink. Your identity is helpful. When those facets of your mind are misaligned, however, your actions can lead to a wayward journey. That route is a bumpy one. You skip the gym, choose the burger at lunch, and indulge in one post-dinner drink. Or four. Your identity is now harmful. Every action you take determines what you become. Who you become determines every action you take.

Your identity forms the foundations of your dieting mindset. It's easy to see why the type of person you are spawns the bedrock of any successful weight loss transformation. *Believing* you're able to lose weight has more of a profound effect than eating a cucumber kefir salad will. *Thinking* you have access to the tools for change is more effective than downing another protein shake. *Telling* yourself you're in control of the decisions you make has more far-reaching consequences than grinding out an extra set or two at the gym. *Feeling* excited at making changes to your physique influences more powerful outcomes than hopping onto the Peloton® for another spin class.

These actions are, of course, important, but your identity and mindset keep the bus (your beliefs, thoughts, words, and emotions) together. This is why my university friend failed with any diet she attempted; she wasn't the *type* of person who was able to exercise regularly, eat healthily, and sustain a reduced bodyweight. Her beliefs, thoughts, words, and emotions weren't aligned. It's also why you must start with your identity and work your way up.

Unearthing Your Identity

Actor Ethan Suplee had always been overweight. He has said that, since his grandparents put him on his first 'diet' at the age of five, he's lost and gained at least a thousand pounds of weight over the course of his life.[10] From an early age, he quickly learnt that food was something people didn't want him to have. Despite having these damaging narratives instilled in him as a child, his size hasn't affected his acting career. He's appeared in numerous feature films and successful television shows, such as *Remember The Titans* and *My Name Is Earl.*

The problem? He always played 'the fat guy'. The endless, 'overweight person' leads kept coming his way; so much so that, whenever he lost weight, he struggled to secure acting roles. He said he felt 'too thin' and, whenever he reached a smaller size, 'wasn't comfortable in his own skin'.[11] He was 'the fat one'. This was everything he knew. It was his *identity.*

Every comment from family members, each character he portrayed on screen, every role he failed to secure, each diet he's been on, and all the flashes of success he's achieved from being overweight, have merged to form the person he believes he's meant to be. He's even joked that he had the 'fat-guy-who-can-act' niche cornered, in Hollywood.[12] Why lose weight when everything he's known and understood has brought him success? Why bother changing when this is the person he, and others, expect him to be? Your identity – who you are – will dominate your life; in the case of losing weight, it will influence your ability to acquire a desirable physique more than you realise. It's no wonder Suplee felt vulnerable whenever he lost weight.

There is hope, however. Suplee has recently embarked on a journey to shed both his identity and his protective layering of body fat. From tipping the scales, at nearly 530 pounds at his heaviest, he now weighs half of that. He regularly lifts weights, is often revered for his impressive transformation, and has set up his own podcast, *American Glutton,* to share the highs and lows of his journey. The actor managed to go from 'the fat one' to 'the ripped one'. He was able to conquer his enduring self and become someone new; someone who was able to exercise regularly, eat well, and live a healthy lifestyle. He has shown that, while your identity will lock you in a seemingly-unbreakable chokehold, it is possible to slowly prise yourself away from your current existence and become free – evolving into the person you desire to be.

Before you work on moulding a new identity, you must first unearth the foundation on which your current one resides. Excavating your current beliefs and values will make it easier to decide what new path you must take. Identifying and bridging the gap between the 'Current You' and the 'Future

You' will then make it easier to implement the pertinent behaviours that can lead you to that future identity. The more congruent your 'current' and 'future' identities are, the better chance you will have of succeeding. Just like Ethan Suplee.

What Do I Value?

Values are extensions of ourselves. They're defined by what we elect to find meaningful in our lives. They're the fundamental component of our psychological make up and, ultimately, our identity.[13] Decide that you value camaraderie, along with Friday night drinks with your work colleagues, and you'll neglect the chance to eat a healthy meal with your family, so that you can attend the office gathering. Value family and health, though, and you'll happily miss the alcohol-infused debauchery to be with your loved ones.

Whatever you decide is important in your life, will manifest itself in your behaviours. This is why our values shape our identity. We're defined by whatever we choose to highlight in our lives. Not only do values ensure we focus on particular character strengths over specific dieting methods – for example, being kind and displaying self-respect over banishing chocolate from our lives – but they promote greater internal motivation as well.[14] Ascertaining your values before anything else will provide you with direction. These are not necessarily defined by what you want to achieve; however, they do reflect your deepest desires for how you want to behave as a human. They will always matter, even if goals, emotions, and circumstances change.

Would someone who wants to be kind and demonstrate self-respect plunge into a 28-day juice cleanse? I think it's unlikely. Would someone who values perseverance, and displaying responsibility, give up on their weight loss journey if they overate at the weekend? Probably not. Those who pursue their values are more likely to achieve any aspirations they possess and derive greater fulfilment from doing so.[15] This clear sense of self-directed meaning provides us with an essentially inexhaustible supply of motivation.[16] This is why we should always take a values-based approach to dieting.

Let's take the dreaded scales as a good example. If you value 'weighing less' as the focal point of your worth, then you'll inevitably feel distraught when you find you've put on two pounds on a Monday morning. You may then go and consume four croissants and a muffin for breakfast, in a fit of frustration. Were the nineteen-year-old teenager desperate to look like Arnold Schwarzenegger – who valued displaying strength and dedication – experience the same situation, and find out he'd *put on* two pounds, he would undoubtedly be delighted. He'd head straight to the gym to continue his muscle-building endeavour. Notice how the same scenario can be interpreted in completely different ways, simply by what is being valued?

Uprooting the set of standards that you have for your life will provide insights into how you already live and how you can choose to live in the future. This will, in turn, dictate any future actions you take. If you realise that you value your worth by the number on the scales – and that it drives your behaviour – you'll also be able to alter the definition of your true wants and desires. If, for example, you begin to value strength as the elixir to your physique, and/or if you value the ability to adjust to everchanging circumstances over what you weigh, you'll be able to interpret that Monday morning number differently. That number will now be anchored in with contrasting values – ones that dictate which direction you will take. While, in my opinion, weight loss should never be the sole purpose of your identity, when it's rooted in with philosophies that transcend any superficial reasoning, it then has the potential to become representative of your hard work and commitment, instead. That two-pound increase is no longer so terrifying.

Crucially, utilising values to steer your journey means that *you* get to decide what they are. It's no longer about what a specific diet instructs you to do, or even what your personal trainer decides. You are now in control of how you want to lead your life. Society doesn't necessarily aid the cause, unfortunately. We often mistake a quick hit of gratification for a sense of meaning – whether that be losing a couple of pounds, or purchasing a new coffee machine. We lose sight, subsequently, of what truly motivates us. We may often seek a catalogue of socially-mandated 'shoulds', in favour of working towards what honestly provides us with a sense of worth. This is why individuals will say they value 'aesthetics', when what they truly value is acceptance or love. By stating they want to chase fat loss, they're convinced they'll be accepted or loved by others; in reality, they may need to focus on self-compassion, or self-love, first.

By simply defining what matters to you, however, you create purpose and meaning to your existence. Values guide, rather than constrain, you. You're now willing to deal with the discomfort of change, because it mirrors the type of person you want to become. You're now willing to keep persevering with the task of a physical transformation, since that's what a 'patient' person would do. You're now prepared to keep going to the gym, as you appreciate the benefits of operating as an individual who 'relishes challenges'.

To work out what you value, you need to start laying your priorities bare and questioning their prominence. Focus on your influences, your passions, how you choose to spend your time, where you spend your money, and what values you hold in other areas of your life. Start placing these in an order that aligns with your weight loss goals. Every action and feeling is irrational without the awareness of a value structure.

Who Do I Spend Time With?

The people you surround yourself with will also shape your identity. If you unite with those who fail to care for their health and fitness, then you will subconsciously do the same. If, instead, you stand with those who emblazon the healthy identity you crave, you'll start to adopt similar habits and beliefs to them. Social psychologist, Henri Tajfel, proposed the concept of *Social Identity Theory*.[17] The groups you belong to provide an important source of pride and self-esteem. They give you a sense of social identity and belonging. This is why you will act like a student if you are a student, and act like a football fan if you're a football fan.

When people are aware of the groups they belong to, they're more likely to demonstrate the values that epitomise that crowd.[18] Have you ever wondered why dieting clubs, like Slimming World and Weight Watchers, are so successful? It's less because of the dieting principles they advocate, and more to do with the collective identity they promote. In another context, of individuals applying for a job, those candidates who believed their potential employer valued intelligence over personal development submitted to those precise values.[19] They answered questions in line with what they believed the interviewer wanted to hear. Simply believing what other people value will subtly change your perception of your own self-concept. Who you spend time with goes well beyond a trip to the fish and chip shop with friends on a Friday evening. It includes being inclined to submit to others' values, even when you don't always share those principles.

This isn't always a negative, however. One study showed that dietary adherence is better among people attached to certain eating patterns, such as going vegan, or gluten-free.[20] Vegans often have no issue avoiding, not only meat dishes, but, also, dairy-based desserts when out for dinner – compared with non-vegan friends who may struggle to say no to the plethora of dairy-based desserts on offer. Willpower and restraint are not issues for animal-product-free individuals; they are enactments of what they – and the social group they belong to – value. This same mechanism explains why religious dietary laws, such as for Kosher and Halal diets, promote such strict loyalty. Finding confidence and commitment in a dietary pattern supported by others will enhance adherence. Unfortunately, there's not a 'Say No To Dessert' movement, yet.

We now know that associating yourself with the core part of a social identity dictates success.[21] As one vegetarian in that same study said, *'It is an important part of who I am.'* You adopt the emotions, feelings, and actions of those around you. This, in turn, forms your very own identity. Examining what groups you represent will enable you to peel away and expose another layer of the individual you are – and how this influences the actions you take. Who do you spend time with?

What Do I Think About Myself?

Everyone has ideas about themselves. Whether you think you're intelligent, attractive, outgoing, or the opposite of any of those, it's your perception of reality that dictates how you feel about yourself. If you believe that the sight of you exercising is akin to that of an elephant traversing the balance beam – for example – you'll probably avoid the gym at all costs. If you're convinced that you will always be the heaviest one in your peer group, you'll likely conclude that losing weight is pointless. A past trigger often reinforces negative thoughts, which then sets off a flurry of internalisations and narratives. These arise as limiting beliefs, which cause decisions to be made on current feelings, rather than on objective reality.

The conclusions you derive from judgement of your characteristics will influence how you act. Taking inventory of these thoughts will, however, allow you to identify whether they're helpful or harmful. Do you habitually focus on your flaws and limitations? How are they interfering with your habits and ambitions? How can you let go of those beliefs?

Do you say to yourself, noticing you just gorged another chocolate bar, 'You fool, what were you thinking?!' Fixating on imperfections will send you into that vicious dieting cycle; failures are heightened, emotions are sent spiralling, and behaviours stem in accordance with all the fear and negativity that's been generated. This unhealthy self-image reinforces the way you look. If you don't believe you're worthy of looking slimmer, or feel that your cooking skills limit your ability to consume healthy meals, you'll do everything to support those judgements. Your mind searches into your past and filters your choices – and therefore your potential – from previous events; this ultimately limits future actions. Continually telling yourself you've always failed, and concluding it's pointless to try again, is self-limiting. Or, rationalising that, since you've never been able to turn down a bowl of cereal at eleven o'clock at night, why stop now – you'll continue to prevent yourself from instigating change.

Are your thoughts influenced by others? Ethan Suplee assumed his family wanted him to avoid food, which only hardened his propensity to overeat in private. Living up to others' expectations triggers distrust within ourselves. Ask yourself, 'Am I shaped by what I believe others think or want of me?' 'Have I been modelled into someone who believes they'll never lose weight, or that they're destined to be fat, simply by what I've been told in the past?' This 'accidental identity' has, and continues, to mirror your life. All these thoughts unite to form a path you're forced to take. Just because you've always been told you're better suited to academia – as opposed to physical activity – or that you're lazy, instead of hard-working, doesn't mean any of it is necessarily true.

By recognising the thoughts you have about yourself, therefore, you'll be able to craft an identity aligned with your goals. If you notice yourself suffocated with negative thoughts about your thighs, your legs or arms, your exercise ability, or cooking skills, you'll be able to flip those ideas. If you catch yourself with judgements that don't align with your long-term ambitions, you'll be able to stop them in their tracks. Extracting that critical voice, and adopting more supportive ideas, will slowly prune the painful frameworks you currently lead your life on. In rewiring thoughts, you can, instead, take action that's in alignment with fresh, healthy assessments of yourself.

How Do I Act?

Every action you take is another brick built in the foundation of who you see yourself as. If you believe you're a terrible cook, then you'll reinforce that idea every time you order a takeaway as the logical alternative. If you believe you're lazy, you can unwittingly manage to cement that belief every time you miss the gym. If you're sure that a scoop of your whey protein tastes like a double shot of fermented anchovies, you'll underline that expectation every time you avoid it.

Recognising the gap between current actions and required actions will also allow you to minimise that disparity. If you want to lose weight, you need to start on executing the tasks that will take you closer to that goal. This isn't about performing a particular action once or twice, but about repeating them over and over again. Slowly but surely, these recurring behaviours will accrue to build your identity. It's not about creating a Michelin-star dinner every night, either, but simply about becoming the type of person who cooks. Similarly, it's not about completing the perfect training session every time, but about being the person who goes to the gym. Your focus should be on the *action*, not the results. These behaviours may not necessarily deliver the progress you desire straight away, which can prove frustrating at first. But, the more behaviours you execute that align with your goals, the easier it will be to craft a suitable identity for the aspirations you possess. This will, in turn, lead to results.

Thinking – and believing – that you want to, and can, lose weight, is imperative, but it isn't enough, alone, to move forward. You must *embody* these thoughts and beliefs. An identity is built through experience. When you start, you begin to establish faith in yourself. It turns out you're *not* so lazy. You're *not* a bad cook. You *can* have that protein shake. You start to believe you can achieve any weight loss goals you have, simply by taking the pertinent actions. When the evidence begins to shift in alignment with those intrinsic motives, the narratives you live by begin to change as well.

Changing Your Identity Is No Small Feat

Let's be honest; changing your identity is hard. It strips you naked and leaves you standing on that school stage in front of your gawking friends. The 'fat girl' is no longer the 'fat girl'. The 'loud and bubbly bloke' is no longer the 'loud and bubbly bloke'. The 'lazy one' is no longer the 'lazy one'. Newfound narratives may be hard to embrace, inflicting intense discomfort. As we prefer the warmth our comfort zone provides, we'll do everything to nest there. You know what you know, and you're used to what you're used to. Attempting to become someone new stabs at your identity, at every office party, social gathering, conversation, and family outing. If the pain becomes too great, then the craving to return to your former self may threaten to outweigh the gratification of looking and feeling a new way. It suddenly seems that baring all on that stage isn't that appealing.

Dr Maxwell Maltz, an American cosmetic surgeon and author, discovered just this. He stumbled across the value of a person's identity – and their limiting, self-beliefs – in his surgery. His patients frequently believed that, if he could fix their physical deformities, they would become new people. They assumed their confidence and behaviours would improve and, subsequently, so would their standing in life. Much like losing weight, however, fixing a wonky ear or protruding nose did *not* lead to enhanced self-efficacy. The feelings of dejection and misery still held strong – wonky ear or not.

Maxwell, in his book, *Psycho-Cybernetics,* says, "[after surgery]…the patient continued to feel inadequate and experienced feelings of inferiority. In short, these 'failures' continued to feel, act, and behave just as if they still had an ugly face."[22]

He goes on to detail the story of a Duchess who, all her life, had been terribly shy and self-conscious, because of a tremendous hump in her nose. "Although surgery gave her a classic nose and a face that was truly beautiful", he says, "she still continued to act the part of the ugly duckling, the unwanted sister who could never bring herself to look another human being in the eye. If the scalpel itself was magic, why did it not work on the Duchess?"

Your current self-image reigns strong in the face of any physical transformation. While you may like to physically transform yourself from fat to thin, you need to *psychologically transform your identity* from fat to thin. Your ability to create long-lasting change goes well beyond your skill at counting calories, or deadlifting your bodyweight; your weight loss journey isn't just physical.

You don't suddenly adopt a new identity. It takes time – often shaped from former life events – to form this collection of values and beliefs. Each event you encounter forms and deposits a droplet in your very own 'identity bath'. Bullied at school for being slightly overweight? In it goes. Attempted, and failed at, every diet under the sun as a teenager? In it goes. Constantly tell yourself you 'can't resist unhealthy snacks?' In it goes. Repeatedly proclaim that you 'hate exercise?' Now the bath is overflowing. Each of these life episodes compounds to form a nice, warm, soaping that your identity hates abandoning. If you've become convinced that these deeply ingrained beliefs are true, no amount of weight loss will change them. *Which is why it's so hard to change.*

The longer you hold onto these narratives, the less aware you are of them.[23] They're always lurking, ready to pounce whenever something surfaces to prove – or, even, threaten – them. In a famous set of experiments, subjects who were primed with different elements of their identity performed differently on tests.[24] Asian-Americans are often perceived as more intelligent in certain subjects like mathematics. These women, who were primed with their Asian-American ethnicity, performed better on numerical tests than a control group – and even better than those prepped with their gender. If you're simply told you possess a certain identity, you subconsciously react per that belief system, like it or not.

It should now be clear as to why the latest diet probably won't work. If you don't *believe* you're that new individual, you won't sculpt a physique resembling that person. Once your identity is threatened – by attempting the latest diet, for example – you become resistant to change.[25] You put up a hardened wall around your exterior and do everything in your power to retain everything you've told yourself over the years. The bus, its petrol, its driver, and their ticket inspector, are all thrown off course. Your impenetrable identity simply doesn't know how to react. Change launches you into unchartered waters, which not only puts you at risk for loss but, also, gain – which is why your biggest fears are brought to the fore. What will people think of you if you lose weight? Will you be able to still enjoy takeaways? Will you have to start taking gym-selfies? Self-sabotage works to stem this 'threatening' invasion. When you change your identity, you're essentially killing off who you used to be.

Similarly, where you're proud of a part of your current identity, you'll do everything to protect it.[26] Should you firmly believe you represent something – you're the strongest girl in your group of friends, or the guy who can run for the longest time, for example – you'll do everything to act in alignment with that belief. You'll now continue going to the gym to maintain that strength, or keep on running to ensure you're still regarded as the best. This also happens to be why certain prejudices occur. If you believe your identity is superior to others, you'll adopt a 'them' and 'us' mentality.[27] Whilst that may be controversial and undesirable in the wrong context, for our purposes here, the underlying premise – aligning your behaviours with your identity, both personal and social – will allow you to start chipping away at forming a character that will allow you to diet successfully. Whilst I advocate that you shouldn't become so viciously attached to a particular diet movement or belief system that it blindsides you, and leads to bias and closed-mindedness, I believe it's still important to be proud of who you are and what you represent. You must be honoured at becoming a new individual.

How To Change Your Identity

Review Old Beliefs And Predict Future Ones

In one of the most vulnerable scenes in the Netflix, biographical documentary *Miss Americana,* singer-songwriter, Taylor Swift discusses how she feels while examining a paparazzi photo of herself. Her lifelong habit, she explains, is to detail what's wrong with her appearance; to instinctively scan her body and conclude she must lose weight. Suddenly, she lingers on the photo she's surveying, realises her chronic and toxic habit, and says, "No, we don't do that anymore". She identifies the version of herself that doesn't do *that* anymore. She's aware she's someone different now.

As we've discovered, your current identity is built on a sturdy foundation. A foundation that has taken years to assemble and will now do everything in its power to sabotage your actions and ability to diet successfully. While telling yourself that you'd never be as slim as the girls in your school class – or that you hated exercise – seemed beneficial at the time, it's now to your detriment. It's why Taylor Swift's always telling herself that she needed to lose weight was a catastrophic slight on her mindset. It's time, therefore, to look back, review those old beliefs, and start moulding new, productive ones.

Summoning the long-held judgements around your body will allow you to re-examine what was true and what wasn't. Was Bob-The-Bully right, in calling you "fat" every day at school, or was he cloaked in his own insecurities? Did you actually hate exercising when you were younger, or just hadn't found something you loved doing? Were you unable to eat healthily for all those years or had you just not discovered meals you enjoyed? The answers you buried yourself in helped create an identity that has influenced the type of person you are now. Unearthing different answers to these difficult questions will lead to the person you now wish to become, such as:

"Bob wasn't right; I do deserve to be leaner."

"It turns out I actually prefer lifting weights to toiling away on the cross trainer every day."

"I actually enjoy home-cooked Thai food, instead of the cauliflower pizza I forced myself to eat in a bid to be 'healthy' when I was younger."

As soon as you feel a long-held principle pop into your head, ask yourself, "Is this true?" If it isn't, then change it. Predict a new one. Such as:

"I now enjoy lifting weights."

"I now value the adventure of cooking a meal for myself/my family."

Through envisioning a *new you*, with new beliefs, new principles, and – ultimately – a fresh identity, you'll be better set to travel through the journey of serious behaviour change.

Those who've experienced a debilitating life, of constant restriction, were shown, in one study, to act in line with this premise.[28] Initially, they avoided social interactions and adopted a 'short-term' dieting mentality; this restrictive approach epitomised who they were. As soon as they freed themselves from the stunting confines of this typical approach – and adopted a more flexible, liberating attitude towards food and exercise – they experienced long-term changes. Accepting a revised way of judging their nutritional habits, and the type of individuals those represented, dictated their chances of losing weight. Think about your previous dieting experiences: do they now predict what exercise and nutrition programmes you attempt, and whether you'll succeed or fail? If you've always adopted a short-term mentality, is it really a great surprise if the results last for a mere, few months?

For anyone having been 'out of shape' for a long time, it can mean that visualising a new identity feels problematic, initially. What *does* being 'in shape' look like, after all? What do those beliefs comprise? We're possibly unaware of half the notions we tend to buckle to. They are so deeply ingrained within the self that we barely notice their dominant influence on our decision-making. Failing to expose these, however, is why you can get trapped in a perpetual dieting cycle. It's not because you can't stick to any particular diet; it's because your thoughts about your evolution aren't braced to diverge yet. Realising it's not the diet's fault, but perhaps an issue with your ideologies and beliefs, can be a life-changing breakthrough in shaping an altered mindset. What are you feeling? Why do you feel this way? How can you integrate these answers into your life?

Failing to consider what your future life will look like – what your new identity will resemble, and what beliefs you'll uphold – means you'll continue a cycle of trying, failing, and trying again, and then again failing. Trying to diet without breaking out of your current identity hasn't worked so far – and won't work until you do so.

Create A Value-Based System

Firefighters value saving lives. Whether it's grabbing a lost cat from a tree, or rescuing a human from a burning building, they get up each day with the same drive and determination. They don't wait until they're 'motivated' or 'feeling it'; they wake up with the intention of saving lives because that's *who they are.* If they fail to rescue someone, or otherwise have a bad day, they don't clock off, or declare they'll start again on Monday. Their values always keep them committed to the cause. This is why you don't necessarily require unreserved supplies of motivation or discipline – common impediments to many dieters' adherence and durability – when embracing a values-based system.

Values are, importantly, always present in the *now.* Unlike 'losing ten pounds for a holiday' or 'dropping a dress size for a birthday party', they provide an inexhaustible source of meaning. It's never about 'getting there', when fulfilling values; you'll always be 'going there'. Should you value 'care', for example, no matter how many caring acts you engage in, there will always be more caring deeds to perform. Should you value 'self-awareness', for example, there'll always be more opportunities to be perceptive and cognisant of your thoughts and actions. Fat loss will arise as a consequence of respecting values, not because you set out with the intention of dieting again, necessarily. Fat loss isn't a value. You approach other aspects of your life from a values-based approach – for example, your job or family – so why embark on a dieting venture any differently?

Ask yourself, 'What profound words do I want to be etched on my gravestone?' While it might be nice for Aunt Nora to know you lost twelve pounds from the ketogenic diet (twice), she would probably respect you more if she knew that you were loving, trustworthy, humble, and responsible. Not only that, but you'd probably have lost those twelve pounds if your eating and exercise behaviours aligned with those values, anyway. Start by focusing on just two or three values that will run parallel with every decision you now make. You don't have to search for hundreds. They don't have to be perfect from the outset, either. You just require a framework upon which to match your actions.

Ask yourself, 'What character strengths do I admire?' What do you want to stand for? What do you want to *do* in this area, that reflects what you respect? It could be anything from compassion, to courage, to persistence, to understanding, to friendship. Once you've figured these out, discern how your actions will express these values. If you value self-care, will you sacrifice your mental health, in the name of posting a provocative selfie on Instagram for a few 'likes?' Or will you take the time to look after your mind and body, by learning how to portion out your carbohydrates, protein, and fat on the plate at each meal?

It has been shown that writing down and connecting with authentic values has more impact on behaviour change and health than simply selecting them from a values menu.[29] Think of this as a wish list for Father Christmas. It's an inventory of what *you* want from your life and others. Of course, values require action; writing them down isn't enough. You must start practicing the appropriate behaviours, as values are won and lost through life experiences. If you value independence, are you being self-supportive? If you value patience, are you always adhering to the plan, no matter the emotions you're experiencing?

Ensure you reflect on your values consistently. Those who do are the ones who make better decisions and generally triumph.[30] Constantly question whether the habits you're executing right now express those principles. Do they relate to the decisions you'll need to make in the future? Once you become more attuned to letting these shape your choices, the demand to lean on them won't be as forceful. They'll almost become second nature. That's the beauty of placing a value-based system above any other approach.

Change How You Act

The process of changing your behaviour is the process of changing your identity. Focusing on *who* you wish to become is far more effective than plucking a weight loss number out of the 'random-weight-loss-figure' tombola and hoping for the best. James Clear, in his book, *Atomic Habits*, proposes a two-step process for shaping a new identity:[31]

1. Decide the type of person you want to be.
2. Prove it to yourself with small wins.

How do you decide the type of person you want to be? I'm sure you've got a friend, or even a role model, whom you admire. This could be an individual with a figure you desire or who can change direction with their fitness goals at the click of a finger, for example. While their proficiency at maintaining a preferable physique, or ability to execute optimal, healthy habits often creates a burning desire to hit them around the head with a kettlebell (which I probably don't recommend), I want you to ask yourself, 'What do they do? What do they think? How do they act?' Determining the successful behaviours and habits of others allows you to form a blueprint for the person you wish to embody one day. Just like a prosperous entrepreneur may be good at staying resilient, or a successful salesman may be effective at being persuasive, anyone succeeding at maintaining a great physique will display certain attributes that contribute to who they are and what they look like.

You don't want to be 'skinnier'; you want, instead, to be the person who always plans throughout the process. You don't want to 'weigh less'; you want to be the person who consumes a vegetable with every meal. You also don't want to 'lose ten kilograms'; you want to be the person who showcases resilience through times of adversity. It's no longer about focusing on the outcome but on the *process*. Since these processes will fuse to carve a new identity, you'll soon find it easier to stay the course and reach your destination.

Of course, once you've identified the person you wish to be – whether that's the guy who's the strongest at the gym or the girl who actually likes exercise – it's time to take action on cultivating that identity. To prove it to yourself with small wins. Executing behaviours that fail to align with your new identity won't get you anywhere, but starting to act like the person you wish to become will get you somewhere. You're not expected to be completely competent or flawless from the outset – to do so encourages resignation and feelings of failure. You're invited to establish an appreciation of the intrinsic satisfaction of *developing* competence. It's not about the outcome but the value of trying – and, rather than focusing on an instant result – of continuing and trying again.

Let's take the act of minimising alcohol consumption when out with friends, as an example. You'll need to practice being the type of person who doesn't drink. If this isn't what you're accustomed to, it's going to be a distressing experience. However, being the *type* of individual who orders a zero-calorie beverage while others are glugging bottles of wine, is more far-reaching than the act itself. This small victory reinforces the notion that you now represent that certain standard, which will go on to pay off in the future towards your weight loss intentions – and probably benefit your sense of wellness the following morning, too.

While neither one raspberry-sunrise-smoothie nor a single trip to the gym will instantly construct a new identity, they can go a long way in altering what you personify. Such change-based actions will feel uncomfortable at first – like having dinner with your partner's parents for the first time – but, gradually implementing these behaviours into your routine will begin to craft the new person you must epitomise. Most people give up after a few attempts; they don't like this 'new person' they've become. The trick is to slowly add to that collection of evidence that you *are* now this new individual, until it all becomes natural.

Think Of Your Identity As Interchangeable

Have you noticed how professional athletes fail to deal with retirement? From Michael Schumacher to Shane Warne, to Tom Brady, each one has toiled with the gaping crater left by relinquishing professional sport. They've had to swiftly return to it, to fill the void. When all you've known and breathed is one thing, throughout your whole life, it becomes incredibly hard to adapt to something else. All these sportspeople made the mistake of assuming that their identities were rigid; that, by retiring, they were no longer 'the Formula 1 driver', 'the cricketer', or 'the American football player'. Were each of them able to accept that their identity could be interchangeable, however, they'd have allowed themselves to live a new life while still appreciating any previously held identity.

Extreme identity shifts can prove challenging. If you've decided you're now the type of person who goes to the gym, for example, you may then avoid social events in favour of training. Or, if you now value carting Tupperware around with you to every social event, containing pre-made meals, you'll never eat out with your friends. This, of course, is where new identities can become detrimental. We don't want the view we have of ourselves to limit us. It *is* fine to attend social events or take a day to rest from training. Allowing yourself to shift between identities – ones that still align with your goals – will enable long-term change.[32]

Establishing an inflexible existence that fails to allow for different life scenarios will only serve to underline any failures you experience. Every unique situation will threaten your identity. If you now treat yourself as a person who only ever 'cooks a home-made meal on Friday night', you'll experience self-deprecating thoughts should you succumb to the occasional takeaway on a Friday. 'Why bother?' you might think to yourself, 'Maybe this just isn't me'. You'll subsequently find it harder to modify your behaviours. Were you to still appreciate being that person who cooks the home-made, Friday night meal, but accept you're also the type of individual who's able to allow themselves the occasional takeaway, you'll avoid heightening any feelings of failure. Accepting that one belief or value doesn't represent your whole self will enable you to live your life to its fullest.

Start thinking of your new identity as fluid. While the bulk of your existence should align with the weight loss goal you have, it shouldn't completely detract from other values you possess. You may now be the individual who tracks their food at a restaurant; is, however, taking the occasional night off, to spend an evening of undivided attention with your partner, going to help breed long-term well-being for both your mental health and relationship? Allowing yourself to consciously shift between identities, when applicable, will lead to long-term success. Redefine who you are, so you can uphold your identity even when circumstances change.

Your 'Why'

What Are You Looking For In A Potential Partner?

There always exists some iteration of a dating show on television. While nothing compares to the fabled Saturday nights in, watching *Blind Date* in the 90s, a new programme will pop up every few months, promising love, fairy tale endings, and, usually, a large, cash prize. Each show starts with the same format. They pan onto a new 'hopeful', focus on a notable physical attribute, and ask them what they're looking for in a potential partner.

"Kind. Funny. Generous. Good personality," the optimistic individual replies.

Unfortunately, such archetypal descriptions are worthless. Why? Because the way in which human brains are wired means they can only provide hollow and meaningless explanations when presented with questions like, "What are you looking for in a potential partner?" and, "Tell me why you're best suited to this job" – or, "Why do you want to lose weight?"

We have two distinct mechanisms in play within our brain: a rational system and an emotional system. The rational side, powered by a part of the brain labelled *the neocortex,* is responsible for methodical answers. It is revealed through language. When individuals describe what they're looking for in a lifelong companion, they're utilising a rational outlook on things. Justifying the extensive list of character traits that they're seeking, with arbitrary words like "kind", "funny", and "nice teeth" is easy. They, and their audience, understand them. What those phrases fail to do, however, is expose the *real* reasons any contestant is searching for a potential soul mate.

We also possess the emotional system, simultaneously chuntering away. That side, powered by a part of the brain called *the limbic system,* is responsible for feelings and emotions. When presented with the question, "What are you looking for in a potential partner?", the person's limbic brain arena lights up and churns out a host of reactions and sensations. What is sensed could be encapsulated in sentences such as, 'I want to feel the love I missed as a child', or, 'I crave someone who can make me feel secure in myself'. Alas, though, they can't actually communicate these cryptic feelings and desires. They, therefore, turn to the neocortex to provide superficial and typical answers, in phrases like, "A good sense of humour". Logically, they know the answers they provide aren't the real reasons; they're simply words used to describe facets of what they want. The answers from the limbic brain provide a true understanding into these honest justifications; they explain *why* they want certain traits in a partner, rather than focus on the *'what'* of any named, specific traits.

Feelings are the real driver behind people's wants and needs and, subsequently, also behind change. This disconnect – between their *'what'* and their *'why'* – can, however, provide us with a deep insight into how we can achieve, and sustain, dieting success.

A few weeks into my university friend's diet, the same thing would always happen. Midway through another gulp of her protein shake, or reluctantly nibbling on another plate of pasta-free pasta, she would always say, "I really don't know why I do this". Again, nothing but a throw-away comment, but it was exactly this – her failure to understand *why* she was eating what she was eating and doing what she was doing – which was further suffocating her chances of succeeding.

Ask anyone why they want to lose weight, or change their physique, and they'll fashion the quintessential answers:

"Because I want to be healthy."

"Because I want to look better."

"Just, you know, because…"

Those are the surface-level, logical reasons that people typically present. They're powered by the side of the brain housed by the neocortex and are akin to the person asserting they want a partner who's 'generous'. These are the responses they *think* will invoke change, but are nothing more than a bulletproof shield, used to protect them from the underlying and genuine reasons that exist. As Henry Ford, founder of the Ford Motor Company, supposedly said, "If I had asked people what they wanted, they would have said a faster horse."[33] Individuals never truly express what they want and why they want it. Yes, the initial reasons they provide for wanting to lose weight appear effective and interesting, but those never enable them to develop long-lasting change.

To successfully lose weight, we need to unearth our 'why' – understanding how shedding a few pounds will make us *feel.* Just like finding a new partner might make us feel comfortable with some of the flaws in our upbringing, or with something we feel we lack within ourselves, losing weight and parading a new physique will expedite other emotions. Purchasing a new laptop may allow us to mindlessly scroll through the internet faster; we purchase it, however, because it makes us *feel* successful. Similarly, buying a new item of clothing may look good on us; but purchase it because it makes us *feel* confident and in control of our body. Going for a run may be beneficial for our cardiovascular health; we do it, however, because it makes us *feel* a sense of achievement. These powerful emotions drive our decision-making.

Harnessing Your 'Why'

People are desperate to lose weight, not because they want to acquire a 'bikini body' or to 'be healthy', but because of the gap between how they currently feel and how they want to feel. This, ultimately, is your 'why' – and is the biggest influence on durable, behaviour change. As Simon Sinek, in his book, *Start With Why,* says, "Knowing your WHY is not the only way to be successful, but it is the only way to maintain lasting success. When a WHY goes fuzzy, it becomes much more difficult to maintain growth and inspiration." [34]

Your current feelings are concealed in a thick, protective cerebral layering. Surmounting that layer and dredging up those feelings is, however, painful. You know those emotions and judgements will reveal issues you don't like, which is why you keep your head above the water, pretending you're content with life, and just want to be a touch 'healthier'. My pasta-free pasta friend probably knew why she wanted to lose weight; she wasn't prepared to accost those uncomfortable feelings.

There is, typically, a host of emotions buried beneath the ironclad exterior people present that's preventing them from eating well, exercising frequently, and looking the way they wish. Some of these emotions may be more pronounced than others but, when these are brought to the fore, they inspire change. For example, you've just broken up with your partner and want to attend your friend's birthday party, finally sporting that dress that your ex once mentioned would never suit you. Or you've just been diagnosed borderline diabetic and would rather live to see your grandchildren reach high school, than miss out on those memories through poor health. This kind of pain is self-evident, but also easy to utilise purposefully. Life events, and the way they're interpreted, impact people's ability to lose weight.[35] Hence, it's easier to say 'no' to the cookies, and get to the gym five times a week, following a relationship break-up, or medical diagnosis. The pain stokes passion and enables change and persistence.

More often than not, however, that pain will be more subtle. You're going to have to dig deep and ask difficult questions to find it. Did someone comment on your last holiday, Instagram-post, saying you'd put on a few pounds? Do you avoid social events because you're fearful of photos being taken? The answers to these questions will reveal your 'why'. It's not because you're scarred from a previous comment on your physique; more so, that you don't feel approval from others. It's not because you don't want photos to be taken; it's more that you're fearful of others' opinions. These are the reasons behind those surface-level arguments for wanting to lose weight. These powerful 'whys' invoke change, provide clarity, and serve as a point of reference for when you're too tired to cook, or someone's brought yet another pyramid of Ferrero Rocher's into the office.

Once you've uncovered your current disposition, you can then look to the future at how you *want* to feel. This will provide you with direction. It will enable your limbic brain to join forces with your neocortex to guide you, instead of veering off into a chocolate-glazed wilderness.

There's a reason why most brides manage to lose weight for their wedding. They envisage how they want to feel on their special day and, subsequently, do everything in their power to make it a reality. They *want* to feel comfortable. Confident. Radiant. Like a celebrity. They know the cameras will be glued to their every movement, and those cogent emotions may be enough to ensure that every preceding decision aligns with the bride's goals. It's why they're often able to diet longer and exercise harder than most. That's a 'why' that's powerful enough to drive significant change.

Viktor Frankl was an Austrian neurologist and psychiatrist, who experienced and survived the inhuman persecution and murder of six million Jews by the Nazi regime during the Holocaust. In his book, *Man's Search For Meaning,* he says, "…any attempt to restore a man's inner strength in the camp had first to succeed in showing him some future goal. Whenever there was an opportunity for it, one had to give them a why – an aim – for their lives, in order to strengthen them to bear the terrible how of their existence."[36]

While it would be injudicious to draw direct comparisons between such a barbaric experience as that, and weight loss, the point remains the same: understand your why and you will gain direction. Once you've discovered that inherent reason, you'll be able to marry your emotions and decisions to form an unassailable mindset. When you understand what's driving your behaviour, you'll have a focal point for every action you take. This is why we *know* we should be eating more vegetables and avoiding McDonald's at 3 pm on a Thursday. We simply lack the right emotional drive to reinforce – and act upon – that knowledge. The stronger your 'why', the better.

How To Find Your 'Why'

Children can be annoyingly inquisitive. Their favourite question to pound you with is, "*Why?*" You'll go from innocently explaining why the sky is blue to suddenly detailing why there are twenty-four time zones in the world. Unearthing your 'why' requires a similar level of curiousness. Tasking yourself with the 'Five Whys' activity will enable you to dig deep and find your compelling reasons for wanting to change.[37]

Start by taking your first reaction to the question "Why do you want to lose weight?" Just like an annoying child, you keep probing, asking yourself "Why?", to each answer you provide. You need to do this five times, at least. Analyse each response, until you find an answer that sets off the sirens in the limbic brain. When you feel that indescribable urge to take action, you know you've revealed your true 'why'.

"Why do I want to change my eating and exercise habits?"
"Because I want to lose weight."

"Why do I want to lose weight?"

"Because I want to feel more confident."

"Why do I want to feel more confident?"

"Because I want to gain more attention."

"Why is gaining attention important to me?"

"Because more people will start to like me."

"Why do I want more people to like me?"

"Because I'm lonely and no longer want to lack connection and intimacy in my life."

Admitting the underlying rationale for your desire to lose weight can feel unpleasant. Answers may, of course, surface that can be unpacked and managed without the need to diet. But, once you've discovered your core, burning reason for change, you'll be able to utilise its power. The person in the example above now knows that every decision they make will be aligned with their desire to remove loneliness from their life. Will avoiding exercising mean they'll acquire that desired confidence? Will being side-tracked by the bright lights of another quick-fix diet align with their 'why'?

You'll frequently find yourself in situations that test your character. How do you deal with the array of sweet and savoury snacks at the table? Or that moment when you're feeling tired and don't want to go to the gym? Reminding yourself of your 'why' will impel action. If you no longer want to fear loneliness, will losing weight help you? If the answer is "Yes", then will avoiding the sweet and savoury snacks at the table take you closer to, or further away from, that 'why'? Remembering the reason that captures your feelings and desires (your 'why') will drive change – at any given moment.

Discovering your 'why' will take time. And, even if you firmly believe you've identified it, you may be wide of the mark. If, when using that underlying reason to embark on a new weight loss journey, you find yourself faltering, you'll know it needs refining. It just isn't currently strong enough to coax the emotional side of your brain to help you change. Go back and ask again. Find those deep-rooted memories and defining moments that have led to this juncture.

"I fear rejection and feel that the bigger I am, the less chance I have of being abandoned."

"My mum used to tell me how big I looked in my school uniform and I now rebel against her wishes."

"I've always failed at dieting and don't want to add another defeat to that collection."

Bingo. That 'why' is more important than any pre-workout supplement you might purchase.

Like constantly redrafting that presentation for work, finding your deep-seated motive will take time and effort. You should end up with an answer that means something truly significant to you. Generic statements such as "Being healthy" should be disregarded; real reasons for change should be glued to and transported around with you, preferably using the world's strongest adhesive. If you don't feel the power coursing through you, then you probably haven't found the right words to describe your purpose yet.

It's the same inner process through which certain brides can transform their physiques with so much more ease than most; their words and emotions follow them everywhere. This is also why many often fail to sustain their weight loss for any lasting period past their wedding day. That impenetrable 'why' has vanished and they have less drive to aid future eating and exercise decisions. Continual sharpening of your 'why' is, therefore, a prerequisite for change. It will often ebb and flow, too, meaning you must constantly keep probing the reasons that define you.

Chapter Summary And Taking Action

- Your identity is the real driver of change. Unearthing the type of person you currently are, along with the type of person you want to become, will create a long-lasting, physical and psychological transformation more than any dieting protocol will.

- Write down the prominent beliefs you have about weight loss (e.g., "It's impossible to stay in shape as an adult"), your thoughts (e.g., "I've never been the gym-type so I'll never lose weight"), your words (e.g., "I always call myself a moron when I choose cake over fruit"), your emotions (e.g., "When I'm stressed, I tend to overeat"), and your current actions (e.g. "I buy chocolate in my weekly shop which doesn't help when I'm trying to minimise the amount I'm having").

- Write down *alternatives* to these (e.g., "I know it's not impossible to stay in shape as an adult because my friends have managed it", or "I now value strength in the gym rather than the number on the scales"). Continue to question and investigate each of the beliefs, thoughts, and values you've written down, and rewrite them where necessary. Keep this list with you as a continual point of reference.

- Start evaluating who you spend time with and how that influences your beliefs. Similarly examine the thoughts you have about your eating habits, your life skills, and your body. Ask yourself whether these are true or not and, whether you can reshape them.

- Create a value-based system. Figure out three values upon which you'll now live your life (e.g., 'adventure', 'strength', and 'self-care'). Think about the actions that reflect these values (e.g., "I will train twice a week, which will align with my values of strength and self-care – and, by taking care of my body, I am able to go on adventures such as active holidays"). Let these values guide your life choices as well as your dieting decisions.

- Think about and write down the actions you need to take to become the type of person you want to end up as. If you want to be slimmer, focus on what a slimmer person does to achieve that physique (e.g., plan meals for the week and/or avoid dessert when out at a restaurant). Add these to the list that you now carry with you everywhere.

- Unearthing your 'why' will also allow you to have a point of reference for future decisions and choices you must make. Complete the 'Five Whys' activity. Dig deep. Create alternatives to that 'why', which will change as your life, and you, develop.

CHAPTER 2
Growth Or Fixed:
Cultivating A Better Perception Of Your Self

Cristiano Ronaldo is one of the greatest footballers to have ever played the game. From athletic prowess to exorbitant skill levels and unrivalled success, it's been argued there'll never be a player like the Portuguese international again. Having won football's most prestigious individual award – the Ballon d'Or – a total of five times, Ronaldo stands at the summit of his sport's elite.

One of his most defining moments came in the 2016 European Championship final against France. After suffering an injury in the twenty-fifth minute of the game – and following multiple attempts to play on – he was forced off the pitch on a stretcher and had to receive immediate treatment to his knee. Devastation took hold. Tears were shed. Most players would have sat on the bench, resigned to the fact they'd play no further part in driving their country to a major trophy; in this case, Portugal's first-ever. But not Ronaldo.

With his knee strapped heavily in tape, and undoubted disappointment pushed aside, he spent the rest of the game frantically prowling the touchline, encouraging, instructing, and pushing his compatriots forward. He was no longer a teammate, but a leader. Limping heavily, he kicked, headed, and defended every ball along with his team and continued to bellow tactical advice to the eleven players still on the pitch. Ronaldo had appeared to appoint himself as joint manager.

No one cared. Least of all the designated coach, Fernando Santos. As the game entered a nail-biting period of extra time, Portugal managed to gain, and hold onto, a 1-0 lead. They were crowned European Champions. Ronaldo, previously accused of selfishness in dealing with his teammates, had brushed any self-admiration aside and believed in his fellow players to triumph through adversity. Despite not joining them on the pitch, he continued to force them onwards from the touchline, displaying characteristics that belied his self-indulgent reputation. This was about effort, belief, and accepting the challenge that had been sent his team's way. They, and Ronaldo, delivered – securing Portugal's inaugural, international title.

What Can This Tell Us About Ronaldo?

Sportspeople are often defined by their 'natural talent' or 'raw ability'. Their success, in whichever sport they compete in, has risen from an innate gift and it's only a matter of time before their pre-destined success surfaces. 'His rise to the top was inevitable', or, 'She just had that underlying talent ready to share', people will declare. Just like Michael Jordan and Babe Ruth before him, Ronaldo would argue emphatically against such deep-rooted and misguided assumptions.

Having endured a rocky childhood, Ronaldo's success didn't surface from any pre-born gift. He worked – often much harder than others – to reach the top. From training with ankle weights to improve his dribbling ability and stepovers at a young age,[1] to spending days and days practicing free-kicks, there wasn't an aspect of his game he left untouched. It's even been rumoured that, as a youth team player at Sporting Lisbon, he would challenge the senior players to 'sit-up' challenges after training.

One of his former teammates said, "I always thought we had several quality players in the Sporting Academy. But that Ronaldo was different because of all the work he put in – not so much during the training sessions, but after the sessions. He would always stay and practice for an extra half an hour on the areas he had most difficulties. The way he trained, the way he motivated his teammates, the way he corrected them, his will to win, his will to impress, was superior to all the others."[2] Even now, still playing in his late-thirties, his social media pages are littered with clips of him in the gym, on the training ground, and sharpening his physical and technical skills.

Former Portugal coach Carlos Quieroz said, "There are some great players that have so much belief that when things are not going well on the training field, they stop. They think, 'I am good, today is not right, but tomorrow it will be fine.' They never think there could be a problem. Not Cristiano. He works and works until everything goes right and only then is he satisfied."[3]

Ronaldo epitomises the culture of hard work and practice. He believed he could always be – and do – better. The benefits of possessing such a mindset manifested in the Euro 2016 final, as his willingness to propel his teammates to reach the pinnacle of their capabilities, despite playing little involvement, delivered victory and status. It was no longer about talent but growth. It was not about succumbing to a limited celling, but breaking through those hurdles and believing his team could emerge victorious. And it's this – his desire to strive for continual improvement, and embracing challenges thrown his way – that can not only teach us about his mindset, but allow us to delve deep into how people can, and should, view their weight loss journey.

Do You Possess A 'Growth' Or 'Fixed' Mindset?

Your mindset explains the theories you use – often subconsciously – to define certain experiences. How you view these certain experiences forms a deep impression on how you lead your life. How did Ronaldo view his setback in the final? What led to his influence throughout that crucial final, despite being consigned to the touchline? How did he arrive at such a malleable mindset, which undoubtedly shaped his glittering career? Answering questions like these will allow you to investigate the perceptions you hold, surrounding your weight loss journey – and their effect on your progress.

Ask yourself what beliefs you possess that drive success or failure. How will you react to victories or setbacks? How do you view the influences that your effort and energy have on your dieting venture? Answers arise from the assumptions you assemble regarding your *ability levels*. Dr Carol Dweck, a pioneering researcher in the field of motivation, explains that our mindset exists on a continuum, from 'fixed' to 'growth'.[4] Unpacking this *implicit theory* is the next part of the puzzle in building that ultimate dieting mindset.[5]

Believing that your physical and mental qualities are pre-set – that your ability to perform specific tasks is set in stone – will limit your chances of successfully shedding weight, or building muscle. This has been coined an *entity* or *fixed mindset*. People who believe that, because of inborn talent, they can't improve the attributes life has given them – whether those focus on their physical ability in the gym, or mental traits, such as discipline – often find themselves stuck. Why bother if their impaired ability won't aid their situation? Why keep persevering if their efforts are in vain? Were Ronaldo to have accepted that genetics and in-built competence were responsible for forming his accomplishments, he would have been less inclined to practice, work hard, and be present on the touchline in that final. If he, or others, couldn't get any better, what would be the point? The same applies to you: do you trust you have the ability to transform your physique? *Can* you change?

Believing your qualities can evolve – through effort, appropriate planning, and constant adaptation – will lead to greater achievement and mastery.[6] This is known as an *incremental* or *growth mindset*. People who believe they can transform their physique through hard work, and a modification of diet and exercise habits, provide themselves with a sturdy foundation on which to thrive. Why worry about failure, when it serves as an opportunity to attempt something new? Why eschew an opening to undertake a unique challenge and boost competence? This is akin to Ronaldo's mindset; improving, and subsequently helping others raise their game, is a gift. One that can be achieved through purpose and intention. If evolution is plausible, then we should utilise that prospect. When crafting the ultimate dieting mindset, we must take refuge closer to the 'growth' end of the continuum.

The way you view your efforts play a prominent role in defining success. It's not about the perfect training programme, polished meal plan or flawless, high-protein snack list – but in appreciating the importance of managing the way you *think* about your skill set. From your capacity to improve the execution of weight loss behaviours, to displaying resilience during unexpected challenges, placing confidence in your capability at improving will lead to long-lasting physical changes. Individuals with a 'fixed' mindset seek to validate themselves; those with a 'growth' mindset focus on developing the inner self.

Do You Believe You Can Lose Weight?

Possessing a growth mindset has been found to improve academic,[7] sporting,[8] and even business performance.[9] Dweck, in her book, *Mindset,* says, "Instead of being held captive by some intimidating fantasy about the Great Writer, the Great Athlete, or the Great Genius, the growth mindset gave [students] the courage to embrace their own goals and dreams. And more important, it gave them a way to work toward making them real."[10] Can the same be said of the weight loss domain? Can the thoughts and assumptions that relentlessly shuttle through your mind forecast your ability to diet successfully? From how you perceive your exercise ability to your competency at cultivating nutritional habits, embracing an incremental mentality will, indeed, help. *Believing* you can change forms the foundation for a successful dieting mindset.

It's been found that individuals' beliefs about their bodyweight can affect whether they're able to lose weight or not.[11] Those who believed their weight was fixed (for example, agreeing with the statement, "You have a certain bodyweight and you can't really do much to change it") were less likely to display the trait of perseverance. This fixed mindset not only predicted their chances of evading effort and hampering positive expectations, but meant they *lost less weight* than those operating with a growth mindset. The take you possess on your exercise behaviours, eating habits, and bodyweight will often dictate progress more so than the actual tasks themselves.

The majority of people continually fail with dieting attempts. No matter the effort, there's minimal progress. No sooner has the weight disappeared, than it returns. It's easy to see how individuals become cornered into this fixed mindset. "If I could have succeeded, I would have done so by now", they tell themselves. "What's the point? I'll never get to where I want to be". The cycle persists and disillusionment with dieting emanates.

Taming the growth mindset, however, allows people to prosper. Not only can they achieve more, but their feelings and optimism improve. Failures soon become openings. Activities become challenges. Succumbing to four scoops of Ben & Jerry's ice cream now shifts to an opportunity to practice portion size control, instead. Similarly, missing a gym session now transforms to a chance to sharpen planning and preparation skills. Growth itself becomes the vessel for change.

This impressionable mindset is derived from people's expectations. *Expectancy Value Theory* surmises that if you not only expect to do well but *value* the task in hand, you're more likely to succeed.[12] If you expect your efforts to contribute to weight loss – and likewise value those same efforts – you're more likely to pursue the dream of sustainable results. If you expect your application to be worthless, however, you're less likely to engage in the appropriate weight loss behaviours. When you set out on another diet, therefore, what expectations do you convey? Do you start your latest venture forecasting dieting victory, or are you still soaked in those negative assumptions hoarded from previous failures? These levels of self-efficacy will not only dictate how likely you are to continue exercising and dieting, but whether – and how – you overcome any obstacles.[13] Expectations matter.

If you believe you're someone who's proficient in the gym and generally holds training with a positive attitude (for example, "I *enjoy* training and believe exercising will change my physique", as opposed to, "I train because I *have* to, to lose weight, but don't believe it's otherwise worthwhile"), you're predisposed to express perseverance in the future. Embracing challenges leads to greater expectations and increased exercising frequency – and, of course, training consistently is linked to a healthier and fitter physique.

Similarly, your approach to dieting is predicated upon your values.[14] Holding the idea of character development in reverence – along with engaging in activities that define who you are – will not only elevate enjoyment, but also engender trust that those activities are worthwhile, too. If losing weight is the sole purpose of your life, however, then engaging in more harmful, diet-based practices – and potentially forgoing the fulfilment and joy of social interactions – will characterise your existence. Those who fall in love with the idea of getting stronger, improving their lifestyle, and building resilient and confident qualities, often find it easier to maintain a desired, body fat percentage. This isn't because they've discovered some secret supplement, or mystical, fat loss exercise, but because of their immersion in the process. From taking the focus away from the 'diet' or 'training programme', they are permitting their character strengths to regulate progress.

Is your identity closely linked to your expectations? If you've always told yourself you're 'a failure' or 'lazy', this will surface as a fixed mindset. You don't *expect* to succeed. Building the ultimate mindset, therefore, sits perilously between whether you view dieting as something to be embraced and attained, or an arduous endeavour that will inevitably lead to disappointment.

You Can Change Your Brain, Too

There are, of course, fragments of apprehension surrounding the purported benefits of crafting a resilient, growth-based mindset on dieting success. These can often be parked, in the style of doubting attitudes, with enigmatic palm readers and psychic mediums (I am, as it happens, still waiting to come into that large chunk of money). There is evidence, nonetheless, to show that claims of ambiguity are based on false accusations. Just as we can amend our behaviours and habits, it's possible to physically reconstruct our brains, too. This is commonly known as *neuroplasticity*.[15]

Neuroplasticity refers to the brain's ability to adapt and change shape. When you learn a new skill or behaviour, the pathways that information travels on lay down a labyrinth of circuitry, called 'grooves'. These new grooves form in the wake of learning, activity, and experience. Just as repeating the act of riding a bike will reinforce and sustain that skill, the brain will similarly strengthen and grow when it encounters frequent thoughts and actions. Every time you rehearse a belief, feeling, or habit, you bolster the pathways between neurons – those 'grooves' – and essentially rewire your brain to adapt to new situations.

Most importantly, it's possible to modify these connections (learning, being creative – and even reading fiction – can all help to develop the neurons in your brain).[16] Even as adults, long after we've learnt how to ride a bike or swim, we can improve existing capabilities, as well as develop new skills. The ability to reshape those pathways, therefore – and become someone new well into later life – is not only possible, but incredibly beneficial, as well. Learning and evolution never stop.

The connection between a growth mindset and neuroplasticity is significant; the two concepts mirror one another. An incremental mindset asserts that your innate skills, talents, and abilities can be cultivated and improved upon, just as neuroplasticity refers to the brain's ability to adapt beyond the usual developmental period of childhood.[17] Both indicate that change is possible. Merely believing that you can transform your body shape will not only beget a superior mindset, but enable the brain to thrive and regenerate in a similar way.

As might be expected, this is no easy feat. Establishing new, neural, growth-related connections is comparable with building a bridge to negotiate a bottomless canyon. The first time you traverse that canyon, and start assembling the bridge, is the hardest; it requires a plenitude of effort and concentration. As an example, the first time you try eating until you're only eighty per cent full seems demanding and commands extra focus. Every time you make the same journey, however – or practice listening to hunger cues with each meal – it becomes gradually easier. With each crossing, that bridge is eventually built, and the journey becomes your new routine. You're now able to eat your mum's mouth-watering, crisp, roast potatoes to satisfaction, without feeling like your stomach is about to implode. As difficult as it may at first seem, it is possible to remodel behaviours and rewrite the instruction manual that lies behind them.

We know that a study group of obese children, who read articles about a growth mindset, adopted better perceptions surrounding health and nutrition;[18] by reading this book, you'll be able to achieve a similar outcome. By learning that you can overhaul not only your mindset, but your brain, too, you're relinquishing any previously-held, limiting beliefs. You no longer believe that failure is inevitable, or that your old habits will prevent you from thriving. You're now able to, hopefully, both see and believe that change *is* possible.

Adopting A Growth Mindset With Exercise

My friend, whom we met in Chapter One, knew that exercise – specifically, resistance training – would aid her fat loss aspirations. The only problem was in ensuring that she persisted with her gym plan long enough to notice progress. Akin to many budding dieters, she would set out with all the enthusiasm she could muster, eager to sample a host of new exercises, training protocols, and – what she frequently described as – 'hot guys at the gym'. While, following each session, she would often complain about her inability to dismount the toilet owing to the crippling muscle soreness that ensued, she'd continue to lift, push, and pull weights every day. As the weeks passed, however, that same enthusiasm waned and her exercise habits hastily fell by the wayside. She'd then berate herself for not being able to 'stay motivated' or 'stick with it long enough', to observe worthy change. That gym membership swiftly became redundant.

Why was this? Was it possible that my friend indulged in an unsuitable and unsustainable exercise programme? Or was it because she lacked the necessary mindset to facilitate her exercise frequency? Did her perception of her movement ability and confidence dictate her persistence level, rather than it being simply about a lack of 'motivation' or 'loyalty to the cause?' There's evidence to say that it was, in fact, her underlying attitude towards exercise that failed to provide sufficient adherence – not necessarily an absence of discipline, desire, or self-restraint.

How much you *believe* in your ability to transform into a fitter individual will dictate your chances of increasing long-term exercise frequency, and your capacity to fulfil your physique's potential.[19] If you believe that strength, technique, and ability are all fixed attributes – that your efforts to change are unavailing – you'll curtail opportunities to make progress. Those who struggle to visit the gym consistently may believe that all their efforts are futile and, because they can't see results immediately, that there's little point in trying any further. Or, because they're collared to the idea of a genetic ceiling, that they'll never reach the apex of physical eminence. Enthusiasm withers and those gym visits soon diminish. This is the *fixed* mindset in play.

Those who train consistently, however, assume a different viewpoint. They believe that exercise is an opportunity to improve healthy behaviours. That their efforts in the gym will help them acquire their desired physique, even when results may seem concealed behind an elusive dream. This is what coaches mean when they harp on about, "trusting the process". Were my friend to have viewed her gym experience as a chance to develop her exercise abilities, or discover an activity she enjoyed, she would have flourished. If she'd not only expected to still be returning to the gym six months later, but valued the consistency that the act of exercise brought, she would have been able to keep clocking in those gym hours. Positive perceptions of physical activity have been found to induce significant, long-term effects on health, through shifts in motivation, emotion, and physiological responses. This is the *growth* mindset at play.

Let's consider the activities of hotel maids, as an interesting example. They're on their feet every day, continually moving, ferrying heavy trolleys, as well as bending and scrubbing. Ask them if they're physically active, however, and they'll often respond with an affirmative "No". Given that their activity levels easily eclipse most sedentary workers, it seems strange that their mindset rests in the 'idle' camp.

A group of researchers at Harvard University decided to examine this very situation.[20] They briefed a group of maids, who far exceeded the definition of an 'active lifestyle', on the number of calories each of their daily tasks burned. They weren't instructed to exercise more, nor eat less.

One month later, following the surprising information that they had been primed with, it was found there was a remarkable decrease in those maids' weight, as well as their waist-to-hip ratio and blood pressure markers. While the busy cleaners reported no significant changes in their subsequent behaviours, it was evident that their physiological improvements were affected by the footing their mindsets held. How you *perceive* your activity levels will govern your ability to change. By simply believing your efforts are aligned with a certain goal, or that you possess the skills to cultivate progress – no matter what your baseline competence may be – you can make significant changes to your exercise frequency, effort level and, ultimately your physique.

Have you ever heard of the performance-enhancing drug OxyRBX? I'd tend to assume not.

That's largely because it doesn't exist. However, runners who were told to self-inject this mysterious, but fictitious stimulant – which supposedly improved oxygen delivery to the musculature – improved their personal bests by an average of 1.2 per cent.[21] They were taking nothing more than an ineffective, saline placebo, yet managed to record superior race times. Notice how by simply believing you will improve, or that you possess the necessary tools to raise performance levels, elevated results will follow?

It has also been found that previous exercise experiences will dictate future efforts.[22] The confidence you possess in your ability to exercise will govern how likely you are to adhere to any training programme you undertake. Those who embrace this challenge-based mindset experience greater rewards.

Think back to your last stint at the gym. If you now uphold it as a numbing failure that resulted in nothing but a depleted bank account and a sore back, you're more likely to channel those beliefs into future pursuits. If, however, you continue to view the previous experience as an opportunity to improve fitness levels, and strengthen your fragile lower back, you'll increase the likelihood of trying again. If you believe exercise embodies who you are, and employ it as an invitation to improve on previous endeavours, you'll enhance adherence.

Interestingly, participants in one study who were wrongly primed with the information that they carried a version of the 'CREB1' gene – which has been found to reduce people's aerobic capacity and make exercise generally more unpleasant – performed *worse*, physiologically, on a subsequent treadmill task.[23] Additionally, they reported feeling more worried and less in control of their overall exercise capacity. The participants' belief that they were genetically indisposed to exercise proved to be more damaging – physiologically and psychologically – than the actual gene itself. It's evident that forming negative expectations of your exercise ability, before you've even started, can have towering consequences.

Perceptions matter. We know that individuals who viewed themselves as 'less active' than others were 71 per cent more likely to die in a follow-up period, than those who regarded themselves as 'more active' [24] – and why those who were exposed to a 'flexible' definition of physical activity, with lower expectations, were more likely to continue exercising in the future.[25] Adopting this 'positive activity adequacy' mindset – the belief that what you're doing is enough, and that physical activity isn't consigned to a dedicated, exercise 'hour' – is more likely to foster a healthy lifestyle and subsequent behavioural changes. The mere belief that one is engaging in exercise has been found to account for half of the mental health benefits of movement.[26]

While this growth-based outlook on exercise habits may appear to soothe the, 'Just believe in yourself' and, 'You can do anything' artillery, it's important to remember it's not a route to idolising motivational memes, and hoping you'll shed a few pounds just by watching YouTube videos in your pyjamas. We shouldn't expect results to fall into our laps merely through hoping, or wishing. Those are empty reassurances. Not only must you take time to craft this productive mindset, but, also, build upon the right behaviours to engender progress, too. It's not about simply *having* a growth mindset; you require the companion component of *acting* on it, as well.

It's worth noting that there isn't a direct relationship between a growth mindset and exercise frequency. Espousing an incremental mentality enhances other aspects of your life inadvertently; this, in turn, improves your ability to reform your exercise behaviours. It doesn't, however, instantly transport you to the gym. From reinforcing the correct values and identity, to strengthening your perseverance, and improving self-efficacy, a growth mindset augments other parts of your character – which *then* leads to sustained exercise habits.

Adopting A Growth Mindset With Nutrition

Just as my friend had struggled to last any longer than the all-too-familiar, three-week stretch at the gym, she also failed to see it through with any changes she'd made in her eating patterns. One by one, those diets came and went. Why? It's been found that the category of mindset that individuals hold – relating to beliefs about whether their physique is malleable or fixed – will also regulate their eating behaviours and, subsequently, chances of losing weight.

Researchers in one study set out to test whether peoples' eating choices were influenced by the type of mindset they displayed.[27] They found that, when offered raisins – a 'healthy' snack – there were no differences in the number of calories consumed between *fixed* and *growth* mindset groups. When, however, they were offered M&Ms – an 'unhealthy' snack – those who possessed a growth mindset consumed *fewer* calories than those exercising a fixed outlook.

If you believe that dietary choices have little impact on your weight loss journey, (for example, "I've always been overweight, so another few M&Ms won't make a difference"), you're less likely to implement healthy eating behaviours. If you believe the decisions you make are linked to dieting success, however, (for example, "I can make a difference to the changes in my body, so I'm going to choose the fruit instead"), you'll be more inclined to favour healthy eating habits.

Eating 'healthily' requires less self-regulation to resist overeating. We've been programmed to believe that apples and broccoli are 'good' for us; it's not hard to say, 'no' to another piece of fruit, is it? Eating 'unhealthily', however, encourages a constant battle between the two sides of your brain. One moment it's telling you to eat nutritiously; the next, it's urging you to inhale one – or maybe, even, all – of the fourteen custard doughnuts at the breakfast buffet. If you believe you're in control of your ability to change, however – that each decision *will* influence results – then you'll invariably adopt smarter choices.

It's why the belief that dieting is inherently difficult (a *fixed* mindset) can become a self-fulfilling prophecy. Participants in one study who agreed with statements such as, "Eating healthy means sacrificing taste", and, "Things that are good for me rarely taste good", displayed a greater Body Mass Index (a measure of weight relative to height), and were less likely to consume 'healthy' food.[28] The mere expectation that losing weight can be a struggle, or that consuming certain foods makes dieting more challenging, leads to a greater propensity for weight gain.

While many dieters set out believing they can transform their physique, their underlying mindset continues to nudge at them like a hot, iron poker, until they eventually fall. Do they *truly* trust the decisions they make will have an impact on their physique? Whilst many will assume, on the surface, that declining the extra cookie, or piece of cake, will help them reach their aspirations, they may not believe, more deeply, that one, small decision will have any impact at all.

"One won't hurt, right?"

And while, admittedly, one single moment won't damage people's chances of long-term success, the frequency of such moments will do. Those who attain a physique they're content with remind themselves, regularly, that every decision they make will influence progress. They no longer believe that "One bite won't matter", but, instead, that every small conclusion carries weight (no pun intended). They're no longer convinced that their physique is encumbered by pre-set limitations; rather believing that every meal and snack they consume can influence how much body fat they're able to lose.

There's a profusion of articles constantly fortifying the impression that losing weight is impossible. From the "97% of dieters regain the weight"[29] narratives, to the anti-diet movement mantra that "Diets don't work", it's easy to see how people can become glued to the supposition that their efforts will be insufficient. Why even make any attempt, when the odds are stacked against them? If everyone gains back what they lose, then why should anyone bother? Such beliefs can become quickly embedded in the brain, distracting and tormenting us when faced with important decisions. How *confident* you are in the eating choices you make, therefore, also play a role in long-term success.[30] Overlooking any negative perceptions surrounding dieting, and possessing the determination to simply try, will provide a far greater foundation than embracing thoughts of failure.[31]

It's important to avoid showering yourself with beliefs like you, "Can't say no" or, "Can never stick to the plan". Cynicism and dejection, from the outset, will never work. Optimism and a degree of positivity truly matter. No longer are you reluctantly, "Attempting to see if this one finally works", but, now, excitedly, "Trying this flexible approach to finally make a change". Neither are you "counting down the days" until you give up, but, now accepting that newfound eating skills exemplify your life. Although converting from a pessimistic outlook to a hopeful one could seem trivial, the level of self-confidence you hold will abet progress more than you realise.

Such self-efficacy plays a large role, not only in your ability to change, but in how you react to relapses as well. When you – inevitably – deviate from the plan, the positivity you possess surrounding your eating habits will forecast how swiftly you'll get back on track. Believe it's yet another failure, to add to the cauldron of disconcerting slip-ups, and you'll have trouble in restarting. Believe, however, that you possess the strength to persevere – and make improvements – next time around, and you'll have no issue hopping back on that wagon. As the familiar saying goes, if you had a puncture in one of your car tyres, would you then set about piercing a hole in each of the other three, or simply focus on fixing the broken one? I'd hope for the latter.

Accepting that your diet is a challenge – and not an enterprise destined to fail – is crucial. Differentiating between a growth and fixed mindset, and subsequently adopting the former, will lead to healthier eating intentions and higher expectancy-value beliefs.[32] Even by merely valuing a nutritious diet and its impact on health, you're more likely to engage in healthier eating behaviours.[33] Start adopting this line of thinking: rather than viewing healthy eating as a chore, see it as a chance to experiment with unfamiliar recipes, flavours, and cuisines. You now no longer believe you're 'addicted' to junk food but, instead, possess the ability to make healthier choices in any situation – even an uncomfortable one. You're no longer convinced that engaging in yet another diet initiative is a futile task but, instead, see it as an opportunity to rehearse and expand your depository of eating skills. The domino effect of crafting these small-scale mindset adjustments will quickly surface.

Adopting A Growth Mindset With Stress

I'll never forget one of my first clients. Andy was like no one you've ever seen before. From juggling 50-hour workweeks as a lawyer, with spending time with his wife and three kids, to being an active member of his religious community – and still managing to partake in weekly tennis tournaments – his life was full-on. Not to mention, he also trained with me three times a week and was determined to get into – what he described as – "the best shape of his life by 60". He was the human equivalent of a high-functioning machine.

With such a relentless schedule came problems, however. Coping with so many facets in different areas of his life created stress. Work, social commitments, and others' expectations would escalate, before he could sustain a manageable grip on things. He often arrived at sessions with his phone by his ear and a look of despair etched across his face. He would frequently compare his life to a game of Whac-A-Mole; as soon as he quashed one stressful situation, another would emerge – almost immediately. When he first solicited my help – perhaps not surprisingly – Andy struggled to get into the shape he wanted.

Chronic stress can be harmful.[34] Elevated cortisol levels not only interfere with sleep and energy, but cause problems with hunger, cravings, and muscle growth. They inevitably impact on your ability to transform your physique. While too little stress can keep you from reaching your potential, too much can harm your health.[35]

Avoiding stress is tough. It's almost unavoidable. Are there proven ways to deal with such situations, however? While meditating and sipping on green tea may alleviate some of the pressures of life, there may be another, simpler method to combat those stressful situations. Analogous to exercise and nutrition, how you *view* each demanding plight life throws at you will foretell your ability to lose weight.

I knew that Andy was crumbling inside. He was becoming stressed about stress. He was succumbing to the pervasive notion that all demanding situations are harmful. In reality, this mental pressure and sense of alarm were nothing more than conditioned responses to specific stressors. The act of believing that 'stress is bad' was detrimental, in ways that stress, in itself, was not. Our feelings towards adversity are crucial.

Stress is placed on a 'mindset continuum'. That is, people perceive disturbing events in their lives as either "stress-is-enhancing" or "stress-is-debilitating".[36] This pertains to that same, *growth* (enhancing) or *fixed* (debilitating) mindset. In addressing this with Andy, instead of attempting to tackle each problem, individually, we set about changing his *perception* of each situation. If we could get him to accept – and utilise effectively – the stressful moments that arose in his life, he would be able to make better decisions and, ultimately, engage in the behaviours that would promote dieting success.

Together, we helped Andy adopt a, "Stress-is-enhancing" mindset. There is evidence to show that 'eustress' – that, is, *good* stress – is useful.[37] It enables you to perceive a situation as something within your control, and empowers increased focus and performance. A racing heartbeat and crippling anxiety are no longer an indication of failure, but a sign of energy and preparedness for an important and potentially rewarding event. People with optimistic and positive attitudes are, therefore, more stress-resistant.[38] This includes those who choose to reframe their stress-inducing busyness as a positive state. Meeting goal conflicts with constructive excitement – as opposed to perceiving the need to accomplish multiple things at once – can reduce feelings of stress.[39] Even US Navy SEALs who believed their stress enhanced health, performance and well-being, were found to display greater persistence through training, faster obstacle course times, and fewer negative evaluations from peers and instructors.[40]

In the case of Andy, we decided to flip each onerous moment on its head. No longer were work problems 'looming'; he viewed them, instead, as chances to improve his resilience. No longer was each tennis match a battle with nerves, but viewed as a possibility to improve his game. People who view stressful events as a challenge, and recognise overwhelm as one of life's guarantees, possess a larger recovery zone. They're simply less vulnerable to hardship. Even students who employ a growth mindset have been shown to display lower levels of cortisol during exam time.[41] That's not to say that stress will be eradicated from life entirely, but, flicking the switch to a growth mindset is often easier than dissecting each situation individually. I formally give you permission to dispose of that green tea.

Andy continued to adopt his newfound mindset with each part of his routine. The weight began to shift. He started to notice when stress would begin to take over; instead of succumbing to daunting feelings of panic, he'd alert himself that his body was simply preparing him for a new challenge. This was him letting his brain know *he* was in control of how he reacted. Every scenario that crept up on him was viewed as an opening for growth. It was no longer the case of, "I've got fifty tasks to do", but, instead, "I possess the work ethic to get all of these done". No more were there cries of, "I can't cope with everything"; his new mantra was, "I'm preparing my body to perform under pressure in the future". Just as challenge was the new apprehension, so improvement replaced the former trepidation.

Equally as important as your stress load, is your ability to handle it. Adopting a growth mindset will change your perception of each scenario. Instead of bowing to feelings of tension, start being flexible and creative with how you resolve them. You could move from, "I've got too little time to get to the gym" to asking, "How can I improve my time management, to ensure I have enough time to train?" Or, from, "I've got too many chores to finish to make a healthy meal for the family" to, "Overcoming this taxing situation will develop my consistency". When you decipher the symptoms of stress as a 'call for action' as opposed to a 'call for fear', you foster emotional balance and rational thoughts.

As with our exercise and eating habits, adopting a growth mindset around stress won't directly lead to weight loss, since implementing the right actions is still imperative. Changing your perception of stressful events will, however, go a long way in helping you do so. If you can interpret stressful situations as mandatory for growth, as opposed to drowning in life's chaos, you'll become more resilient, mindful, and tenacious in your dieting attempts.

The Problem With A Growth Mindset

One of my favourite cartoon strips involves two men discussing their recent dieting endeavours.

The first man turns to his friend and says, "I've tried Atkins, South Beach, and The Zone, and not one of 'em did a bit of good!"

His companion replies, "A new study says you should just cut calories and exercise."

The first man responds, "Oh, no way, if it doesn't work, I'd have no one to blame."

While satirical, this subtle point delineates a problem we may encounter when harnessing a growth mindset. By endorsing a mentality that promotes effort and responsibility, we then have nothing to blame but *ourselves*. Engaging with this 'blame game' may appeal to some but, for others, it has the potential to be damaging.

The trouble is, it's easy to overlook failure when snuggled deep in a growth mindset. This outlook can act like a security blanket, absolving people from incompetence and inaction. It seems that, if you simply blame hard work – or the lack of it – you'll be fine. Comforting yourself because you overate at the weekend but 'adopted a growth mindset' isn't, however, going to achieve results. Ascribing any failure to insufficient will fails to ignore the often intransigence of the body if there is no challenge made to it.

As discussed earlier, reassuring yourself that you can 'do anything' seldom creates change. When failure arises, that perspective only compounds any feelings of disappointment, since you end up blaming yourself. Instead of blaming hard work, it's imperative you unearth other skills and methods of behaviour change, to work on. Relieving yourself of responsibility for failures by solely embracing – or even condemning – a growth mindset is flawed. Yes, the choices you make have an impact on results, but it makes sense to use this approach to think and act fittingly, rather than as an excuse for another dieting failure.

It's also important to acknowledge the unbalanced playing field that some are participating on, when it comes to weight loss. From socioeconomic to demographic factors, effort and mindset aren't the only attributes that create, or hinder, an ability to change. Social determinants are also powerful. This is why any reprimanding of people who struggle with their weight – suggesting that they 'don't want it enough', or 'lack discipline' – is caked in delusion and oversight. It's not *just* about personal responsibility.

Max Weber, a German sociologist, coined the term 'life chances', to describe probabilities a person has in their life to realise their needs or desires.[42] Everyone possesses the opportunity to make healthier choices, but can only choose from what is available to them. The overweight person whom you see struggling to walk down the street is probably desperate to lose weight – it may be almost constantly in their thoughts – but what if they can barely afford to pay the heating bill, let alone worry about purchasing an acai smoothie bowl for breakfast? Socioeconomic status plays a defining role in people's chances of adopting a healthy lifestyle, therefore. As an example, this is why it has been reported that African Americans consistently present fewer healthy eating habits compared with White Americans.[43] Cultivating a growth mindset can sometimes exacerbate feelings of personal responsibility – that, if you possess the ability to change, then your weight, size, and shape is all *your* fault.

This double-edged sword is often overlooked when discussing the purported benefits of an incremental mindset. Embracing your ability to grow and improve as an individual – and, therefore, increase your chances of losing weight – is important, but blaming yourself, when, in reality, other factors are at play, is a recipe for disaster.

Similarly, judging others for their supposed lack of discipline can be a misguided attempt at utilising a growth mindset. Weight stigma is rife in modern society,[44] and the pervasive belief that everyone has complete control over their decisions is distorted.[45] This paradox – those who possess optimistic ideas around weight loss can occasionally hold negative attitudes towards others – exacerbates hostile judgement around 'fat', and around 'overweight people'. We must consider the diverse circumstances that influence body shapes and people's accessibility before any of us *solely* accepts total responsibility for self or others. While it may be nice to believe that *anyone* can achieve sustained weight loss, it's not always possible – not for everyone, at least.

Once this is acknowledged, you can then start tackling better choices. Completely absolving yourself from change because of the situation you find yourself in, is, however, also indefensible. It's not about effort with your body per se, but the effort cultivated with *individual tasks*. While 'losing weight' may be the overall goal, harnessing a desirable mindset to manage keeping a food diary, improving your relationship with food, or increasing strength in the gym – as examples – will dictate your ability to create a long-lasting transformation. We know that those in disadvantaged societies have still been found to experience greater benefit from adopting a growth mindset, thus indicating it still includes some importance.[46] It may not be the complete solution, to be revered like a magical elixir, but the concept of a growth mindset can still stand firm in the face of certain situations.

How To Create a Growth Mindset

The type of mindset that you nurture will surface in your life the most. If it's that *fixed* mindset, it will occupy your life in various ways. You'll blame others, avoid challenges, and concede defeat, before you've even started.

Embrace a *growth* mindset, however, and you'll adopt resultant behaviours that help to reform and elevate you. You'll accept each challenge with vigour; you'll take failure as a chance to improve – and you'll persist with the necessary skills required for success. Simply acknowledging that your physical fitness is within your control – and can be developed – will ensure you maintain motivation, rather than spiralling into self-defeating rumination – a seemingly glaring point that many people, nevertheless, forget.

While striving to implement a *growth mindset* is crucial, it's important to remember, however, that people don't exclusively fit into one mindset camp only. They tend to flit between the two, depending on the task. While you may view a 'chin-up' as an exercise you'll never be able to master, you may have faith that your cooking skills will improve with practice, for example. Although another bad weekend at the pub could deter you, you may still believe you can make better decisions when ordering a takeaway. Ultimately, it's about identifying those activities and beliefs that can infiltrate the *fixed* mindset camp and slowly chipping away towards improvements that direct you towards the *growth* outlook.

You're Just Not There, Yet

Weight loss isn't black or white. A weight loss plateau, or being unable to observe physical changes for a while doesn't mean you've failed – just like surpassing your calorie goal for the day, or missing a gym session doesn't make you a chronic underachiever. Whatever the task or goal, you must appreciate when you're not there *yet*. Assuming this expectant attitude ensures you're more inclined to remain adherent, and consider the future, when faced with moments of despondency. It's no longer about acquiring instant results *now*, but polishing and embracing the process until you *do* get results. Practicing this inspirited mentality will pre-empt dedication and durability.

You must appreciate that every aspect of your weight loss journey is a skill. Just like playing chess, or learning to draw, each can be improved with repetition. From learning to consume a vegetable with every meal, to practicing self-acceptance, each, continually-refined behaviour contributes to that overarching ambition. You can use each, demanding opportunity you encounter to better yourself – to improve. It's not always about dropping those ten stubborn kilograms, nor fitting into that swimsuit, but using each part of your journey to refine your character and your ability to work hard.

Just like sportspeople whose only focus surrounds talent, and teachers who believe some children are destined for the top, while others can't be saved,[47] viewing your weight loss journey as another, pre-destined endeavour, that you'll never transcend, will only facilitate those 'fixed' feelings. Switch your mindset to one that lauds gradual improvement and can overcome any challenge thrown at it, however – and not only will you blossom, but your brain will change, too.

Developing a growth mindset means you're able to overlook the current obstacle you're faced with. Reminding yourself that you'll experience plenty more opportunities to fine-tune skills, or forge progress, is the principal mechanism to practicing consistency and remaining adherent. Throwing your hands in the air, and hoovering up the contents of the biscuit tin – because you believe everything is lost – will only feed that fixed mindset. Welcome imperfection, as opposed to berating it. Allow yourself to overcome your weaknesses. It's not that you've failed, you just haven't discovered the right method, or practiced a certain eating skill enough – thus far. There is still time.

Whenever a thought, or flurry of negative words, infiltrates your mind, simply place the word "Yet" at the end of the self-induced remark that's attempting to penetrate your belief system, such as:

"I haven't lost the weight, *yet.*"

"I'm unable to overcome the guilt I feel surrounding consuming certain foods, *yet.*"

"I don't have the motivation to get to the gym consistently, *yet.*"

The addition of that simple, three-letter signal remodels your thinking from one of fixed to growth. This seemingly trivial extension now promotes a mindset comprising persistence and anticipation. By accepting that you haven't obtained those ambitions, or mastered that reformed mindset as it stands, you permit yourself to remain devoted to the direction you wish to take. You're now a work in progress, as opposed to something that can't be rebuilt.

Learn From Your Failures

Expecting to swim seamlessly through your weight loss journey, without the occasional hiccup, or cookie-induced coma, is flawed. You will likely fail at some point. *How* you react to these failures, however, is the true sign of a growth mindset. Just like Steve Jobs left Apple in 1985, but returned to lead the company to its towering eminence years later, the mindset you adopt – when faced with hardship – will signpost your probability of success. When you ditch the healthy, nutritious meal for a takeaway, how do you subsequently behave? When you miss the gym because you're feeling tired, what outlook on the situation do you uphold? In adopting a growth mindset, not only will you improve reactions to such setbacks, but also get better at detecting when they arise.[48]

Those with a fixed mindset will accept failure as part of who they are. They're less likely to proceed and display levels of robustness. "I'm not cut out for losing weight", they'll tell themselves. Setbacks are viewed as inevitable. Adopting a growth mindset, however, will help when confronting failure. When you overeat, you'll be more likely to interpret the reasons why that event occurred, and endeavour to make your next meal a healthy one. When you take measurements to gauge progress and realise you haven't lost any centimetres from your waist, you'll be more likely to focus on the process and keep visiting the gym. Setbacks are viewed as a chance to progress, not quit.

Those with a fixed mindset will often avoid failure altogether. If they believe their body shape is confined to a pre-destined narrative, or they've always been – and will continue to be – 'the fat one', then they'll summon up excuses and justifications as to why trying is worthless. Failure scares them. They'll state they're 'happy with the way they look' or that 'they don't have the time to concentrate on losing weight right now'. This avoidance-mindset only serves to toughen the outlook and physique they're currently unhappy with.

To cultivate a growth mindset, instead, it's therefore important to not only accept failure as a necessity, but forecast how you'll react to those inevitable slip-ups. Prepare for how you'll behave in the face of defeat. If you do overeat needlessly, will you have a nutritious, 'go-to' meal that you can create immediately, to rebuild that momentum? If you realise you haven't lost any body fat since your last progress check, will you have a method of reminding yourself of your values? Having these actions and thoughts written down, ahead of time, will ensure that you'll know how to proceed when any such disconcerting moments arise. It helps to start embracing the notion that pain, suffering, and failure will usually precede goal achievement.

Take The Right Action

Cultivating a growth mindset doesn't arise from poring over a treasury of self-help books and declaring, confidently, that you'll "…work harder next time". It isn't just about effort. It's important to remember that changing your physique is the ultimate aim at play, and, by only endorsing determination, you're restricting the tools you have available to succeed. It's also about continually refining the learning process and ensuring you're always advancing towards the end goal, with the *right* actions. When we admire effort exclusively, ignoring the outcome, we submit to what's commonly known as a *False Growth Mindset.*

Just working harder, whilst implementing the wrong strategies won't yield the transformation you seek. While you may be able to run a faster, 10-kilometre run, through constant practice, is that going to be effective in helping you acquire the physique you want? Is adopting a growth mindset, when undertaking the Carnivore diet – despite the Carnivore diet causing you untold misery – going to be beneficial? Is working hard, for the sake of working hard, a productive strategy? People can easily fall into this widespread trap. They believe they need to implement more behaviours, more training sessions, and more effort, when, in fact, they just need to work smarter. 'More' doesn't always equate to 'better'. Every action, whilst underpinned by character and determination, must be bound to the outcome.

Researcher, Carol Dweck, when talking about the oversimplification of a growth mindset within students, said, "Teachers were just praising effort that was not effective, saying "Wow, you tried really hard!" But students know that if they didn't make progress and you're praising them, it's a consolation prize. They also know you think they can't do any better. So, this kind of growth-mindset idea was misappropriated to try to make kids feel good when they were not achieving."[49]

Return, now, to a moment where you displayed a similar channel of thought. Did you shower yourself in praise for trying hard when, in reality, it wasn't warranted? Did you avoid the difficult and appropriate task, because you were focused on breeding a mindset of growth and improvement? It's imperative that you detect when inaccurate endorsements for hard work emerge, when, instead, implementing timely actions is of greater significance. Just because you read a chapter on the growth mindset, in a dieting book, doesn't instantly mean you've won.

Dive Into Tasks That Scare You

Enveloped within the pretexts people lather their ego with, exists fear. The fear of failure, of embarrassment, of change, and of responsibility. People can become scared of exposing any home truths regarding their behaviours, so that, instead of being open to learning and improving, they avoid activities that fill them with unease. They may avoid the gym, shy away from keeping a food diary, or flee the work required to improve their relationship with food and their body image.

When people want to present themselves as smart, they may become fearful of appearing foolish or as a 'failure', should they get the task or question wrong. When the anxiety of attempting something new, and appearing naïve, is greater than the pleasure received from staying safe and looking intelligent, they may freeze. They will tend to avoid the responsibility required to make mistakes – and any subsequent progress. When individuals operate from this place of fear, they resist learning; they procrastinate, and tend to recoil from pursuing new callings. This entity-based mentality drives behaviour, but not in a good way. It radiates as laziness.

Unravelling and embracing this fear will enable you, instead, to cultivate a growth mindset. When you welcome the inevitable apprehension experienced with attempting something untested, you'll start to crave repetition and increase determination. No longer will fear forestall your actions; excitement at tackling a novel challenge, and potentially making mistakes, will emanate. Instead of enduring anxiety, therefore, at appearing potentially defeated, you'll be able to pinpoint that underlying feeling and quickly flip it to a willingness to master new experiences. Discovering such clarifications can provide critical insights into your flaws and subsequent cover stories. Are you actually too busy, or are you fearful of confronting mistakes once you start? Is your bodyweight 'set point' really fixed, or are you fearful of what a personal transformation will do to your life? Is it really not the 'right time', or are you fearful of the uncertainty that starting can provoke?

When you realise that fear – and, subsequently, inaction – has no place in your life, moments previously defined by inactivity can turn very quickly into flashes of persistence and progress. No longer are you hesitant at starting a food diary, but eager to improve nutritional habits. Now you're not nervous about visiting the gym, but, instead, raring to add another skill to your toolbox of life's quality experiences. No longer are you stuck in the fixed mindset, but, instead, excited to grow. Every time feelings of resistance and laziness surface, ask yourself why they've appeared. You'll usually find it's because you're avoiding the task due to a fear of failure, and of being recognised as irrational and/or lacking judgement. Embrace growth, however, and you'll foster enthusiasm at the opportunity to fail, to try something new, and, ultimately, to lose the weight you've always wanted to lose.

Chapter Summary And Taking Action

- People stuck in a fixed mindset will become entrenched in a belief system that asserts that they're powerless to improvement, unable to change their body shape, and that their weight loss journeys have already been mapped out for them. They subsequently avoid challenges, quit easily, and are fearful of change.

- People who embrace a growth mindset firmly believe they can improve, that they can influence their physique, and have control over their fat loss journey. They subsequently try new activities, persevere, and are eager to learn and improve. Those who adopt a growth mindset possess heightened expectations, partake in increased exercise frequency, display better coping strategies, and hold greater nutritional habits.

- Consider what thoughts and beliefs you have about certain activities (e.g., "I've never been good at going to the gym", or, "I never seem to get better at saying 'no' to the cake"). Adopting a mindset that encourages growth – and believing your brain can physically change, too – will enhance exercise, eating, and stress-related behaviours.

- Start changing your thoughts. Examine what is required to flip fixed thoughts to ones that promote growth (e.g., "I'm going to go to the gym so I can work on my squat technique", or, "Even if devour the cake, I'm still going to attempt to improve mindful decision-making"). Acknowledging that your physical fitness is within your control – and can be developed – will ensure you maintain motivation, rather than spiralling into self-defeating rumination.

- While relieving yourself of responsibility for failures by solely embracing – or even condemning – a growth mindset is flawed, to improve your outlook on things, start adding the word 'yet' to any negative thoughts you have, surrounding your ability or effort levels – and embrace the opportunity to attempt new tasks that scare you (e.g., "I haven't lost any weight, *yet*", and "I may be busy, but now is the best time to start").

- At every opportunity, start to cultivate that growth mindset and avoid any pre-destined and fixed thoughts that surface regularly. Make a note of every time one of these thoughts pops into your head and make an effort to change it – there and then.

CHAPTER 3
Your Expectations Suck:
Mastering The Art Of Goal Setting

The Sydney Opera House perches elegantly on the edge of Sydney Harbour in Australia. Its famous roof, consisting of a string of large, precast-concrete 'shells', showcases its distinctive aura. Its value as a national symbol makes it one of the most iconic buildings in the world. From ballet to the theatre, and opera, the world heritage site hosts over 1,500 performances and is attended by over 1.2 million people each year. Its unique appearance has been said to have, "…changed the image of an entire country".[1]

The construction of the building wasn't all plain sailing, however. The planning, development, and assembly of the symbolic landmark was nothing short of disastrous and, were it not for a significant overhaul of the original design and project timeframe, it may never have happened at all.

In 1959, after a lengthy design competition, Danish architect Jørn Utzon was commissioned to produce a venue that would host large, theatrical productions.[2] The project, described as 'genius', was initially budgeted at 7 million Australian dollars and expected to take four years to complete. It appeared straightforward. These estimates were made, however, even *before* drawings, designs, or funds had been granted. Utzon hadn't even visited the harbour himself. Things – inevitably – started to unravel.

Following pressure from government officials, changes of original contract documents, complications with the initial brief, and unexpected weather complications, the Opera House was already running *forty-seven weeks* behind schedule, just two years later. Some of the striking interiors were pulled out and disposed of midway through its construction, while acoustic and seating designs were discarded completely. Disputes between Utzon and the government ensued and, along with significant iterations to the design, the project soon began to drag. Completion seemed a long way off.

In 1973, a whole *ten years* and *102 million Australian dollars* later, the much-compromised Opera House was finally completed; the planning, design, and construction eventually dovetailing over a decade beyond its initial inception. The project's original cost and duration forecasts turned out to be wildly misguided; nothing more than a couple of slapdash figures plucked from thin air. Projections of four years and 7 million Australian dollars seemed like a blip on the horizon. The now-nostalgic venue still holds the world record for the largest cost overrun, at 1,400 per cent.[3] For you and me, that's akin to buying a £1 punnet of goji berries for £14 – and receiving them ten years after making the purchase.

Despite its prominence throughout world culture today, the project has since been labelled as a lesson in what *not* to do. The Opera House itself states its story as, '…one that started as a fairy tale, had a tragic middle, and emerges as a tale of reconciliation'. Its timeframe and cost proposal were nothing short of a disaster.

Sagas of misinformed predictions, budget oversights, and planning blunders don't end there, unfortunately. In the mid-1980s, the United Kingdom grossly underestimated the cost and total production of 232 Eurofighter Typhoon, multirole fighter jets, for its Royal Airforce. Each plane ended up costing 75 per cent more than predicted and, while the number of planes initially ordered dropped to just 160, the bill for development and production *rose,* by 20 per cent to £20.2 billion.[4] A new tolling system based in Germany lost an unpredicted 156 million Euros per month, owing to optimistic predictions from software developers – and led to a cancellation of the contract in 2004.[5] Time and time again, it seems, gaps between expectations and outcomes have ended up askew.

Erroneous predictions surrounding times and costs were wildly off the mark. Under such circumstances, no one benefits – least of all those making the original forecasts. Simply put, you, me, and every other ambitious individual out there, are not very good at making predictions. We underestimate, overhype, and miscalculate on a daily basis.

These prevalent and wild, cognitive biases are obviously unhelpful when dieting.

Specifically, people fall into the 'planning fallacy' trap – a well-established bias that states people envision a typical occurrence of how long something will take to be completed, only for it to then take *much longer*.[6] Our expectations aren't aligned with reality. This fallacy – the propensity to narrowly focus on the end goal and ignore additional, influencing factors – is possibly nowhere more prominent than when attempting to lose weight. Our expectations surrounding weight loss and its outcomes are so fiercely afield, that we then end up with a defective, and potentially damaging, dieting mindset. Could we, therefore, reshape our expectations? Might we adopt a new line of thinking, which means we don't succumb to improbable assumptions – and our own, Sydney Opera House disaster?

Why You Have Unrealistic Expectations

There are a plethora of outlandish claims circling the health and fitness industry, which have led to a steady stream of unrealistic and unattainable expectations affecting anyone embarking on a new diet. From how much weight you can lose in a week, to how long it will take to reach your overall goal – and how easy you'll find the whole process – people fail to start any physical transformation with the right calculations and rationality, straight from the outset. These quixotic endeavours lead to misjudgements, dejection, and – ultimately – failure. We all have our own, 'Opera House' quest inside us.

The 'planning fallacy' is the umbrella that conceals several destructive, mental biases.[7] From optimism to focal and impact biases, many are often submerged in murky waters when starting any diet. Research has shown that these excessive discrepancies, between expectations and actual outcomes, can be demoralising; they may lead to negative self-thoughts and, even, self-blame.[8] This invariably results in aversive self-focus, impaired performance, and the eventual abandonment of long-term goals. The more ambitious the expectations, the more harmful the outcome.

The better you can get at unpacking these kinds of falsehoods, the better you'll be at navigating the perils of the dieting process. Adherence, motivation, and feelings of success will all increase. You'll be able to persevere when faced with obstacles. No longer will you want to take a sledgehammer to the scales every Monday morning. Nor start dieting just three weeks before your friend's wedding, when you realise three weeks isn't actually a very long time. You'll begin to craft a mindset that will take on board what to expect – where, perhaps, you've ignored and failed to surmount such challenging hurdles before. No longer will your expectations suck.

Should You Lose Two Pounds A Week?

Did you know that there are approximately 36,000 McDonald's restaurants in the world, of which around 7,200 are based in the UK?

One of the figures in that statement is inaccurate, however. While there are, indeed, roughly 36,000 McDonald's restaurants worldwide, there *aren't* 7,200 in the UK.

I want you to now guess what you believe the real answer to be (it's probably best to make your prediction before you read on further).

If your estimate was *higher* than 1,300 (the real answer), then you just fell for the *anchoring bias.* That is, when individuals are asked to estimate a quantity; it's been found that their final response is influenced by any numbers they've recently observed.[9] My proclamation was over five times the actual answer. Whilst you probably had no idea what the true amount was, your guess was undoubtedly influenced by my original – albeit arbitrary – figure. You didn't know how many McDonald's branches were in the UK, so unwittingly used my extravagant suggestion as a guide, resulting in a higher, chicken-nugget influenced, figure yourself (I, again, apologise for my undue act of trickery). People form a judgement from an initial projection, and then adjust that estimate – which is labelled an 'anchor' – to construct a final decision.

How many times have you heard that you should always aim to lose two pounds of bodyweight a week? Or, in some magazine articles, 'ten pounds in just ten minutes'? Or, that some people should be a certain size or bodyweight? Hearing these auspicious claims over and over again tends to lead to a mental block. We anchor in others' predictions and use them as guides for ourselves. If others are losing that much, or can lift that much weight in the gym, then why can't we?

One study showed that patients entering a diet and exercise programme expected to lose an astounding – and simply speculative – *20-40 per cent* of their starting bodyweight; figures that can only be realistically achieved through bariatric surgery.[10] 'Impressive' and 'fast' is what people have always heard; 'impressive' and 'fast' is what people use to form predictions about their own journey.

Such claims are often unattainable, however. And, when individuals *don't* lose two pounds a week, or fail to achieve their desired goal in the specific timeframe they've set, they view themselves – and their endeavours – as failures. Even when provided with the opportunity to adjust initial estimates, people have often been shown to stand by any opening predictions they made about how long a task would take.[11] People's weight loss expectations are guided by numbers and predictions they've frequently espied. Using those blanket claims, to regulate their journey, sets them off on the wrong path from the outset, unfortunately. Even experts in the property market fall into this trap, and estimate higher house prices when receiving misplaced information before viewing a house.[12] Misguided forecasts arise from assuming we all follow identical quests.

Failing to comprehend the wealth of factors that can influence any weight loss journey – from age, gender, and muscle mass, to metabolic adaptions suffered from previous dieting endeavours – will only lead to disappointment. Just because you've witnessed a particular rate of weight loss, or learnt of impressive and speedy results prompted by a specific dieting protocol, it doesn't mean you should use those as a baseline for your own pursuits.

Are You Fixated On The End Goal?

Dieters will often become infatuated with their weight loss goal; the result is all they focus on. It's all about the number, the look, and the reduced body fat percentage they'll acquire when their journey is 'complete'. Confining attention to the result, leads, however, to the oversight of factors that can influence progress – as well as what will occur when that goal has been attained. From the process taking longer than expected, to encountering inevitable difficulties along the way, this negligence of all that precedes the outcome evokes poor expectations from the outset. This is known as *focal bias.*

People often perceive their problem – in this case, their weight loss journey – as unique.[13] They neglect to consider past attempts, not only from others but by themselves as well. It doesn't matter if they know friends and family who have taken years to achieve long-lasting changes, or whose last diet took longer than expected; they continue to underestimate the complexities of their latest challenge. "It will be different this time", they tell themselves. Interestingly, ask those very same people how *others* will fare in the same situation, and they'll hold pessimistic views about their friends' chances. Optimistic predictions about their own endeavour still reign strong, however, and, when any unaccounted-for moments inevitably rock the boat, failure looms.

At the outset of any venture, people also often only consider the best possible outcome.[14] They can only envisage the pair of jeans they'll be able to slip into, for example, or the number of times they'll visit the gym each week. They – mistakenly – fail to consider the complications that will arise, and other possible outcomes that may transpire subsequently, such as not being able to slip into the pair of jeans after all, or that lounging in the park on a sunny day is more appealing than going to the gym. Disregarding these unforeseen problems – from social events and holidays, to injuries and moments of discouragement – promotes flawed expectations. Even those who've been asked, specifically, to *not* provide a realistic prediction of how many times they'll exercise, in the two weeks following their projection, overestimate how many times they'll jump on the treadmill.[15] Such unrealistic optimism has far-reaching, negative consequences on goal setting, decision-making, and planning.

We gaze into the future and are convinced we'll have more time, energy, and motivation reserved for the tasks we don't want to perform today. Take, for example, the study that involved students being asked to drink an unappealing, ketchup-and-soy-sauce concoction (practical research for the book didn't extend this far).[16] Those who were told they'd have to drink the liquid in the *next* semester were willing to drink twice as much than those asked to take a swig in the following few minutes. We're convinced that we're more likely to execute a certain behaviour in the future.

How many times have you said to yourself that you'll exercise tomorrow, or later, only to find it doesn't quite pan out as planned? Or, that it doesn't matter; you'll choose the healthier meal next Friday night – only to find yourself ordering the same takeaway, again? This impaired hopefulness compounds unrealistic expectations surrounding exercise and nutrition habits. You believe you'll do more – and better – next time, than you actually will.

Both the oversight of previous weight loss attempts, from ourselves and others, and the optimism surrounding our future habits and motivation, create rose-tinted visions of the journey ahead. We underestimate how long things will take and romanticise adherence to future plans. Our fixation on the end goal, and not necessarily the highs and lows of the process, will only ameliorate false expectations. The future version of you won't be as motivated or as kind to your ego as you'd like to believe.

Do You Believe Your Current Thoughts Will Remain The Same In The Future?

I wonder if, at some point, you've made plans to see a friend, only for that day to arrive and you then realise that you don't actually like that friend much, let alone want to share a cocktail with them. When we make goals or plans that seem distant, or abstract, we tend to fail to account for the intricacies of that plan. We believe everything will be fine. When that day approaches, though, or finally arrives, you'll begin to focus on the concrete features of your arrangement – such as remembering that your friend isn't a very nice person who once kicked your cat. You then instantly regret agreeing to meet, in the first place.

This is the essence of *Temporal Construct Theory*,[17] which can be applied to your weight loss efforts as well. That, when goals and plans are somewhere and sometime in the future, you'll fail to account for obstacles, time constraints, and potential emotions that may occur between 'now' and 'then'. It's known, more specifically, as *projection bias.*

Abstract plans seldom lead to results, unfortunately. People are aware of the start and finish lines, but the blurred, middle period clouds their calculations. They fail to account for how long and difficult it will be to get there. Dieter's project their feelings *now* onto how they believe they'll feel in the *future.*[18] They have no concept of what the challenge should, or will, look like – which only enhances unrealistic expectations. It doesn't help that the men and women in the magazines make it look so simple.

If you're unaware of the potential obstacles that will surface in the coming weeks – such as, an unplanned birthday party, or your car needing to be serviced so you can't get to the gym – you'll only amplify any misguided projections. When such obstacles naturally arise, you likely get confused. "This wasn't meant to happen; maybe I'm doing something wrong. Maybe I'm not meant to lose weight?"

Taking a moment to detail all the potential hurdles that will arise in the future, however, will strengthen predictions about the quest ahead.[19] This is why transformation photos and extravagant weight loss claims from some personal trainers, or media outlets, tend to be more harmful than helpful. Only contemplating the 'end goal' – and not the hardships we must conquer to achieve sustainable changes – leads to problems. People only see the 'before and after' and not the 'middle'. In truth, the middle matters more.

Allowing assertions such as, 'Lose ten pounds in three weeks', to guide your journey will only exacerbate any current, starry-eyed expectations you possess. In an ideal world, it should be, 'Lose ten pounds of body fat in at least six months, while navigating unplanned work projects, spontaneous social events, feelings of despondency, and a potential, world pandemic'. Unfortunately, that directive doesn't sell quite as well. Even so, when planning a diet, you must focus on time points that are closer to your current state.[20] Stop focusing, therefore, on how you will feel six months down the line – focus on the next six days, instead. This will not only enable you to establish reasonable timelines, but also outline the actions required to overcome any likely obstacles.

Do You Think You'll Be Happier Than You'll Actually Be?

On the surface, many people equate a thinner, leaner body with instant happiness. From feeling lighter, and being able to purchase smaller clothes sizes, to feeling more comfortable without any clothes on – sporting a slimmer shape is the ultimate achievement for most.

"Just look at how happy all those people are who have leaner physiques", they think to themselves.

This positive, exaggerated future that people project onto themselves is, unfortunately, misguided. Losing weight, and acquiring a perceived, 'ideal' body isn't all that it's hyped up to be. It doesn't often bring the joy, acceptance, and approval that many people believe it will. Frequently, these other, seemingly 'successful' and 'smaller' people are no happier with their bodies – or lives – than they, themselves, currently are.

It's been found that people consistently overestimate the affective impact of future events.[21] Utopian predictions lead to faulty assumptions about the power of a specific goal on their happiness. It's why a new iPhone, or promotion at work, never leads to sustained levels of joy – it turns out that, funnily enough, you *still* hate your job.

People tend to forecast wrongly how much pleasure losing weight will bring. Visions of bliss – perhaps along with an influx of social media followers – may be eagerly anticipated when armed with a 'six-pack' or toned legs; yet those heightened feelings of satisfaction are never quite attained. While self-confidence, energy, and a positive body image may increase up to a certain point, there'll never be an occasion where you're completely fulfilled. You'll *always* find body parts, or elements of your physique, that you're not content with. Meanwhile, any negative feelings surrounding self-worth and esteem are still prominent, no matter the number on the scales, or your hip-to-waist ratio.

When people set out on any weight loss journey, they automatically expect their levels of happiness to increase. They infer, wrongly, that they'll feel 'better' or 'happier' for losing weight. When such gratifying feelings don't emerge, however, people assume they're doing something wrong. They may continue chasing a 'perfect' set of abs, in the hope it will pacify any raging self-doubt, criticism, or self-objectification. Until they focus on repairing those insecurities, however, that cycle – the tendency to pursue one pleasure after another – will never end.

Individuals also tend to neglect how their feelings will potentially be affected by other life events, whether a change in job, or finding a new girlfriend or boyfriend, for example. They subsequently also overestimate the future impact of losing weight. Dan Gilbert, in his book, *Stumbling on Happiness,* says, "We assume that what we feel as we imagine the future is what we'll feel when we get there, but in fact, what we feel as we imagine the future is often a response to what's happening in the present."[22] The reality of the future is never as rewarding as you predict it to be. Don't ignore how your current situation is affecting your thoughts, and promises, surrounding any goals or expectations you possess.

While you may exude more pride and self-esteem towards your physique when fat loss occurs – which is, of course, never a bad thing – you must remember that your happiness levels will spike for a fleeting moment, but then always return to a baseline afterwards. It's the *promise* of happiness that sets us off on a journey, with the expectation of developing a contented self – which means you invariably end up chasing the wrong ambitions.[23] While you should pursue reward, you should seek the *right* type of reward. Happiness will surface from self-improvement and cultivating expedient life traits, not from exclusively weighing less or looking slimmer. Focusing on character development, the process, moments of planning and preparation, as well as learning from mistakes, will cultivate more happiness in reaching that desired bodyweight or body fat percentage.

How To Set The Right Expectations

It Will Always Take Longer Than You Think

Strict dieting timeframes can *occasionally* be useful. When people fail to consider modifications, however – along with slip-ups, and lessons learnt from the past – they'll be no better off than their work colleague who's attempting the same diet with no knowledge of those potential implications. It's time to accept that long-lasting change probably won't happen in that ideal timespan you might initially envisage. Just like the Chinese Bamboo Tree, which fails to grow for the first four years of its existence – only then to sprout an extraordinary, twenty-seven metres in just five weeks – you must expect results to take time, not surface immediately. Successful fat loss is a long, arduous game.

More often than not, charting short and specific weight loss timeframes will set you up for setbacks and – ultimately – frustration. Hofstadter's Law, a form of the Planning Fallacy, states that, "It always takes longer than you expect, even when you take into account Hofstadter's Law."[24] Allowing yourself more time than you originally planned for – and, potentially, even *more* time than that – will encourage pragmatic expectations. No longer will you start dieting for your summer holiday six weeks prior, but six *months* earlier. Neither will you believe you're able to squat your bodyweight in one month, but, more realistically, in one *year*. No longer will quick-fix timeframes cloud judgement, hope, and rationality. It will *always* take longer than you think.

The more complex a task – and none more so than attempting to lose weight – the more steps, and delays, are going to be involved from start to finish. Those who accepted more steps in the planning of their wedding, for example, were less likely to succumb to the planning fallacy.[25] And perhaps avoided an argument over the colour of the invitations. Whether it be having to look after your children when they're ill – and therefore missing the gym – or a spontaneous weekend away with your partner, and dining out at various restaurants, there'll always be developments that occur unexpectedly. You simply can't account for such moments. Therefore, putting pressure on yourself to lose a specific amount of weight in a certain amount of time serves only to heighten feelings of anxiety and stress. You start taking unnecessary risks to adhere to that pre-set deadline, and may even end up worse off than before – if you haven't given up already, of course. Either allow yourself more time, or start sooner.

Similarly, let history be your guide. Delve into the success stories of others and unearth the timeframes they adhered to. By exploring similar situations, and their outcomes – commonly known as *Reference Class Forecasting*[26] – you can make better predictions about the future. If people have always regained the weight they lost, in following the diet you're now attempting, why assume you'll be any different? If friends have consistently lost motivation around three weeks of their journey, then uncover methods to overcome those same struggles.

Be wary of the types of brazen assurances that pervade the internet. While the individual you can see on social media may have transformed their physique in twelve weeks, did they manage to sustain that transformation? While that same individual may look great, how much effort did they have to implement *before* the start of those twelve weeks? What challenges did they have to weather, to get there? Not only will you likely discover that the process took longer than you think, but you'll also discover the outbreak of problems and misfortunes they faced. Avoid thinking your journey will be any different. Taking precautions, and canvassing previous scenarios, will prevent you from expecting instant results – and will encourage a patient, long-term approach instead.

There Will Always Be Hurdles To Overcome

Nobody's fat loss journey is going to cruise along, obstacle-free. There will always be life events that surface, such as social gatherings, holidays, weddings, and work projects. There might also be injuries, and the times when you spend forty-five minutes having to clean the dog's poo off the kitchen floor instead of making dinner – along with other, crippling roadblocks. Expecting your journey to run smoothly is short-sighted. Unless you live a charmed life, it's a recipe for failure. Pre-empting such roadblocks – and installing diversions to overcome them – will curb any unrealistic expectations from the outset. When those hurdles arrive, you won't be surprised; you'll be prepared.

Whenever people are asked to identify just three obstacles that could transpire during a given task, their predictions about how long the activity will take increase – and their optimism over any quick-fire results subsides.[27] You must do the same. From anything on a weekly level, such as work drinks or a family meal out, to a yearly level, such as a holiday or a stressful period at work, figuring out potential solutions to any problems those situations could present will allay impractical aspirations. If you anticipate difficulties, you won't be as inclined to chuck that diet book in the bin when things go awry, and will appreciate how to maintain your exercise and nutrition habits.[28]

One favoured approach to overcoming obstacles is utilising a technique called 'implementation intentions'.[29] When people form conditional plans, within which they forecast the precise behaviours they'll execute in response to specific cues, they increase their chances of succeeding. Telling yourself, "When situation X arises, I'll perform response Y", is effective for adhering to goals and habits. Plans made to quell any arising obstacles are what often dictate progress.[30]

If you've got a work event coming up, which you know always ends with a few too many drinks and late-night kebabs, setting yourself a specific plan for how you'll conquer each situation will increase your chances of successfully navigating that stressful scenario. It's not about possessing enough willpower or motivation, but adopting a meticulous course of action. Detailing every point of the evening will ensure you're more likely to align your behaviours with your long-term goals – and prevent emotions from clouding your judgement. For example:

"IF I know there'll be food on offer at the event, THEN I'll have a protein shake before I leave."

"IF someone offers me a drink, THEN I'll always follow it with a zero-calorie beverage."

'IF I know it'll be a late night, THEN I'll prebook my taxi, so I don't find myself stumbling into the kebab shop on the way home."

Creating a specific plan for when, and where, you'll perform a particular behaviour will reduce your chances of having to make decisions in the moment.[31] Even devising a specific strategy for how you *feel* in a particular situation can be helpful, in allowing you to replace unwanted habits with new ones.[32] Using these 'if-then' patterns by linking the critical stimulus (e.g., feeling bored) that usually elicits an *undesired* response (e.g., eating chocolate) to a new, *desired* response (e.g., eating an apple instead), will evoke behaviours aligned with your goals.

While broad plans can be useful, it's essential to be precise in your preparation. Being vague is like saying you 'want to be rich one day'. Think about the smallest of actions that reinforces the bigger picture. Such as, actually buying a lottery ticket. You'll no longer succumb to feelings of laziness when it's time to go to the gym, but already have your gym bag – with clothes, membership card, and a bottle of water – at the ready. Neither will you let feelings of tiredness influence whether or not you eat in front of the television; you'll remember to emphasise it's an opportunity to practice a growth mindset. In breaking down each potential obstacle, right to its core, you'll have a plan in place to combat each problem. This will enable you to understand what skills you'll need to utilise in every situation.

Mental Challenges And Boredom Will Always Surface

Magazines, supplement companies, and social media influencers will always peddle 'the easiest route'. Why market hardship and struggle when you can sell – and make money from – seemingly effortless, quick-fix solutions? While promises of 'losing ten kilograms while sitting on the sofa eating what you want all day' can appeal to the desperate dieter, along with guarantees of 'becoming four inches slimmer in a week', they're only inflating the unrealistic expectations surrounding fat loss. Losing weight *will* be a struggle. There will be times of despondency, dejection, and demotivation. There'll be hunger, tiredness, and monotony. It won't be the easy road you've been sold. In expecting those mental challenges from the outset, however, you'll place yourself in a better frame of mind to see your ambitions through to the end.

It's been found that people who realise tasks require more effort often perceive a potential deadline to be closer in time.[33] They become aware of the difficulties they'll face, and they realign their expectations. Expecting struggle and frustration – over and above any easy dream you've been promised – will elicit a superior mindset. Expect adversity, and you won't give up when progress plateaus. Expect monotony, and you won't be surprised when that excitement after 'week three' of the journey subsides. When you accept there'll be slumps in motivation and ease, you'll be well prepared for what lies ahead.

The famous truism, Murphy's Law, states that '*Anything that can go wrong will go wrong*'. Whilst acknowledging such a hard line may seem undesirable, predicting the worst is encouraged when dieting. Fragments of pessimism, propagated at the start, will allow you to set pragmatic timeframes and deal with future challenges – setting a 'premortem' on your goals, as such. While confidence is imperative, you'll know how to react when things go awry and can ensure uncritical optimism is grounded in reality. No longer will you feel like a failure when you lose motivation or deviate from your plan; you'll appreciate that it's *meant* to happen, whilst being more inclined to keep pursuing your weight loss goals.

Researchers have found that those who possessed positive fantasies (dreaming about a positive outcome in the future) about certain life events (e.g., getting a job and finding a partner), performed *worse,* in achieving their goals, than those who had negative fantasies (dreaming about a negative outcome in the future).[34] As humans, we're able to simulate our achievement of future events in all its glory. This is often to our detriment, however. Instead of dreaming about the perfect outcome, we should start dreaming of failure, slow progress, and stepping onto the scales and *not* seeing results. While seemingly counterintuitive, this can set you up for success more than you realise.

People expect a diet to be exciting. They envisage the finished product and forecast a wild journey filled with thrill and adventure. It's never this exhilarating, however. It's more like having to sit through your Grandma's knitting club AGM for twelve straight hours, on repeat. Weight loss isn't filled with enchantment and riotous celebrations, unfortunately. The ennui of eating similar meals will invoke boredom; the process of copying the same gym sessions will elicit mental fatigue – and having to continually grind out improvements will demand stringent routine. Never expect anything other than monotony when dieting. There won't be too many highs, and there won't be too many lows.

It may also appear those who have little issue with motivation, self-control, and acquiring results are passionate about everything related to health and fitness. They'd participate in an all-inclusive, egg-white pub crawl, if they could. This prompts many to believe that their life should revolve around eating healthily, exercising hard, and cherishing every part of the journey. While enjoyment is undoubtedly a factor associated with adherence,[35] expecting to treasure every moment is unwise. Continual joy isn't mandatory for solid achievement.

Triumphant dieters are the ones who can turn up every day and execute the right actions, regardless of how motivated or inspired they are. Despite feelings of boredom or apathy, they still manage to get the job done. They no longer seek excitement in a new diet, or exercise programme, but focus on putting the reps in each day. Skipping days because you're 'not in the mood' will never work. Choosing an unhealthy meal because you're 'tired' won't inspire progress. Snacking in the evenings because you've had a 'hard day at work' won't take you closer to your goals. The concept of daily practice – while possibly seeming like a monumental challenge to overcome – will breed gradual improvements. You'll never be always motivated, nor inspired, to exercise and eat well; you will, however, need to always take repetitive steps forward to achieve what you set out to.

Your Body Has A Mind Of Its Own

We know an energy deficit creates fat loss. As we're able to influence our total calorie intake, macronutrient quality, training volume, and energy expenditure, we may therefore assume we can dictate how much weight we're able to lose on any given day or week. While people possess some control over their response to the laws of thermodynamics, presuming *complete* command over progress is a prominent, unrealistic expectation.

How many times have you hopped onto the scales on a Monday morning, fully expecting to have dropped another pound or two, only to discover that the number hasn't budged at all? Envisaging dropping a percentage or two in body fat, because you devoted maximum effort to the week, ate nothing but green beans and chicken breasts, and trained 'really hard', is leading yourself down the wrong mental path. Correlating effort with progress gives the impression you can 'work the fat off', which isn't strictly true. As Amir Siddiqui, owner of Dubai's 'Symmetry Gym', states, "Results don't happen at the rate your mind desires, they happen at the rate your body allows."

People who believe they have power over certain situations often succumb to more optimistic time predictions over tasks.[36] Assuming you're able to 'squat the weight off', or, 'chug down a few kale and turnip smoothies to lose a couple of pounds', reinforces the unattainable notion that you're in complete control of progress. Your body has a mind of its own, unfortunately. From water retention to the differences in fat and muscle loss, to metabolic adaption, and changes on either side of the 'calories in calories out equation', predicting rates of progress down to the last gram is impractical. So, stop trying to. Fat loss isn't directly correlated with the amount you're doing, or the measure of effort you're exerting. Setting yourself the expectation of losing 'two pounds a week', or, 'a jean size in a month' will, more often than not, set you up for failure. You can't speed up results nor fully predict how your journey will pan out. This is why obsessing over numbers and figures is unhelpful for most people. Focus should be directed, instead, towards other measures of growth. Increases in strength, developments in energy levels, improved sleep patterns, greater fruit and vegetable consumption, and 'feeling' better are often more fitting standards on which to gauge results.

This doesn't mean you're not in control of *any* progress. We don't want to wield that fixed mindset. Adopting a bulletproof, dieting mentality means ousting emotion from each measure of results and taking an objective stance on your actions. We need to appreciate that improvements will never be linear. Daily and weekly fluctuations will always emanate. It's imperative, therefore, to stop expecting change to be straightforward.

It's also important to remember that, whilst you seldom execute control of external results, you can exhibit control of your *actions*. Focusing on maximum effort in the gym, implementing the pertinent habits for change, and making the best choices at every social event will, in turn, affect results; they just won't do so directly. Don't expect the perfect week, or month, of eating and exercising to elicit the perfect result.

You'll Never Be Happy With What You've Achieved

People tend to want fat loss to be twice what it is. If they lose a pound; they'll want to have lost two. Should they drop two inches from their waist, they'll want that to be four. Dropping one dress size isn't enough; they want another. One study showed that obese women seeking weight loss treatment characterised a 25 per cent weight loss as, "One I would not be happy with", and a 17 per cent weight loss, as, "One that I could not view as successful in any way".[37] Following forty-eight weeks of treatment and a 16-kilogram weight loss in the same intervention, a shocking 47 per cent of participants didn't even achieve a weight they could regard as 'disappointing'. Even when patients are repeatedly informed that their weight loss goals are unrealistic, they still expect to lose *twice* as much as has been advised.[38] People who become disillusioned with their results – no matter how realistic they are – tend to engage in self-critical statements, set unattainable behavioural goals, and, eventually, abandon their dieting efforts.[39] You can see we have a problem.

People are constantly pounding away on that hedonic treadmill; the never-ending hamster wheel of euphoria that dictates they'll always circle back to an equilibrium of happiness, whatever they achieve. With this thinking, however, even when you reach a certain goal, size, or shape, the chances are you still won't be happy. So, stop trying to be. Expectations will always rise with results, meaning that you'll inevitably want more. Instead of losing weight to increase joy, use it to better yourself – to push yourself forward. We know that, although losing a specific amount of weight may seem like the logical goal, the desire to lose more will never cease. True happiness surfaces, instead, from engaging with the process.

While lasting gratification won't increase explicitly through the amount of weight lost, confidence and volition will. It's about finding autonomy and self-determination before you reach the end. You should never base your contentment exclusively on figures; it should come from the improvements in cultivating discipline, overcoming pitfalls, and mastering the skills that accompany any weight loss achievements. Jonathan Haidt, in his book, *The Happiness Hypothesis,* calls this 'The Progress Principle'. He says, "The final moment of success is often no more thrilling than the relief of taking off a heavy backpack at the end of a long hike. Pleasure comes more from making progress towards goals than from achieving them."[40]

While you may never be pleased with the look of your current physique, you should always strive to be happy with self-development. In freeing yourself from the 'seeking,' you focus on the 'doing' – you detach from the reward and focus on the work. In doing so, you stay true to your honest wants and desires. Being content with making progress *towards* the overarching goal is often the marker of a truly successful person – as opposed to whether or not they can slip into a smaller shirt size.

To increase appreciation of your journey, recognition of current achievements is crucial. There seems to be a predisposition in the human mind that overlooks the previous months' hard work and progress, and ends up focusing solely on all that's left to achieve. This 'void of desired progress' – the fixation with everything still left to accomplish – supersedes the awareness of everything that has paved the way for this moment. You can subsequently end up neglecting the same methods and dedication that led to your current shape, size, and weight, and become impatient and frustrated with trying to achieve more. Instead of appreciating where you've come from, you become infatuated with where you need to go. Revelling, instead, in any progress you've made, rather than all that's left to do, will offset unrealistic expectations and increase happiness.

Mastering The Art Of Goal Setting

The tale of the Ford Pinto cuts American pop culture deep.[41] In the late 1960s, the Ford Motor Company were desperate to wrestle with foreign competitors to dominate the small-car market. CEO, Lee Iacocca, announced the goal of producing a new car that would '…weigh less than 2,000 pounds', and '…cost under $2,000'. It would be available for purchase in 1970, a mere, twenty-five months later. This demanding task – coupled with a similarly tight deadline – caused problems. It meant that many levels of management became so fixated on the goal they'd been set, they signed off on unperformed safety checks, to expedite the development of the car.

Disaster ensued.

Problems were soon discovered in the fuel tank design. Lawsuits later revealed a glaring issue; the Pinto could, worryingly, ignite upon impact. Subsequent investigations declared that, even after Ford finally identified the hazard, executives *still* remained committed to their goal. The pressure and belief they had to get the new vehicle out the door as quickly as possible, meant overlooking potential disasters. The goal they'd been set was the sole focus – and nothing else mattered. Instead of repairing the faulty design, they calculated that the costs of lawsuits associated with Pinto fires would be less than the cost of fixing the problem. Shockingly, the rebuild was ignored – and the Pinto went into production.

Complaints, injuries, and disputes followed. In 1978, all Ford Pintos were recalled and had to be upgraded, due to the deficient and fatal design. In the following years, reports ranged from 27 to 180 deaths, experienced in the wake of the dangerous oversight. The company endured a damaging reputation, in the years following, for putting profits ahead of product quality.

If ever there was a lesson in the problem with goal setting, this was it. Specific, challenging goals were met by Ford executives (speed to market, fuel efficiency, and production cost) at the expense of other vital features that weren't considered (safety, ethical behaviour, and company reputation). Goal setting, in this instance, came at a price.

While setting goals can, of course, be useful (we don't want to become cemented purely in the ceaseless world of self-improvement), as its impact can be similarly damaging. From harming our motivation, to creating unsustainable habits, and exacerbating failures, setting objectives – and destinations – isn't as straightforward as many would like to believe. Goals need to be dealt with delicately. They require a process that creates an effective mindset; not one that leads to a narrow focus, complications, short-term change, and ultimate failure.

The Problem With Setting Weight Loss Goals

When dieting, everyone has a goal. Whether it be losing a certain number of kilograms, or desiring a specific physique, everyone sets off with a perceived destination in their sights. We've been told that 'having a goal' is a prerequisite for any weight loss journey. If you don't know where you're heading, how can you plan ahead? If you're unaware of what's left to achieve, how can you follow the plan?

While long and short-term intentions can, and should, play an integral role in any diet,[42] such intentions are often based on harmful footings. The methods and tactics we've been taught are simply unfitting for individuals building an ultimate dieting mindset. As Scott Adams, in his book, *How To Fail At Everything And Still Win Big,* says, "[most of the time] goals are for losers."[43]

Ask any dieter why they've selected that particular number of kilograms to lose, and you'll probably be greeted with a shrug of the shoulders. Ask them if they know how they're going to get there, and they'll respond with a blank face. Enquire as to what they're going to do *once* they've got there, and you'll be lucky to avoid being 'unfollowed' on social media. From plucking a few aimless numbers out of the air, to racing towards a wayward and arbitrary destination they've conjured up inside their minds, goal setting has become a misrepresented and miscalculated aspect of dieting. It's often what causes people to lose sight of what they actually want, and – ultimately – to fail.

Most Weight Loss Goals Elicit Hope, Not Change

Have you noticed how galvanised you feel when you set a weight loss goal? That dream physique piques motivation, and hope and excitement emerge. It's probably why New Year resolution fanatics will typically make the same pledge for five years, or more, before they manage even a six-month success,[44] and those who resolve to start exercising will rate themselves as more confident in being able to increase their exercise frequency than when they'd rated themselves a week previously.[45] This hope, however, leads to sizeable, unattainable, and elusive goals being set. The euphoric promise of change wields its influential arm and, instead of ascertaining the likely speed, amount, difficulty, and consequences of self-change attempts, individuals set grandiose goals that serve to stimulate gratifying feelings of optimism. Simply deciding to change produces a number of reinforcing feelings of being in control – as well as providing the impression that progress has been made. "I'm going to join the gym, cut out all the alcohol, and lose it *all* by Christmas", they declare (at the beginning of December). These beliefs surrounding change induce repeated attempts, because the inbuilt assumptions are, in and of themselves, rewarding. *Setting* the goal is more exciting than the process itself.

Of course, such satisfying feelings rarely last beyond the first bite of broccoli. Those once-excited individuals quickly succumb to feelings of guilt and shame because they can't keep pace with their initial hopes and dreams. They wind up feeling worse than before, and may attempt to soften each disappointment by making attributions to explain why. This *False Hope Syndrome* masquerades as action[46] – just as people will spend hours researching the perfect drill, instead of putting the shelves up, or on deciding upon the ideal font for their work presentation, rather than actually creating the slides. Goal setting is, in reality, nothing more than a short, sharp burst of dopamine that's utilised to increase self-esteem and garner feelings of perceived progress. Worryingly, people will also remember that initial 'success' and siphon those same feelings when wanting to change – or diet – again, ensuring the process is continuously repeated.

People often engage in the goal setting process longer than they need to, as a way to convince themselves they're making progress. The mere act of committing to change enables feelings of discipline to emerge – ultimately masking their ambient fear of failure. The less time spent in taking action, then the less chance someone has of dampening their motivation. Setting goals feels like they're accomplishing something, when, in fact, they're basking in their comfort zone and avoiding the inevitable blunders – and hard work – that arise when embarking on a diet. Goals become important when you champion them with change, rather than just relying on hope.

Most Weight Loss Goals Encourage A 'Quick-Fix' Mindset

Most dieters become so fixated on their overarching goals that they'll do everything in their power to reach them. From crafting unsustainable eating habits, to damaging their relationship with food, the process behind most weight loss goals is seasoned with a dash of chaos. People may not consider what destruction they leave in their path; they're just concerned with crossing the finish line. Long-lasting behaviours are substituted for bullish ones; damaging dieting protocols are favoured over sustainable methods – and deprivation and punishment are championed over satisfaction. If that 'ten kilograms' needs shifting, everything will be done to shift it.

People can end up chasing the same goal over and over again because they fail to focus on the pertinent *behaviours* that lead to long-lasting change. They, instead, weigh themselves religiously, check their bodies obsessively, and only experience happiness when they're moving towards their goal. They may, subsequently, start pummelling away on the treadmill, instead of lifting weights; they'll slash calories carelessly, instead of implementing a periodised, nutritional approach. They'll possibly ignore a higher-protein diet, in favour of munching on bland lettuce leaves at every meal, just to expedite the process. Instead of adopting a calculated, manageable method, they exclusively focus on the number, size, or percentage they want to achieve. People focus on these *performance goals* as opposed to *learning goals*.[47]

Performance goals concern an individual's focus on the outcome. This is what dieting ambitions are frequently founded upon – the figure someone must attain before moving onto the next goal, or diet. This, unfortunately, encourages the 'quick-fix' mindset. Ignoring learning goals – the focus of acquiring the ability to perform a task – fails to induce a sustainable approach to weight loss. Individuals will do anything to reach their destination at the expense of health and adherence, resulting in repeated dieting attempts.

These weight loss goals lead to stress, anxiety, and perceived pressure.[48] If an individual has set themselves a specific target, they're encumbered with the burden of success. Their attention becomes diverted away from strategy development and learning, towards a preoccupation with high-pressured – and often unethical – actions. It was found that, because health companies in China were providing discounted premiums for individuals who consistently acquired daily step counts, those people began developing electronic cradles that would rock their smartphones and 'cheat the step counter'.[49] Any inappropriately set goals typically promote negative consequences.

In the end, individuals find themselves back at square one. A lack of understanding for everything that occurs between those start and finishing points results in limited adherence and fickle dieting attempts. Yes, an overarching goal dictates the resultant journey; it shouldn't, however, negate the important tasks, behaviours, and challenges that must exist in between.

Most Weight Loss Goals Indicate An 'End'

Have you ever noticed it's harder to order a taxi on a rainy day? Common sense would assume it's because everyone else is similarly hailing cabs, to avoid the torrential downpour. While this is one potential reason, there's also another interesting argument to consider; there are simply fewer cabs on the road.

One study found that, as a day progresses, cabs start disappearing quickly from Manhattan streets on rainy days, more than on sunny days.[50] This is not owed to a collective agreement amongst taxi drivers to leave us all drenched by the side of the road, but because of the specific, daily goals they set; the goal to earn double the amount it costs them to rent out their cabs for a 12-hour shift. On rainy days, drivers make money *quicker* than on sunny days, simply because demand is higher. They hit their daily goals sooner, and, feeling chuffed with a successful day's work, then head home – leaving no cabs left for wet, miserable people like us.

Herein lies another prominent problem with goal setting; when we set ourselves specific goals, we often relax, rest, pause – and head home, once they've been achieved. Most problems with weight loss objectives arise not when people strive to reach their target but when they actually *get* there. The discrepancy between their current state and the goal – and, thus, their resulting motivation – disappears.[51] That foot comes off the pedal and old habits start to creep back in. "I've done it", they think, as they sit back with a refreshing glass of wine on Christmas Day – believing all the work is done. This newfound lack of direction lures them away from their original goal. They neglect the skills and habits they established to reach their destination, and lose focus. "Dieting is easy", they convince themselves; "I deserve a break".

When people achieve a significant goal, they have nothing left to work towards. The wedding is over, the holiday has finished, or there are no more inches to lose. Where that goal once dwelled, an emptiness now exists. Setting a 'finish date' with any diet or training programme, while helpful in rare instances, seldom leads to long-lasting success. It was never really the 'finish date' they wanted – this masquerading as a proxy for something deeper – it was something *else*.

People often pursue goals that are at odds with their values, leading to one-dimensional and quick-fix bursts of effort. This is why sprinters are always told to run *through* the finishing line; when that tape across the line is in their sights, their automatic reaction is to start to slow down just before reaching it. When they're told to focus on a point *beyond* the winner's tape, however, they're impelled to keep going. Most weight loss goals, similarly, indicate an 'end'. Losing a definitive amount of weight isn't the goal; nor is attempting to reach a specific, societal standard of perceived beauty in a particular timeframe. Instead, these are the *problems*.

Most Weight Loss Goals Corner You Into Being A 'Success' Or A 'Failure'

Achieve your goal, and you're a success. Fall anywhere short of that goal, and you're deemed a failure. There's nothing in between. Which is, unfortunately, where most people tend to exist on the goal setting spectrum.

Cornering yourself into one of those two, possible categories, damages your chances of celebrating other worthy wins, goals, or achievements. If the goal was to lose ten kilograms and you only lose five, you're judged a failure. If you haven't dropped a dress size but have managed to increase your strength in the gym, it seems you're still considered a disappointment. Restricting your sense of fulfilment to an 'either/or' scenario fails to appreciate the numerous, other accomplishments you can earn by continually striving to improve.

Such feelings of failure typically dictate future actions. If your goal was to lose five kilograms in six weeks, but you only lose two, you're more likely to avoid trying again next time. If you set yourself the challenge of going to the gym six times a week, but only manage three, you may engage in more detrimental and restrictive behaviours in the future. Reductions in self-efficacy, through repeated failures – which arise from striving for specific weight loss goals – are harmful. If you lose confidence in your ability levels, this will tend to inhibit your perseverance and resilience. It's for this reason that being 'specific' – which is what the 'S' in the accustomed 'SMART' strategy stands for – isn't always helpful. It turns out that this blueprint, frequently touted as the elixir to all goal setting problems, might not be so smart after all.

Appreciating the collection of additional achievements accomplished through embarking on a weight loss journey, and not solely the set figures and timeframes, will enhance greater success in diet maintenance. Think back to the last goal you set; if you didn't achieve it, did you accomplish something else instead? If you didn't lose a required number of centimetres from your hips, for example, did you nonetheless manage a streak of visits to the gym? If you failed to practice your value of flexibility, did you still manage to adopt behaviours aligned with your value of persistence? You'll discover, quickly, that, while you maybe didn't reach the overarching goal you set out towards, you still achieved other, disguised jewels as part of your journey. Those are just as important as that single, long-term goal you may have had. This is not least because they remove the detrimental, binary criteria – either of only two options to 'fail' or 'succeed' at the one, fixed goal – that haunt the goal setting process.

Common Weight Loss Goal Setting Mistakes People Make

Adopting A One-Size-Fits-All Approach

Whether it be one, three, five, or twenty kilograms to lose, there's always a number and timeframe involved when people set themselves dieting goals. Rarely are these targets productive, however, let alone possible. People create an image in their mind as to what they'd like to weigh or look like; they decide when they'd like to achieve that by, and then wildly set off with little consideration for their gender, training experience, lean body mass, current lifestyle, or previous dieting history. Plucking capricious goals out of thin air on impulse – ones that have no well-thought logic behind them – is a fruitless task. If you failed to reach a goal that you'd set yourself, perhaps you weren't destined to achieve it in the first place. Maybe it was founded on nothing but momentary wishes.

While aiming for a 'two-pound per week loss' could be beneficial for some, it may be detrimental for others. Although it might take a 120-kilogram male only six weeks to shed ten kilograms, it could take a 75-kilogram female triple that time. While a person who's never dieted before may find it easy to lose weight consuming 1500 calories every day, a serial, yo-yo dieter may find the same calorie target less helpful. It's not a one-size-fits-all approach when goal setting.

Many dieters will set goals that they believe they've selected themselves. In reality, they've possibly been influenced by their identity, their peer groups, and their culture – along with prevalent societal standards. If your grandma has always made remarks about your weight, you'll likely submit to her expectations, even if her sentiments offend you. If your culture favours those with a slimmer physique, your ambitions will tend to match those preferences. Many will set goals because they feel like they *have* to, not necessarily because they *want to*. Adopting such a one-tiered approach to goal setting may well lead to increased body dissatisfaction, though, or body preoccupation – and even body image avoidance. Ultimately, those point towards failure. You must spend time reflecting on what *you* want and how *you're* going to get there, because aligning yourself with others' specious expectations and standards won't promote a timeless transformation.

It should be evident, by now, that shoehorning yourself into a broken, all-purpose, goal setting process is flawed. Two different athletes or businesspeople may achieve the same level of success, yet experience contrasting paths, as well as different, eventual outcomes. We can't *all* chase the same goal, can we? Pursuing random, unconsidered goals that others have fashioned is a heedless task. Defining success on your own terms is far more important than pursuing any sweeping ambitions that aren't specific to your wants, desires, opportunities, and ability levels.

Setting Too Many Outlandish Goals

While the idea of waltzing around with sub-ten per cent body fat all year round, or shedding an 'easy' 25 kilograms, may appear inspiring, setting extravagant aspirations will only set you up for disappointment. Unreasonable weight loss goals are overpowering – partisans of feelings of failure. With so much work to do, time to pass, and uncertainty surrounding the overwhelming target, people become stranded in a position of passivity. The more there is to achieve, the more they'll fail to take action.

Even when people do manage to make some strides forward, that intimidating goal still appears untouchable. It can feel like constantly treading water. While unknown and seemingly impossible aspirations – or what some have coined 'stretch goals'[52] – may have benefits in other domains, rarely do they have a significant impact in the weight loss field. Admittedly, we probably wouldn't have landed on the moon, nor created a Wi-Fi hotspot near the North Pole, were it not for lofty ambitions; but, setting such grandiose targets when it comes to weight loss will often lead to failure. Not only does all the work-left-to-achieve incite feelings of dejection, but fails to account for the countless steps required to move forward. When you set yourself goals that are too challenging, you're leaving yourself at more risk of damaging your self-esteem, your trust, and the opportunity to make progress.

Appreciating what's going to be required, to achieve a particular look, is vital before starting. If you want a six-pack, do you know how hungry you'll have to feel each day? If you want slimmer legs, are you already aware of how much time you'll have to dedicate to training each week? If you wish to participate in a photoshoot, have you considered how many social events you'll have to decline to make it a possibility? Ascertaining what trade-offs you must make is at least as important, if not more so, than the activities themselves. In doing this, you'll avoid the temptation 'to go big, or go home'. It'll become clear that hasty and outlandish weight loss goals rarely breed sustainable motivation and adherence.

Similarly, setting too *many* goals, too soon, typically results in failure. Boundless dreams tend to lead to confusion surrounding what to focus on; they also stir eventual overwhelm, alongside diminished interest. It's like competing in an arduous tug of war with yourself. Each goal is pulling you in a different direction; instead of making progress, you wind up in a period of stagnation. Creating a catalogue of desired achievements and chasing them all at once will only result in a distracted and confused mindset. This 'goal competition' bleeds attention and drains focus. It's not a goal *setting* problem, so much as a goal *selection* problem.

Focusing On The Outcome And Not The Process

The 'Big Dog Backyard Ultra' is the toughest of ultra-running events. Its premise dictates that the competitor run a single loop, measuring 4.16 miles, within a single hour. Once completed, they do it again. And again. And yet again, until there's just one man or woman left standing – literally. It doesn't matter if you finish a lap the quickest or the slowest; every runner begins a new loop tied for first place. There is no finishing line.

Some runners have been known to clock a staggering 246 miles, in completing the event. That's 59 loops over 59 consecutive hours. I can feel the blisters forming, just thinking about it. Yet, this brutal race teaches us an important lesson; when there is no destination, you just *keep going*. Pacing yourself, like those repeatedly running the same loop in the same amount of time, delays fatigue and enables a longer race. One former champion said, "You're never overwhelmed by what you have left to run because you simply don't know what you have left to run."[53]

This concept has been coined *Teleoanticipation.*[54] It's the notion that the anticipation of a finishing line will not only dictate physiological reactions, but psychological ones, too. Our knowledge of a distinct destination dominates the entirety of the experience. While this can be useful in certain situations, when it comes to a successful weight loss journey, the reverse may be a better answer – *not* having an end point. Asking yourself, "Can I keep going?" instead of, "Can I make it to the finishing line?" will elicit positive reactions – including increased perseverance and greater adherence. This helps to explain why dieters, much to their detriment, will set off like sprinters, at breakneck speed, to complete a six-week detox, only to wind up mentally and physically exhausted, once that short stint finishes. Like the 'Big Dog

Backyard Ultra', however, they must complete one loop. And another. And then another. The race should never end.

Most weight loss success stories are accompanied by a sensationalist headline and/or an impressive set of before-and-after photos. That moment of the visible weight loss result becomes the main focus. Everyone craves that transformation and may then set off with exactly that *outcome* in mind. Just like those competing in a running event, they're always looking to the future, wondering when that 'finish line' result will surface. The obsession with a desired conclusion – a certain appearance, bodyweight, or shape, for example – hinders weight loss maintenance, unfortunately.[55] Look closely at those who've succeeded, however, and you'll realise it was never about the goal; it was to do with everything that *preceded* it.

While goals are useful for setting an initial direction, focusing on the process is essential for making progress.[56] Rather than consuming yourself with an 'end' figure, it's more productive to pinpoint the *behaviours* and *systems* that will lead you there. These process goals focus on the execution of skills and strategies crucial to performance. They've been associated with enhanced concentration and less anxiety, alongside greater satisfaction and confidence levels.[57] The smaller facets of the journey combine to create the end goal.

Those people we discussed previously, who possess an entity-based mindset, are often at the mercy of performance-based goals. They presume there's little they can do to change their physical or mental attributes, and subsequently blame external factors, whilst feeling defined by past failures. As we know, pursuing performance-based goals only serves to emphasise the belief of being 'not good enough' or not possessing the necessary skills to even come close to the end result.[58] Adopting a fixed mindset reinforces those feelings of failure. If you've always failed at dieting before, what would make this attempt any different?

With process goals, there's always something to strive towards. It may be the amount of exercise you can complete, or how much effort you can put in to improve the required skill set for weight loss – as examples. Either way, harnessing an approach that focuses on your beliefs and ability to change will lead to results. Concentrating on improving your abilities allows you to compete with yourself. When you become the centre of competition, you can ignore the perils of external feedback and validation. Your focus is fixed firmly on beating your own performance level in that contest.

How To Craft A Bulletproof Goal Setting System

Realise Goals Are Tools And Nothing More

Goals drive behaviour.[59] We can't escape that fact. We wouldn't brush our teeth if we didn't care about dental hygiene, nor get ready for a night out if we didn't care about our appearance. We need goals, to avoid submitting to the ambiguous quest of continual 'personal growth'. Problems arise, however, when we direct *all* our focus and attention towards the end goal. Just like we utilise the feedback from food tracking apps or smart watches, goals should also be employed as tools and nothing more. They should serve like a simple litmus test, for where to budget time, energy, and focus.

The beauty of effective goal setting is that you're in control of the process. You decide what's suitable for you and your life. Overlooking the core tenets of goal setting – from ability level, to commitment, to the resources at hand – provokes a host of detrimental effects. Once you've figured out how best to utilise a structure to the journey you're about to embark upon – through considering circumstances and key factors (as outlined in the earlier, "Adopting A One-Size-Fits-All Approach" section) – then you'll be better placed to establish suitable objectives.

Goal setting is ultimately a matter of efficiency. What is it that inspires you the most, to act in alignment with the bigger picture? If you decide dieting is the overarching ambition, but tend to fail to follow through with the pertinent behaviours, then perhaps this isn't the right goal for you. Maybe you're succumbing to the goals of others? Maybe you're seeking a different change to your life, masked by the supposed zenith of life's achievements that is successful dieting? Set yourself long-term goals, but don't allow them to induce feelings of failure, nor provoke a change in your behaviour, mood, or focus if – and when – you reach them. Don't become cornered into heading towards one specific destination; remember that goals should drive you forward but not govern your whole journey.

If a congruence between your ambitions and your identity isn't evident, you'll likely face conflict – friction between what you want and what you're able to give. You'll be battling with limiting beliefs, doubts, and trouble with prioritising, probably being pulled in countless directions. Greater perceptions of failure, attention demands, and inhibition of learning may surface. Take time to think about the goals you want to set and what's required to make them a reality. Are they what you really want?

Your goal setting system should be spearheaded with an *unspecific* intention.[60] Setting yourself a general target, at the beginning, of 'dieting', 'reducing overall body fat', or 'building muscle' is acceptable; encouraged, even. It eliminates the pressure and burden of reaching a certain destination in a particular timeframe. No longer are you thrust into a 'success' or 'failure' disposition. You're always winning, if working towards that broad yet powerful objective. You wouldn't strive to earn £17,693 per year more than you currently do, in only three years' time, so why set similar, clear-cut goals when dieting? We're not saying *never* be specific with your ambitions – such exactitude and purpose may well arrive when examining the process. But overlooking precision, whether that be the number on the scales, or the weight on the bar, will strengthen continual progress.

Create A Goal Hierarchy

Creating a bulletproof, goal setting system stems from establishing an entire goal network – what we call a goal *hierarchy*.[61] Establishing an entwined, behavioural map of pursuits will foster greater motivation, adherence, and resilience in the face of setbacks – instead of homing in purely on specific behaviours, or fixating on the bigger picture. From top to bottom, each specific goal within this hierarchy is interconnected, so they can activate or inhibit one another. Following a well-assembled structure supplies you with the mandatory tools to unite each goal in a cohesive manner – from identifying your values, to recognising the necessary day-to-day behaviours you must implement.

Sitting atop this tree are what is known as *superordinate goals.* These reflect what you find important; they are soundly linked to your identity and sense of self – what we term, in essence, as your values. The beauty of superordinate goals is that they act as 'guiding principles' – goals that exist over a longer time scale and exist across a broader concept. 'Acting with patience', 'living a healthy lifestyle', or 'displaying constant commitment', being prime examples. In pursuing concrete, yet abstract goals, you're provided with reasons for targeting specific behaviours. They enhance *meaning.*

In pursuing character strengths and a clear direction, you're less likely to cheat the system. For example, participants who thought about *why* consuming multivitamins was important to them increased their intake over two weeks, compared with those who didn't think about the reasons behind their decisions.[62] Ask yourself, 'Do my goals represent my core values? Do the goals I have support the type of person I want to become?'

Chasing broad aspirations reduces the likelihood of sacrificing long-term goal pursuit in exchange for short-term reward. 'Losing body fat', for example, can be supported with other goals further down the tree for when motivation is low, or unexpected obstacles arise. Increasing sleep, consuming more protein, or developing strength are all smaller goals that contribute to the wider ambition – and can be executed regardless of how you're feeling or when encountering unforeseen circumstances. Focusing on a sense of self encourages continual progress rather than the 'stop/start' cycle many find themselves imprisoned in. There's no specific endpoint. Striving to *be* someone, rather than achieve *something,* provides a feeling of orientation, strengthens guidance, fuels motivation, and reduces the discrepancy between who you are now and who you want to be in the future.

Of course, these superordinate goals can't be achieved without the support of other, less abstract intentions. Formally known as *intermediate goals,* they sit a rank lower on the goal hierarchy and are more specific. Increasing daily movement, reducing stress, and building muscle are all objectives bound to a certain behavioural context and underpin the goals sitting higher in the hierarchy. Walking, relaxing, and lifting weights are behaviours that reinforce the idea of someone living a 'healthy lifestyle' or striving to 'display commitment'. They contribute to an individual's identity and are important in ascertaining *how* to achieve that ideal self.

Stationed at the bottom of this hierarchy are *subordinate goals*. This is where most people *start* their goal setting journey, unfortunately, ignoring all that must come before those. Such specific goals are important, of course. The goal of 'following a Push/Pull/Legs training split at the gym each week' will inevitably contribute to the intermediate goal of 'building muscle', which, in turn, advances the value of 'displaying commitment'. Exclusively focusing on these, whilst ignoring the bigger picture, nonetheless amplifies the previously discussed problems with goal setting. But, when situated in a pyramid of importance, subordinate goals are held within a broader context and bolstered with meaning and gravity. They remain valuable; setting these smaller, sub-goals within that structured hierarchy ensures you can also focus on the next action. Goals such as, 'training three times a week' and 'consuming a high-protein, high-carb meal after each workout' are still crucial targets to work towards. Possessing something concrete and feasible to strive for – within reason – will boost your motivation and provide you with instant feedback.

As a superordinate goal is connected to several subordinate goals, people can still pursue them in multiple ways. This flexibility is known as *equifinality*. The same goal can be achieved through a multiplicity of varying, lower-order goals. If your *only* goal is to train three times a week and you injure yourself, you're left stranded. If you strive for a combination of subordinate goals, however, such as also aiming for 8,000 steps and journaling for ten minutes each day, you can still pursue your intermediate *and* superordinate ambitions in the face of a broken wrist or leg. You're always striving towards being an individual attempting to lose body fat, no matter what happens.

It's clear that establishing a well-connected hierarchy will promote adherence, as well as help you craft a bulletproof goal system setting. Overarching, superordinate goals determine more concrete intentions at the intermediate level; they, in turn, regulate goals at the subordinate level. Deciding upon a panoptic goal, that supports a sense of self as opposed to a specific weight loss target, will encourage sustainable behaviour change and long-term results; it will also produce further goal intentions and aid subsequent planning. Focusing on your identity and your 'why' *first,* creates a domino effect. Motivation is sustained, distractions are reduced, and goal conflicts diminish. Moreover, resilience increases the further down the tree you advance. Of course, visualising how you want to be and act in the future is important, too, but only when that 'possible self' is linked to concrete strategies and actions – ones that indicate intermediate and subordinate goals, which still hold significance and, so, shouldn't be omitted.

Adopt A 'The Way Is The Goal' Mindset

People often become fixated on their overall weight loss goal – where they need to end up – and discount that significant middle part of their journey. They dive in headfirst, expecting to achieve a new physique or bodyweight, without considering the steps needed to reach their desired outcome. Embracing the *behaviours* that lead to the result, and crafting the prescribed skill set are crucial. Focusing on the means of goal pursuit – known as the process – is more beneficial for progress and well-being than simply fixating on the outcome.[63]

Given that we typically spend much longer on the journey than experiencing attainment, it's vital we adopt a process-focused outlook towards our goals. When concentrating on the behaviours and habits required for change, then our persistence, motivation, self-efficacy, and perceived control all improve.[64] This helps to explain why those who focus on dietary behaviours, rather than the amount of weight lost, experience greater success and fewer deviations from their plan.[65] Adopting a mindset of 'the way is the goal' will predict successful weight loss more than any solitary, outcome-based endeavour.

As Greek poet, Archilochus says, "We don't rise to the levels of our expectations, we fall to the level of our training." When we embrace the process – or the training required – we don't have to constantly strive to reach the destination. Whether it be practicing eating to 80 per cent fullness, watching dinner without a screen present, or reducing the number of snacks between meals, pinpointing those behaviours will enable change. The process is where you *can* be specific. You'll eat dinner at the table every night this week, or always wait ten minutes before you reach for a snack – as examples. Those who fall in love with the skills required to achieve their aspirations will reach their destination anyway.

Focusing on the *right* process is, of course, important. If you're not creeping towards the desired result, you must stop to check that your current behaviours are relevant to the journey. Analysing your existing processes and experimenting rigorously will be far more effective than changing the goalposts. If you haven't lost any inches around your waist, then don't continue to chase down that target without making amendments. Look at adjusting your training plan, your ability to deal with snacking, or your weekend calorie intake, instead. These are not only easier to modify but hold greater meaning.

Running parallel to these process-based endeavours is the distinction between mastery and performance-based goals. While performance goals involve judging and evaluating ability (for example, losing eight kilograms in eight weeks), mastery goals involve *increasing* ability and learning new skills (for example, plating healthy and balanced portions and improving mindful decision-making).[66] Focusing on this 'ability-based' mindset will encourage learning, active engagement, and self-efficacy, whilst also removing the 'success/failure' dichotomy. If you fail to lose eight kilograms in eight weeks, you'll potentially attribute this to an inherent inability to diet successfully. If you fail to build strength in the gym, however, you'll appreciate that you may need to train more frequently, or follow a different programme. Mastery goals promote self-evaluation of current efforts and encourage problem-solving for future attempts. Those who focus on *learning* (for example, 'identify three effective strategies to increase your daily step count') are more likely to increase physical activity than those who focus on the *outcome* (for example, 'hitting 10,000 steps each day').[67]

Focus On Other Achievements And Previous Successes

When asked to complete a task, people have been found to narrow their focus. They're blinded by other influences that appear unrelated, but are of significance to the activity in hand. Take the famous 'Gorilla Study', as an example.[68] Researchers asked participants to watch a video in which two teams passed basketballs amongst each other. One group wore white shirts; the other group wore dark shirts. When given the task of counting basketball passes among people wearing only white shirts, subjects unconsciously blocked out the black-shirted individuals. As a result of this tapered focus, most participants failed to notice when a man wearing a black gorilla suit sauntered into the middle of the screen, pounded his chest, and then walked off again. Intense concentration on the *counting* task had caused people to overlook an extraordinary and unusual element of their visual world. Do you do the same with your weight loss journey?

It's important to remember, when setting goals, that it's not *always* about your weight, your body fat percentage, or your transformation photo. Neither is it always about fixing flaws, relentlessly dieting, and trying to repair your body image. Restricting your focus to only those achievements can obstruct your application, causing you to forget all the other, equally important aspects – those of exercising consistently, eating well when at social events, and getting enough sleep each night. You fail to notice the gorilla in the room.

Although most people set dieting goals for appearance-related reasons, spending time focusing on other motives during weight loss maintenance can improve chances of success.[69] Exercising can be a way to connect with friends, enhance mental clarity, and improve health. Cooking home-made meals can be a chance to bond with family, practice new skills, and boost confidence. Don't become blindsided by the archetypal dieting goal of meeting any collective measure of perceived beauty. Other benefits arise from focusing on the same behaviours.

Improved confidence and self-esteem can emanate from seeking out other achievements. Whether it be building as much muscle as possible, completing your first, unassisted 'chin-up', improving your mobility, or simply *feeling* better, a host of other victories are attainable. Sometimes, opening up a constricted focus and pinpointing what else you can achieve will ease the pressure of trying to reach a desired weight or shape. Concentrating on other behaviours and skills will incidentally lead to an improved physique.

Achieving those small wins – whether related to physical appearance or not – will continue to boost motivation. Just like those of us who enjoy video games are immersed in feelings of joy and success when we complete another level of 'Angry Birds', if we're able to move onto the next level in our weight loss journey, we'll keep returning for more. When you complete another, lower-body session at the gym, you'll feel a sense of accomplishment. When you choose the healthier snack over the chocolate bar, you feel fulfilled. Each small win will signify progress – aiding further action – even when that distant destination seems a long way off.[70]

When you fixate on the bigger picture, it then becomes too easy to ignore those previous wins. You can become haunted by all that's left to achieve and experience a subsequent dip in motivation. Realising you're further along in your journey than you thought, however, will encourage perseverance. This *Endowed Progress Effect* increases the likelihood of completing the next, small task. Take the study of people who were given a 'car wash loyalty card', for example.[71] Those given the card with two stamps *already* marked off were more likely to fill out the rest of the voucher than those given the same card but *without* two slots already stamped. Both groups still required the same number of stamps to achieve a 'free wash'. The group who had a supposed 'head start', however, were more likely to fill the rest of the card out. Celebrating previous wins – and how far you've come – will encourage persistence. Natural logic suggests, you've already made sufficient progress, so why stop now?

Measure And Refine Your Goal Setting Systems

If you've ever worked in sales, you'll know that targets and performance levels will not only dictate income, but an individual's standing within the company as well. No one wants to be last. While sales goals can be a powerful motivational tool, they also often arrive with a host of unethical problems. People are more likely to misrepresent their performance or cheat, for example, when their actual achievement level falls short of attaining a set target.[72] These uncompromising standards clearly create problems.

When adhering to rigid performance indicators, individuals tend to let their dieting ambitions control their mindset and emotions. If, for example, they haven't lost a pound or two, they'll believe they've failed. If they haven't made it to the gym five times in the week, they won't believe they're deserving of progress. They've become enslaved to the goal and will do everything in their power to meet its pre-set requirements; all with little regard for its influence on sustainability and adherence.

Goals are established to serve you, and not the other way around. Refining goal setting systems, when they no longer benefit you, will overcome this problem. If you're not making sufficient progress, you *can* adjust the process. You're allowed to go to the gym three times instead of five, for instance. You're also allowed to aim for four pieces of fruit and vegetables each day, rather than seven. Trying to squeeze the square peg into the unyielding round hole, simply because you feel the pressure to meet a pre-set target, just won't work. Remember, if you don't meet an objective, it doesn't mean you're 'a failure'.

It's around this logic that conventional diets tend to fail. They demand unabridged adherence to their rules, without any room for modification. Dieting doesn't have to meet an expected performance level, however; that level is specific to you. It follows that recurrent refinement and modification will be needed for goal setting success.

Long-term achievements arise less from single triumphs, and more from continual adaptation. Each goal, and its collection of interlinked operations, is a temporary path. This is why splitting the goal setting process into different stages – whether that be dieting, maintenance, or muscle-building phases – will enable you to reach your long-term ambitions. Permitting frequent adjustments, rather than banging your head against the wall in trying to achieve the same thing over and over again, will promote pliability in your journey. Allow for changes in the ambitions you have, therefore. Embrace them. Avoid succumbing to feelings of stubbornness; instead, accept that your feelings and circumstances will always change. Transitioning through varying routes to reach your destination shouldn't be viewed as a negative; you should measure and hone them based on your progress. They shouldn't corner you into the definition of a success or failure.

Chapter Summary And Taking Action

- People fall into the 'planning fallacy' trap. They envision a typical occurrence of how long something will take to be completed, only for it to then take *much longer*. This mental bias isn't the only fallacy that draws people into adopting false expectations on their weight loss journey (note: Anchoring Bias, Focal Bias, Future Goal Bias, and Impact Bias).

- Before you attempt any weight loss endeavour, start by figuring out what may *actually* happen, not what you *think* will happen. Ignore specific timeframes; use other peoples' experiences and research to guide your journey instead. As an example, think in terms of, "I'd like to improve my body fat percentage so I can live a healthier *life*, not just a healthier six weeks."

- Write down the obstacles you'll have to overcome and how to conquer them (using implementation intentions), as well as preparing yourself for other challenges (e.g., "I'll inevitably experience a drop in motivation, plus have to deal with moving house in a few months – so I know, and accept, that progress will slow down at this point").

- Appreciate that you can't always control your body, and you'll possibly never be satisfied with the end result. Chase down self-improvement as a goal, rather than just a leaner physique (e.g., "I want to become better at maintaining my consistency at the gym. This will, in turn, enable me to drop a jean size").

- The conventional, goal setting process is flawed; most people elicit hope, not change, from it. Such a process indicates an 'end', corners you into a definition of 'success' or 'failure', and assumes everyone is the same. Avoid setting yourself arbitrary weight loss targets and outlandish goals

– which rarely work. Similarly, fend off a fixed mindset, including being confined to one goal you've had for the whole of your life.

- Use goals as a tool (e.g., "I do want to lose weight but am not constricted to everything this usually dictates"). Set ambitions that align with what *you* want to achieve (e.g., "I want to lose weight because *I* want to; I won't let this endeavour define me, however"). Create a goal hierarchy, consisting of superordinate, intermediate, and subordinate goals.

- Learn to appreciate the process (e.g., "I will learn new recipes to make for the whole family and follow a new, strength training programme at the gym"). Focus on other achievements (e.g., "I want to complete my first, unassisted chin-up") and concentrate on the next, tangible action (e.g., "At 5 pm, I'll go for a forty-minute walk"). Goals can be incredibly effective, *when* utilised in the right ways.

CHAPTER 4
Off The Wagon Again:
How To Fail Properly

In late 2020, Netflix released their seven-part mini-series called *The Queen's Gambit*. Based on a book published in 1983, its enthralling storyline centres on the game of chess. While doubts were raised over the appeal of a coming-of-age period drama detailing the intricacies of nothing but a two-player strategy board game, it took the world by storm.

The tale of an orphaned chess prodigy, living during the cold war, was watched by 62 million households in the first 28 days followings its release – and is now Netflix's most-watched, limited series.[1] People subsequently fell back in love with the game. Some toy retailers noted a *1100 per cent growth* in the sale of chess sets, whilst others claimed there was a *608 per cent rise* in chess book sales since the television series hit people's screens.[2] More women are now playing the game than ever, and *The Queen's Gambit* has been said to have opened the forgotten game up to many youngsters who may had never previously taken an interest. It has potentially changed the landscape of chess for decades to come.

Yet, there was a real possibility that the show might never have happened in the first place. Alan Scott, the show's producer – having devoured the original novel in 1983 – bought the rights to turn it into a movie six years later. Production was slow-going, unfortunately. No one was willing to take a chance on the storyline, fearing it was 'too dull' to take off.[3] Rewrite after rewrite was knocked back and, despite, in 2008, it looking like actor, Heath Ledger, was going to take a chance on the unique story, his unfortunate death led to another blow.

Persistent failure did little to stem Scott's passion for the project. It was only in 2017, however, when he met with director Scott Frank, that Netflix agreed to a seven-episode series – almost *30 years* since Scott had initially championed the idea. With a host of failed attempts at finding a suitable director and production schedule, along with copious script rewrites, only in 2020 did it become an 'overnight' success. An 'overnight' success that, in fact, spanned over *three decades.* The story of main character, Beth Harmon's, rise to the pinnacle of the chess world goes well beyond its title of one of the oldest known chess openings. It's a tale of failure, setbacks, rejection, perseverance, and – finally – success.

It begs the question, therefore, is there value in failure? Are we meant to get knocked down and get back up again? Do mishaps and blunders – small and large – always lead to success? *Greater* success, even? And, more importantly, does the way we perceive failure shape our dieting mindset?

What Is Failure?

Failure is commonly defined as 'the lack, or opposite, of success'. It's the matter of not achieving one's goals. If something doesn't go quite according to plan, we judge that we've failed. This perception of failure can arrive in many forms. Some less significant and more avoidable, whilst others are larger or more complex. From scoring an 'F' on a school exam, to causing the death of seven astronauts through downplaying a glaring issue with the tank of a space shuttle,[4] or investing in – and losing – £5000 from 'Steve Down The Pub's' latest investment tipoff, failure is rampant in daily life.

The concept of 'failing' allows us to differentiate between setbacks and triumphs, losses and victories, and slumps and progress. It allows us to evaluate a specific situation and view where we've fallen short of an intended objective – including areas such as relationships, work projects, business ventures, and scientific experiments. Every time we experience a mismatch between expectation and reality, we're able to recognise that something isn't quite right – and can, subsequently, adjust the error. Without failure we wouldn't learn or improve. We might not help others, laud our heroes, nor celebrate achievements; all of which contribute to a functioning, continually developing society. You could say that failure is, therefore, quite important.

The problem is, though, no one wants to fail. It's just not very nice. Like standing barefoot on a plug socket, or asking someone out in high school, to be greeted with the retort of, "I think we make better friends"; these piercing experiences shuttle an agonising wave of pain through your body. No wonder we often spend time running *away* from failure. We've been conditioned to associate defeat with negative experiences, missed opportunities, punishment, and disappointment.

If our first attempt at making a healthy dinner ends up with an overcooked chicken and a broken smoke alarm, we'll likely feel dejected. Healthy eating isn't for us, clearly. If our first experiment with the leg press at the gym ends with us getting entangled in the machine, we'll possibly end up not just feeling embarrassed but also vowing to never set foot near the confusing mechanism again.

Explanations – more accurately, exculpations – that cloud the message of failure follow. Individual's may blame themselves, their effort, or even the task at hand – meaning the lessons learnt are insufficient for future success. The initial cleft of disappointment following a failure is a scary place to occupy. We're not sure how we're ever going to escape. "There's no way I'll ever succeed", we convince ourselves. When we exist in a culture that, throughout our early years, doesn't encourage failure – let alone celebrate it – it's hard to avoid such ingrained feelings.

Failure, therefore, terrifies us. Which means we shirk away from experiences, challenges, and opportunities – including career paths, business ideas, relationships, and attempting that chicken recipe again. The feelings of dejection, embarrassment, and grief tend to repel us from tackling both old and new tasks. We may even believe that downfalls and defeats define us. As if that one, specific moment in time will become some grandiose endorsement of our self-worth. It's as though we'll be judged for falling short of a pre-arranged diagnosis of success.

Unfortunately – and this is important – we have no choice. Failure *will* happen. Not always, but it will. Trying to avoid it is like trying to avoid death, taxes – or annoying quotes like this. Look closely at any skill or task that you're currently proficient at, and you'll likely remember that you fell short of certain requirements on the first few attempts. Maybe you fell off the bike, or failed the mock exam; perhaps you didn't know how to adjust the seat on the leg extension at the gym. The reassuring news, however, is that the majority of successes we encounter now were built on a bedrock of failures. From the famous stories of J.K. Rowling[5] to Sir James Dyson,[6] people who've met their intended objective experienced those same clashes with disappointment. They happened for others and will happen for you. If we've all previously experienced, currently experience, and will continue to experience failure, is there an argument to say that we *need* these defeats, collapses, and inadequacies in our lives? Does growth always emerge from failure?

Now, while I'd love to be able to tell you to put this book down, go and fail at something and subsequently greet success at the next turn, the pendulum has, unfortunately, swung too far in the *other* direction. Because of its inevitability, people now idolise failure. They hunt it down. They tweet about it. The problem with most failure aficionados who parade defeat as a glorified badge of honour, however, is that they overlook the consequences. Damaged relationships. Job losses. Wasted time. Death. Losing the £5000 you were going to treat your family to an all-inclusive trip to Dubai with. Of course, while failing when dieting won't result in such devastating consequences, the ramifications are clear to see; failure isn't always beneficial.

I don't want you to set out with the *intention* of failing. That's foolish. Setting out to endure pain, anxiety, and defeat isn't always a stipulation for success. Failing without purpose is ill-advised. It's simply time to admit that, while it stings, it's going to happen anyway. We should still strive for success but, if failure is going to surface regardless, we might as well face it head-on, rather than deny its inevitability. The lessons we learn from our errors will provide greater value than not trying at all.

Herein lies the deal with – and answer to – failure. It's not about the event itself but about how you *handle* it that matters the most. How do your perceptions and reactions surrounding defeat influence your behaviours? How do you view small disappointments and big implosions? What type of mindset do you adopt regarding mishaps, mistakes, and blunders on your dieting venture?

Why Do People Fail When Dieting?

Because They're Too Rigid

The classic diet arrives with a host of iron-fisted rules. 'Don't eat this; do eat that'. 'Don't eat at this time; eat at that time'. 'Cut out this; eat more of that'. When eating practices are rule-driven, problematic behaviours ensue. Of course, if any of these hard-lined rules worked, there wouldn't be over 100,000 results when you type the term, 'Diet Book' into Amazon. Rigid diet rules and dichotomous thinking lead to failure.

Numerous studies have found that such inflexible dieting methods predict increased bodyweight and calorie intake, along with a loss of control, in both men and women.[7] One study described rigid diet rules as the "…number one psychological predictor of weight loss failure."[8] If we're bound to a host of commands that limit, deprive, and corner us into a 'good/bad', 'clean/dirty', 'on-plan/off-plan' mentality, then we'll end up regressing to our old ways. It's like constantly pulling on an elastic band, until it eventually snaps back and leaves a painful mark on our skin. We simply can't outlast the heavy restrictions imposed upon us.

From completely eradicating certain food items, to following a strict and intense meal plan for 12 weeks, such deprivation and rigidity leads, inevitably, to failure. A small deviation from the plan, or the fierce feeling around the anticipation of, "I can't wait till this is over", results in increased stress levels[9] – and an eventual, 4000-calorie blowout on any previously prohibited foods. Not to mention the torrent of guilt, shame, and, even, eating disorders that accompanies that typical, pizza-ravaged feast.[10] People invariably end up back at square one.

If you engage in eating behaviours that continually grapple with your mind, to the extent that they hinder you more than they help, then your dieting approach is too rigid. The fixation with what you can and can't do – specifically with what you can or can't consume – leads to feelings of failure whenever you make a tiny step outside of the imaginary cage you've locked yourself in. Of course, two individuals can engage in identical behaviours, with contrasting ramifications for each. But following a specific diet protocol that burdens you with a host of uncompromising rules will, more often than not, result in failure.

Some guidelines are, of course, required. Tipping the scales too far in the other direction and allowing people to attempt a dieting phase with complete free reign, tends to lead to confusion and excessive leniency. They also, all too often, end up making little to no progress at all. Some form of structure is required when aiming to lose body fat; we need a certain level of restraint, after all. But implementing too many stringent boundaries invariably leads to problems. It's about installing a framework that doesn't cause you overwhelming anxiety over what you can and can't consume, nor a burning desire to reassume old habits.

Because They're Thinking Too Much

Your heart sinks when you notice the crisps on the table, or the wine on offer at dinner. What if you'll *never* be able to resist the euphonic call from such temptations? "No", you tell yourself – you won't succumb to their tantalising cry this time.

Five minutes pass, however, and the appetising item is still staring at you from across the room. Yet another ten minutes pass, and you're now making a lengthy list of reasons in your head as to why you shouldn't – can't, even – have them. You're not allowed. They're not part of the diet. They're 'bad'.

Then you persuade yourself that you could just have a *couple*. You've been so good recently. You deserve one. Or two. More thoughts swirl around inside your head, before you realise you now feel slightly nauseous from wolfing down four handfuls of crisps and two glasses of wine.

Damn, it happened again.

Relentless ruminating over a decision only serves to emphasise the strain on your motivation and restraint. The inevitable bomb then explodes, and you wind up knee-deep in crisp packets and empty bottles of wine. That constant pressure plays in a loop inside your brain; instead of assisting in talking you down from the roof, it only seems to push you further to the edge. Constantly stewing over a situation, in your head, exacerbates such thoughts. The more you think, the more likely you are to fail.

Unfortunately, the act of trying *not* to think about something sparks a paradoxical effect.[11] We focus on the thing we're not meant to be thinking about *more* than when we intentionally try to think about it. This is why trying to extinguish those thoughts of, 'Avoid the crisps' or, 'I mustn't go off-plan' likely end up, in reality, as going ahead and devouring the crisps, or veering off-plan. Our brain is in a constant battle with itself. One side attempts to sustain focus and control; the other scans for danger and temptation.[12] When we're tired, stressed, or distracted, the side foraging for danger surfaces and feeds our mind with all the things we're not meant to think about. This has been called *ironic rebound* and is the process put in place for when you end up performing the behaviour you promised yourself you wouldn't.

Think of these intrusive thoughts as countless apps open on your phone. While you may not be able to see them in action at that particular moment, they're still hidden and operating, ready to surface when you feel the urge to open up your favourite one for the umpteenth time today. The more we try to avoid those apps – or our thoughts – the bigger the crash from the rebound effect. We know that food thought suppression has been found to result in increased food intake, through cravings, particularly in overweight and obese people, when dieting.[13]

Our thoughts and feelings each play a large role in how we deal with certain situations. Attempting to censor them often results in those same feelings pushing back harder, in a powerful eagerness to emerge. While we may be able to suppress them for a short while – and in some situations that *could* prove beneficial – our always attempting to subdue those thoughts exacerbates feelings of anxiety, stress, and failure.[14] Thought suppression is taxing and, when we exclusively rely on it as a method of avoiding certain foods, failure occurs.

Because They're Always Dieting

A recent survey of two thousand British people showed that the average adult will attempt *126 diets* throughout their lifetime – that's at least two new diets each year.[15] Has there ever been such a prominent failure rate in any other endeavour that the general population undertakes? Apart from the act of taking 101 shots to get the perfect photo for Instagram, you'd assume not. The constant and supposed need to diet often sets people up for failure – not least of all because, most of the time, people don't actually need to focus on losing body fat.

The perceived requirement to meet a societal benchmark of leanness is draining. Supplement that with inadequate, often damaging, dieting methods, and you have a foolproof recipe for failure. Not only do people fail to reach the impervious ideals they've been nurtured with, but they often focus on the wrong aspects of aesthetic change – from fixating on the number on the scales, to always feeling the need to be 'thinner'. When they look at themselves in the mirror and can't yet see what they *perceive* society likes, they diet again. And again. And again.

The common, quick-fix, unsustainable nature of most diets creates a vicious feedback loop. As soon as one diet finishes, another one starts. Not only does this create physiological stress on the body, but a psychological burden, too. The constant and presumed need to think about food – what to eat and what not to eat – along with how much body fat you're losing, and whether you believe you're the right size yet, wears a person down. The same kind of enthusiasm for going gluten-free has usually dissipated by the time people reach their fifteenth attempt at losing the same, elusive ten pounds. They continue to believe they've failed – yet again – and go in search of another method to attempt. Each time, that enthusiasm dwindles.

Eventually, losing weight consumes their life. They place the archetypal diet on a pedestal, as an investment that will pacify hidden insecurities and problems. When the latest, 'Paleo-Inspired Whole Foods Diet' fails to fix those issues, they will continue to hunt for something novel and exciting.

The paradox is this: people will always do better when they *don't* always place changing their physique at the top of their priority list. Even those who feel more relaxed with their food choices, and don't obsess over each decision, will suffer fewer cravings.[16] Losing body fat should be a part of life, at certain points, but not its definition. Realising the need to implement long-lasting, behavioural changes – united with shaping a new identity – will curtail short and long-term failures. While dieting 365 days of the year may seem mandatory for physical change, it is, in fact, counterproductive.

Chances of failure can be reduced by relinquishing the focus on losing weight and concentrating, instead, on other priorities, such as building muscle, learning to cook with the family, and cultivating important values such as passion and self-reliability. People no longer become consumed with aiming to look a certain way, but are absorbed by other parts of the transformation process. Those often promote greater change than continual weight loss endeavours.

Similarly, just as there should be times spent aiming to lose body fat, there should be moments spent *maintaining* weight loss as well. You can still want to diet, generally, whilst appreciating it's not the best goal at *that specific point* in the journey. In embracing maintenance – or, even, dedicated muscle growth phases – you'll remove the overwhelming pressure of dieting.

Practicing skills that enhance awareness of internal cues, and appreciating moments of stillness, are both signs of responsibility and growth. Eating for optimal satisfaction and satiety, and recognising non-hunger cues for eating, for example, will *still* aid weight loss – just not with prevalent dieting methods. By adjusting the process and focus – although not necessarily the overall objective – common failures can be viewed in a different light.

Because They Practice Perfectionist Behaviours

Dieters can become consumed with excessively high standards. They'll strive for flawlessness in everything they do, whether with eating habits or exercise behaviours.[17] They'll believe everything needs to be executed perfectly, or else deemed a failure. If they eat a piece of chocolate, they've failed. If they don't manage to complete all their gym session, they've failed. If they put on one-eighth of a pound, they've failed. This pervasive – and ultimately harmful – mentality is commonly defined as *perfectionism*.

While there are healthy variants of perfectionism, what we call '*negative perfectionism*' dominates the world of dieting.[18] These faultless tendencies – concerns over making mistakes, the fear of negative evaluation from others, and feelings of always falling short of high standards – result in self-criticism, self-contempt, guilt, and shame. The belief that an individual has failed tends to greet them at every corner. Not only does perfectionism result in emphasising mistakes, highlighting a lack of self-esteem, and – ultimately – procrastination, but it's also been found to drive binge eating[19] and enhance body dissatisfaction.[20]

Dieters can become so engrossed in the act of achieving perfection, they believe the small steps they're making are worthless. Because they're unable to see themselves making progress – no matter how slight or steady – they tend to become glued to one spot, unable to move forward. They're so fearful of being powerless to measure up to an idealised model of perfection, that it leaves them functioning from a sense of failure. If they believe they've failed, they have no option but to quit.

It's this *act of quitting* that defines perfectionism. When perfectionists experience a stumbling block, they'll typically abandon their efforts. When those who make progress encounter a stumbling block, however, they'll practice consistency. There's a clear difference. We all have perfectionist thoughts; what counts is how we respond to them. How do we deal with the inner critic, who makes inaccurate assumptions about our work, our progress, and our effort? Do we withdraw from our ambitions or stand firm and persevere?

The familiar dieting mentality promotes perfectionism. From feeling the need to follow a meal plan down to the last gram of chicken, to never overeating, nor drinking at social gatherings, people will rarely live up to their grandiose expectations. If all they've ever known, seen, and experienced is the desire for impeccability, that's what they'll pursue. When they inevitably fall short, they'll change direction and take steps *away* from their goals. Their inability to handle fear sabotages them.

As Josh Hillis, in his book, *Lean & Strong,* says, "Perfectionism is an unwillingness to do work when confronted with our own humanity. It's abdicating responsibility every time we see evidence of being human."[21] Judging your self-worth based on an ability to achieve pre-set, imposing standards results in a persistent sense of failure. Perfectionists see this as an opportunity to quit, resulting in misery and little progress.

How Do You Deal With Failure Right Now?

Caving To The 'What-The-Hell Effect'

We've all been there. One innocent cookie has turned into ten. A couple of crisps from the sharing platter have turned into a salt-and-vinegar-crisp meltdown. One regretful deviation from the (rigid) plan leads to a guilt-consumed bender. This has been formally defined as the 'what-the-hell effect'.[22] "I've already screwed up so, what the hell, there's no point in trying to salvage the situation – bring me *all* the food." Chaos flows, as people contrive to leap off the wagon – hard and fast. Viewing a failure – no matter how insignificant – as the end of the road leads to people throwing in the towel and giving up altogether.

Dieters become beset with feelings of guilt and shame when they perceive themselves as failures. Those powerful emotions, and the sense that the person has lost control, causes them to become stuck in a vicious, *'indulge-regret-indulge'* cycle. In her book, *The Willpower Instinct,* Kelly McGonigal says, "Giving in makes you feel bad about yourself, which motivates you to do something to feel better. And what's the cheapest, fastest strategy for feeling better? Often the very thing you feel bad about."[23] Instead of learning from mistakes – and even implementing a damage limitation approach – dieters let those feelings dictate future actions. That feedback loop induces more guilt and shame, which only serves to breed more overeating or under-exercising. The cycle continues.

The what-the-hell effect manifests as a familiar, 'all-or-nothing' approach. People are either perfectly devoted to the plan, or not following the plan at all. And when they perceive themselves to have failed – whether that be snacking when they shouldn't have, or missing a gym session, for example – they're thrown off course. They declare they'll, "…start again on Monday", or "…wait until it's a better time to start". Instead of aiming for a level of consistency – no matter how trivial – they quit. They're either sprinting ahead at full steam, or sprawled across the floor like a toddler amid a full-blown temper tantrum.

Sitting on that 'all' side of the fragile, dieting see-saw is a perilous place to perch. It seems that, the more you try to meticulously follow the plan and restrain yourself, the more likely you are to breach the adherence barrier. This *'disinhibition effect'* was found in restrained eaters (those who consciously and chronically restrict themselves), who proceeded to eat *more* ice cream after already downing a milkshake or two, compared with unrestrained eaters.[24] These self-confessed 'strict' dieters have even been found to exhibit lower levels of cognitive functioning.[25] The more you try to be all-in, the weaker that see-saw is. When you tip to the other side – even slightly – you find yourself back where you began; on the sofa, with a big tub of ice cream, promising you'll start again soon.

There appears to be no happy medium with failure. We're either *not failing* or *failing completely*. As we've established, avoiding disappointment is a futile task. Absolute thinking clouds our judgement of the situation. Small errors and minor blips are often salvageable; nothing more than a tiny dent in an otherwise progressive, blossoming journey. The all-or-nothing approach is the antithesis to the ultimate dieting mindset.

Giving In To The Magnifying Glass Effect

A trivial slip-up, often nothing but a small incision if seen on a towering, 150-metre skyscraper, will repeatedly get blown out of proportion elsewhere. It's what Aadam Ali at *Physiqonomics* calls '*The Magnifying Glass Effect*'.[26] While a small-scale misstep should be swept under the carpet, dieters often view it as the end of the world. The focus is now solely on that one blunder, and all rationality escapes the mind; the familiar overreaction then ensues. What should have been viewed as a paltry and acceptable failure leads to either an overcompensation by undereating and over-exercising, or a full-blown eruption of overeating and under-exercising. Zooming in on one slip-up, and presuming everything else has been ruined, is a common way of dealing with failure.

It's been shown that we make over two hundred important decisions each day.[27] That's 1,400 decisions every week. One decision – whether it be to consume a few more chips than we should, or favouring the sofa over going for a walk – makes up *0.07 per cent* of our week. Accepting that 0.07 per cent of the week is highly unlikely to make a noticeable dent in our progress should be the norm. When the 'Magnifying Glass Effect' surfaces, however, it, unfortunately, accentuates that error, making it seem more pronounced and detrimental than it actually is. We're unable to take a step back and acknowledge the bigger picture. We assume, instead, that those few chips, or the time we spent on the sofa, have led to weight gain and muscle loss, which mean defeat – and a failed weight loss journey.

These tiny failures are often coined 'lapses'. Lapses are any small, unplanned behaviours that threaten progress. They don't, on their own, cause failure.[28] It's a bigger sequence of these events, labelled a *'relapse'*, that does. It's, therefore, the *frequency* of those small failures that ultimately matter. People become immersed in the moment – and fail to realise that each single disappointment will often have little, to no, effect on the overall, desired outcome. Not only are they inevitable but, in the grand scheme of things, largely meaningless. Failing to ascertain the difference between a *trivial lapse,* which can be improved, and a *significant relapse,* that needs remodelling, reinforces the Magnifying Glass Effect.

Engaging In Learned Helplessness

Those who consistently fail at losing weight start to postulate they'll *never* succeed. What's the point in trying? Each previous failure weighs heavy, with people having to drag those cumbersome sacks of disappointment with them, everywhere they go. Every time they experience another failure, their ability to persevere starts to drain. The psychological hardship of each defeat starts to slowly accumulate, like a gambling addict's debt. Every bump in the road is viewed as another opportunity to give up. This is the *fixed mindset* in play.

Individuals with this implicit frame of mind tend to view failure as part of who they are. This often results in shying away from challenges or situations in which they're uncertain of their ability to succeed.[29] If they've always failed, then it must be written in the stars. Or maybe on one of the fourteen fortune cookies they've just unwrapped. Similar to when dogs avoid jumping a barrier to escape a box, because they've been conditioned to receive an electric shock each time they do so,[30] typical dieters become conditioned to avoid the pain of failure, by giving up. This is formally known as *learned helplessness.* The fear of experiencing yet another distressing experience prevents them from trying again.

These 'helpless-oriented' individuals tend to condemn their own abilities and lose hope for future success.[31] They become fixated on *why* they always fail – and they let those seemingly personal flaws guide their future decisions. They'll firmly believe it's because they lack the necessary skill set, motivation, or willpower to succeed in any physical transformation. They'll start to tell themselves, "I'm not very good at dieting", or, "I guess it's just not meant to be".

Such dieters belittle both their ability and self-worth, resulting in increased anxiety and doubt. Those who engage in the common, yo-yo dieting practice often report a feeling of helplessness when it comes to healthy eating.[32] If all they've ever known is the perception of failure, then they have little reason to try again. If we compare this with 'mastery-orientated' individuals, however, who perceive failure as an opportunity to persist with different strategies, it's easy to see how some people become embroiled in feelings of despair while others don't. Helplessness even changes people's perception of goal setting, from one that focuses on the *self* to *performance-related* goals. Instead of the spotlight highlighting character growth, it becomes about the 'after' photo or jean size – which only serves to exacerbate small deviations from these physical objectives.

Letting the perception of failure dictate your beliefs about yourself will result in feelings of resignation. If self-defamation and suffering indicate that you'll never succeed, you'll give up at the first hurdle.[33] Learned helplessness exists on a foundation of hope and belief and, if you have little left in the tank, the chances are you'll seldom try again.

Fashioning Justifications And Excuses

As the perception of failure invokes feelings of guilt and shame, people will do everything in their power to avoid them. They'll formulate heavy justifications as to their seemingly poor decisions or actions. When they construct such excuses (for example, "It was my brother's birthday, and it was only two (eight) beers, I promise"), they're shifting the blame, that causes those feelings, onto external factors less damaging to their self-esteem. These excuses protect self-image, alongside their sense of control.[34] If they're able to place the disapproval of failure onto someone, or something, else (for example, "There wasn't any other food available", or, "My brother pinned me to the floor and shoved the doughnuts down my throat"), then they're able to avoid the pain of supposedly doing something wrong.

These excuses can arrive in the form of many behaviours.[35] There may be a denial of the ramifications of certain actions, known as 'distorting the consequences' (for example, "A second takeaway this week won't hurt"); to crafting comparisons with other failures, known as 'advantageous comparison' (for example, "I ate far more at the *last* party"). People will always try to protect themselves from the feelings that failure will arouse. They'll even blame others for their decision-making, known as 'diffusion of responsibility' (for example, "Everyone else was ordering drinks at the bar, so I had no choice").

In citing external factors, dieters assume those moments can be changed *next* time. This may explain why individuals will attempt diet after diet; blaming the weight loss plan relieves them from any responsibility for the original failure (except for the possible naivety in choosing an obviously inferior diet). These external attributions salvage hope, whilst averting the need to try harder next time.

One of the most prominent forms of justifications people use is *moral licensing*.[36] This is the notion that you permit yourself to do something 'bad', once you've completed something that makes you feel 'good'. Detrimental behaviours are made personally acceptable when they're portrayed as socially or morally valuable. They create a positive feedback loop, allowing individuals to continue with the very same behaviours that incite failure. It's why people are more likely to splurge on a frivolous purchase, such as a pair of designer jeans, over a utilitarian one, like shopping for a vacuum cleaner, after they've been asked to imagine spending three hours a week teaching children in a homeless shelter.[37] And it's why dieters who perceive themselves closer to any weight loss goals they've set themselves were likely to choose a chocolate bar over an apple, as a parting gift from the study they'd just participated in.[38]

When people believe they've performed an act aligned with their goals or identity, they're more likely to then follow it with a contradictory behaviour. It's why self-sabotage occurs. Individuals relax because they believe they've done 'well', only to engage in actions that eradicates that very same progress. Many will say, for example, "I went to the gym today, so I can consume four of the Nutella-filled doughnuts", only then having to start the same journey again the following day. Excuses serve to placate any feelings of disgrace.

Moral licensing not only dupes us into acting against our true identity, but arrives with other prominent problems as well. When we make justifications for our choices, we avoid the lessons that failure can bring us. Shame and guilt are inescapable but, nonetheless, demonstrate how to act in the future. Examining the lessons that these emotions and failures can teach us is, therefore, crucial for successful, long-lasting, physical and mental transformations. While we shouldn't always chase down feelings of shame and guilt, embracing them will be far more valuable than avoiding them completely.

How Should You Deal With Failure?

Embrace Failure

Failure is temporary. It's nothing more than a quandary that indicates your actions didn't turn out as you planned or expected. It's not a negative; it's merely an *opportunity* to now improve. To discover how you felt in the moment. To establish how you reacted to those feelings and the requirements for a stronger and more effective plan. The act of failure creates growth. This 'solution-oriented' mindset will allow you to *fail forwards.* Through leveraging your mistakes, you're able to avoid those same lapses next time, which, in turn, will help you keep striving towards your new identity, values, and goals.

Embracing failure does, unfortunately, run counter to everything we know. It doesn't come naturally. If we can't pinpoint the positives, then we tend to assume that none exist. And, while not every failure is obviously beneficial (sometimes it just *is*), it's still crucial to start hunting for any opportunities and advantages that prevail. They may be small and tough to find, but, search long and hard enough, and you will locate them.

Ordering three takeaways in one weekend is now *great*, in that it's a sign you need to do your weekly shop on a Friday, so you've got fresh food in the fridge for the next few days. Failing to lose any centimetres from your waist circumference over the month is now *great*; it's an indication that you need to keep a closer eye on your food consumption each week. Overeating at lunchtime is now *great*; it's a warning you need to step away from your desk, so you can focus on practicing the skill of eating slowly without distraction. Embracing your failures is a prerequisite for success.

Wallowing in feelings of negativity and blame, following a blip, will only inflame those cookie-induced blunders. Normalising and welcoming the setback, however, will serve to minimise the negative connotations associated with failure. Once you overcome that fear, you'll reclaim control of your decision-making. You'll unearth a whole new commitment to your weight loss journey, as you're now prepared to accept the hardships those errors bring. Each failure is now an opportunity to gain valuable feedback and adjust accordingly, not an intimation that the dream is over.

You'll probably recognise this outlook, by now, as the *growth mindset*. Possessing these incremental beliefs will protect against the adverse effects of dieting setbacks.[39] As negative reactions to dieting difficulties will clearly predict people's chances of weight regain,[40] it's important to detect how shifting the perception of failure to something constructive increases the probability of long-term weight loss. Motivation and adherence will prevail, as each adverse situation is something to work towards and improve upon – rather than discard or ignore.

The next time you find yourself with an accidental, empty crisp packet by your side, or you overshoot on your calorie budget for the day, work on embracing the failure. Instead of believing you've ruined everything, consider what you can learn from the situation. What led you to overeat? What systems can you put in place to avoid it happening again? How will you deal with the problem next time? Using these accommodating, coping strategies – including positive reframing, acceptance, and even humour – allows people to deal with the day's failures. It can even increase overall satisfaction.[41] As Winston Churchill said, quite aptly, "Success consists of going from failure to failure without loss of enthusiasm." While seemingly counterintuitive, it's crucial to welcome and recognise failures as principal pillars of progress.

Practice Excellence

We know that aiming for perfection when dieting is an ineffective strategy. While you may have one 'perfect' day or week, a 'bad' day – or week – will soon surface. What predicts success is how good you are at minimising the damage of those lesser moments. This is known as *practicing excellence.*

The pursuit of excellence involves trying, failing, and *trying again.* This cycle repeats itself until you become excellent, rather than perfect. You become so 'excellent' that you can minimise the substandard days, weeks, and months. You're always making steps forward, regardless of the outcome. You'll still make mistakes – this is not perfectionism, remember – but, because your skill and mindset have developed, with each attempt, into those emphasising quality, not exactitude, you'll reach a place where precision just isn't necessary. Because you're now committed to growing and learning, striving for anything more would be detrimental.

A person practicing perfectionism will expect every gym session, mealtime, and weight loss attempt to be perfect. Monday should be a high-protein, slow-simmered, burgundy beef stew with not an ounce of chocolate in sight. On Tuesday there'll be a 90-minute intense legs-session, followed by a seafood-stuffed salmon fillet, coupled with a zesty tomato and nectarine salad. Anything misaligned with this paragon is regarded as a weakness. This individual expects to repeat such a level of perfection day after day, week after week – and to achieve results instantly. When it inevitably doesn't happen, they'll simply give up.

A person practicing excellence, however, will expect every gym session, mealtime, and weight loss attempt to be excellent. They may occasionally have a beer with dinner, or throw some chips in the oven instead of having a salad, but they're at peace with those decisions. This is because the majority of their meal is still *excellent.* The bulk of their actions are still aligned with their goals, without serving as some impossible ceiling to reach. The next time they make the same meal, they may aim to have half the beer or half the number of chips.

They've tried, failed, and tried again. Those perfectionist thoughts still occur, but, instead of quitting, they seek excellence.

Marcus Aurelius, the great Roman emperor and Stoic philosopher, said, in *Meditations*, his collection of personal writings, "When force of circumstance upsets your equanimity, lose no time in recovering your self-control, and do not remain out of tune longer than you can help. Habitual recurrence to the harmony will increase your mastery of it." This notion has been labelled *The Equanimity Game.*[42] When you naturally get knocked down, making a game of how quickly you can recover will predict your success.

Practicing the art of recovery elevates excellence. Your ability to return to the norm as quickly as possible will forecast sustainability. If you miss a day of tracking your food, how quickly can you return to monitoring your next meal? If you have one too many bites of the dessert on offer, how quickly can you make your next mouthful something healthy? If you have no reason to throw the towel in when something doesn't go according to plan – because you're so engrossed in the game of equanimity – you'll be able to follow your weight loss journey for longer than you're accustomed to.

You're not opting for mediocrity here – if you *always* make mistakes, you're functioning at a level that's too challenging. The idea is that you're still striving to be the best you can be, but you're not expecting perfection. You're willing to accept failures while striving for premium standards. The pursuit of excellence involves the tenet of repeated, admirable practice. Getting knocked down, but seeing how quickly you can get back up again – and appreciating that this is the natural order of the process – is how you should deal with failure.

Practice Iteration

Since Apple released their first iPhone in 2007, they've designed and released over twenty-three variations of the phone, each one better than the last. Since Microsoft released their Windows 1.0 software in 1985, there's been a total of twenty-five versions of the computer operating system, each one also better than the last. Neither Apple nor Microsoft viewed each progression as a failure of the preceding attempt; merely an opportunity to improve. Each modification an iteration of the previous model. And this is how we should redefine failure; we're *iterating*, not failing.[43]

Just like architects or engineers make hundreds of modifications to an initial design, you should set out to make hundreds of adjustments to your weight loss journey. The belief you're iterating, and not failing, is a powerful concept. It shifts the blame from the individual to the design of the system. And through attributing failure to the *model*, you're not only dislodging any feelings of shame or ineptitude, but also granting room for self-improvement. Each failure is no longer identified as a negative, but as an opening to be remodelled. Employing such an influential mindset allows you to continually upgrade and reshape previous plans, until you unearth a system that works for you and your lifestyle.

Even Walmart, the American retail corporation, has bought into the idea of iteration by partnering with Fresh Tri, a neuroscience-based, habit-formation digital app. The app focuses on the concept of practice and iteration to drive healthy habits and lifestyle changes. One study showed that its use led associates of the company to lose an average of 7.2 pounds over 60 days.[44] It enables users to discern what is and isn't working, and helps them acknowledge personal qualities that promote progress. It allows them to iterate their way to success.

"Traditional goals-and-tracking methods backfire because any perceived failure triggers an area in the brain that kills motivation to keep trying," explains Fresh Tri founder and CEO, Kyra Bobinet. "By training people to iterate — to practice and tweak daily habits — we help them overcome barriers of long-term change such as relapse, weight regain, plateaus, and self-doubt."[45]

The idea that resuming the journey in a different format is worthwhile takes each failure and turns it on its head. It opposes the notion that giving up completely is the only option. The ability to restart – and restart fast – encourages momentum. Each failed attempt at following the design becomes an opportunity to find an alternative solution, which combine to bring about significant change.

Practice Flexibility

Just like a gymnast can contort themselves into different positions depending on the movement required, we must adopt a similarly flexible approach when dieting. We must adapt to the situation in front of us. Whilst we don't necessarily find it difficult to get there, nor become stuck in that one position, we bend and twist our actions, skills, and beliefs, to acclimatise to each new scenario that life brings.

Flexibility opens your world to a new host of opportunities. No longer are you consigned to rigid dieting rules, but can apply the necessary behaviours to each condition as they make sense in that moment. You can now eat out with friends, instead of having to stay at home for fear of ruining your diet; you may enjoy the occasional glass of champagne at a friend's wedding, instead of sticking to the water – and be able to perform a mobility session at home instead of going to the gym. When you forge an effective supply of life-changing skills, such as food tracking, mindful decision-making, or portion control, you're able to tailor these qualities to different situations. Just like choosing which outfit to wear for work each day, flexibility means knowing you possess the necessary skill set to decide which behaviour to employ at any given time.

Flexibility removes the concept of 'good and bad' and 'on-plan or off-plan'. If nothing is good or bad, nor on-plan or off-plan, failure is almost impossible. If eating ice cream is allowed because ice cream isn't 'bad' for you, then eating a bowl of it isn't a failure. If overshooting on a calorie budget for the day isn't off-plan – because you know you can adjust your calorie intake the following day – then having an extra spoonful of potatoes at dinner isn't a failure. If forgetting to pack the turkey for lunch isn't off-plan, because you know you can replace it with salmon to still hit a protein target, switching foods isn't a failure. By practicing flexibility – paying close attention to each situation and amending actions appropriately – you'll flip your mindset from one of intransigency to freedom.

You don't, of course, want to career too far to the other end of the spectrum. Practicing *too much* flexibility will seldom lead to results. Going all out on an anniversary dinner – because you can starve yourself the next day –

will lead to disordered eating. Not training for a week, because you know you can train eight times in the following four days, will lead to physical burnout – and sore glutes. You must position yourself in the middle. Sometimes you say, "Yes"; other times you say, "No". On certain occasions you train with greater intensity; on others you train with less urgency. Sometimes you'll consume all of the takeaway; on other occasions you'll have just the meat and salad.

Flexibility doesn't imply you should 'Do whatever you want'. It signifies periodically turning up the dial and occasionally turning it down. When you're riding high on the waves of motivation, you may follow specific macronutrient targets. When you're feeling sad, you may just focus on hitting a protein target. When you're full of energy you'll maybe aim for a personal best in the gym. When you're tired, you'll likely aim to just complete some of your session. *That* is flexibility.

It's important to remember that you'll still want a number of boundaries to adhere to – we all require some form of direction, of course. You just don't want any of these to restrict and confine you into a mindset that you can't escape from. The key is in finding succinct and personable systems that guide you, and enable you to practice flexibility – for example, not entering the kitchen after 8 pm, not eating food off others' plates, or always drinking a glass of water before dinner. These small, custom-made policies that *you've* set yourself – and not the rules taken from yet another dieting fad – will still provide control, but shouldn't cause an overwhelming desire to return to old, destructive behaviours. A modicum of structure breeds freedom.

The notion of flexibility also derives from your value-based system. If you've honed your values and identity, you'll know when it's appropriate to 'up the ante' – as well as when to lower it. The type of person you want to become will dictate your decisions. If you value time spent with your family, then sharing a frozen yoghurt on a day trip with your children may bring more joy than staying restrained. If you also value health, then sharing a frozen yoghurt while at home on a random, cold Thursday in November probably won't bring more joy than surfing the temptation. Flexibility allows you to exercise those values to decide when it's appropriate to use certain skills.

This will take practice, just like with any other skill; but, being flexible with goals, skills, and values promotes adherence, and helps you avoid getting hung up on a myriad of supposed failures. Now you don't feel the need to 'start over'; you simply *keep going*. Values-based action promotes a high degree of flexibility between different situations, but you're aware of your values-based choice in any *given* situation.

Accept Your Thoughts

Imagine yourself as a tiny insect, sitting on a leaf floating down a stream. What would you see and feel? Perhaps you'd see the green of the leaf, the blue and white of the sky, and feel the movement of the running water. If you left the leaf, to perch yourself on the edge of a tree, you'd now be able to see many more leaves floating alongside the one you were just on. When you were seated on that one leaf, that was *all* you could see and feel. However, looking down on the stream from above allowed you to observe other numerous leaves also floating along. You were able to zoom out and survey the many additional objects, colours, and activities going on apace with the one leaf you were previously sat on.

That one leaf is representative of your one, often negative, thought in that moment.[46] For example, craving a piece of chocolate, wanting to avoid the gym, or believing you're a failure. The rest of the stream represents the many other thoughts and events that are also happening – for example, the desire for a piece of fruit, or remembering your values. Gaining distance from the one leaf denoting a single thought, feeling, or sensation – and recognising it for what it is – allows you to make decisions aligned with reality. You're not confined to that one emotion in that given moment because you know there are many other, concurrent thoughts and sensations around you. By allowing your mind to identify any negative thoughts, you can reframe them in a positive way and choose alternative behaviours. This is what's known as *defusion*.[47]

We know that suppressing your thoughts only exacerbates the feelings attached to them. Trying to avoid thinking about the piece of chocolate sitting in the cupboard is like trying to avoid thinking of a horse dancing the jive in a pink tutu. All you end up doing is thinking of the piece of chocolate – or horse dancing the jive in a pink tutu. *Allowing* yourself to feel a desire enables you to then act independently of the experience. When you're 'fused' with your thoughts and feelings, you automatically act on them (for example, craving, then immediately also devouring the chocolate). When you're 'defused' from your thoughts and feelings, you can act independently from them (craving but *not* devouring the chocolate). Defusion is simply separating yourself – and your actions – from your thoughts.

It has been shown repeatedly that, when dieters try to suppress their thoughts, they experience a significant thought rebound. When the dieters in one study were told to just *think* about their intention to eat chocolate, however, they ate twice as fewer chocolates as when they tried *not* to think about chocolate before a taste test.[48] They were able to uncouple the act of eating chocolate from their desire to do so. This acceptance-based approach to our thoughts results in lower cravings and reduced consumption.[49] You are not, nor do you have to act upon, your feelings.

It may be possible to suppress thoughts in the short-term, and, in certain cases, for certain people, will – and should – work. But, while diets relying on thought suppression always runs smoothly for the few first weeks for *some* individuals, seldom does that fragile restraint continue to outlast such deafening desires. Dieters may convince themselves that it's a viable tactic to ditching the chocolate, only to promptly discover they're unable to contend with the recurrent challenge posed by thought suppression. As soon as the seal is broken, they'll end up relieving themselves of that thought censorship and devour all the chocolate, soon gaining back all the weight they lost. Though it may appear to work for a while, thought suppression encourages food-related thoughts and results in increased food intake.[50]

When you wolf down the chocolate, or cancel your personal training session, perhaps you tell yourself that you didn't try hard enough. This leads you, paradoxically, to try even harder, which then only creates an even bigger rebound. Defusion doesn't mean fighting those thoughts; it's about recognising them, accepting them, and realising they're normal. The next stage is *not* acting on them, because you've been able to detach those inward experiences from your behaviours. Increasing awareness of how you're feeling, thinking, and behaving, in the moment, will help identify the 'why' behind any eating and body-related behaviours, unfurling different avenues for change.

To practice defusion, think about labelling your internal experiences.[51] For example, "I'm currently having the thought that ('*I really want a bag of crisps*')", or, "I am currently having the feeling of ('*tiredness, so I don't want to go to the gym*')". This enables you to look *at* your thoughts as opposed to acting *from* them.

Similarly, you can replace the word, 'but', with the word, 'and', when you experience a sensation that conflicts with your goals. For example, instead of, "I was going to go to the gym, *but* I'm tired", it's now a case of, "I was going to go to the gym, *and* I'm tired". This simple swap allows you to dissociate those internal experiences from your behaviours. Instead of punishing yourself for feeling tired or hungry, you can simply recognise that your mind and body are operating as they should. This process makes it easier to accept that, whilst we have an 'inner critic', we can also revert to performing the habits and behaviours that align with our aspirations.

Practicing defusion is hard; it's a highly developed skill. You've always been taught to push that dancing horse out of your mind. It's been shown, however, that three to twelve months of practicing defusion not only leads to increased weight loss, but also a better quality of life.[52] Honing this technique will allow you to avoid the inevitable failures many dieters experience, promoting perseverance through onerous times. You're no longer defined by your failures; instead, you can accept them and stay true to your identity, values, and goals. And this brings us onto another vital aspect of dealing with failure and adversity: *resilience*.

Building Resilience During Your Weight Loss Journey

Athlete adventurer, Ross Edgley, is no stranger to a challenge. From completing a 26.2-mile marathon, whilst pulling a 1,400-kilogram Mini Countryman car tied to his waist, to completing an Olympic distance triathlon with a 100-pound tree strapped to his back, his latest act of fortitude came when, in 2018, he attempted 'The Great British Swim', a casual, 157-

day, 1792-mile swim around Great Britain. He clearly has a taste for pushing his body to its limits. As Ross explains in his book, *The Art of Resilience*, he relishes challenging his *mind* as well.[53]

During his five months at sea, Edgley drew on three concepts that helped him battle the treacherous conditions, the unnerving pain, and the relentless obstacles that both his body and Mother Nature threw at him. To build a resilient mindset, he needed to cultivate what he states as, "[a] strong body, a stoic mind, and a strategic plan". Those three components allowed him to deal with the host of challenges and dangers he faced during his record-breaking adventure. From taking his body through gruelling training sessions (a 48-hour, sleep-deprived swim, for example) to learning how to control his pain and fatigue, he was able to ensure he didn't break – either physically or mentally. Through understanding how to pace each 6-hour swimming stint of his journey, and how to appropriately refuel his depleted energy stores, he prepared himself for the many ruthless and cutting challenges that would be thrown his way.

Having powered around Britain's shoreline in 157 days, Edgley managed to break a number of world records, including, 'The world's longest staged swim', and 'Fastest person to swim the 900 miles from Land's End to John o' Groats'.[54] He forever etched his name into the history books. While undoubtedly possessing elite-level, physical attributes, it's clear that Edgley's unbreakable mindset helped him deal with the arduous challenge. From countless jellyfish stings, to seasickness, to lacerations on his tongue, and spending almost half a year at sea – had he not spent valuable time crafting that resilience, he would never have been willing to even start his journey, let alone be able to complete it. The same ethos must also be applied to your weight loss journey – save for a few, unexpected moments of wetsuit chafing, of course.

The overarching characterisation of unrivalled resilience is that 'adversity will always precede positive adaptation'.[55] By taking any failure or challenge – no matter how big or small – and using it to improve and grow, you're displaying inimitable spells of resilience. Absorbing, and stabilising, at a higher threshold of pain, at each stage in your journey, will enable you to survive the ongoing chaos of any dieting venture and keep moving forward.

We've established that no fat loss endeavour is going to be plain sailing. From hunger, to sacrifice, to failure, there'll be a bombardment of challenges launched your way. It's not always the challenge itself that will indicate success, but often your ability to *deal with it*. How does your mind react when you've overeaten one day, or you decide to miss your gym session for a trip to the pub? Do you give in or keep going? Do you fear failure or take pride in your errors? Resilience – the ability to successfully adapt to exposure to, and bounce back from, life's stresses[56] – will define your chance of losing weight and keeping it off.

The problem is, people have been conditioned to become averse to distress and pain. As soon as a modicum of struggle surfaces when dieting, the first reaction is to quit. It's evident, however, that no person has successfully transformed their physique without staring into the abyss, encountering failure, and emerging stronger. Resilience is a skill that everyone must master to reach their desired goals.

Welcome And Prepare For Challenges

We've established what to expect during your weight loss journey. There'll be plateaus and moments of exasperation. You'll never be as happy as you imagined when you achieve a certain body fat percentage. Your thoughts will often govern your actions. Instead of shirking away from those moments, however, it's time to entertain and welcome such challenges with open arms. *Purposefully* exposing yourself to taxing situations will help to develop an emotional toolkit that's armed to display significant stretches of resilience.

Just as your smartphone can withstand its fair share of knocks, dents, and trips to the bottom of the toilet bowl, yet continue functioning, so, too, will the seeking of similarly difficult situations provide a form of psychological robustness for your mind. You'll be able to keep operating, no matter what threats to your mental toughness you may encounter. The main difference between you and your phone, however, is that when you get knocked down or, for some reason, take a trip to the bottom of the toilet bowl, you *improve*. While your phone simply carries on, you're able to build an extra layer of confidence, tenacity, and autonomy, following every test thrown your way. This is why a certain degree of fragility is desirable; strength – physically and mentally – arises from moments of weakness. Growth surfaces from a breakage in normality. We *need* stress.

Just like Ross Edgley hunts down challenges that not only pushes him physically but, also, mentally, our pursuing moments that demand defiance will build pillars of resilience. The stronger and tougher those pillars are, the better chance you'll have of overcoming obstacles in the future. Whether that be dealing with temptations, or noting plateaus on the scales, getting better at experiencing such challenges will enable you to grow mentally stronger – and ensure you'll be better set the next time those junctures arise.

There's a reason they say you should attempt things that scare you. Take the story of Admiral James Stockdale, for example. Captured as a prisoner of the Vietnam War, he was held hostage and tortured for seven years. Where others failed, Stockdale prevailed. The reason? Stockdale explained, "You must never confuse faith that you will prevail in the end - which you can never afford to lose - with the discipline to confront the most brutal facts of your current reality."[57]

This *Stockdale Paradox* – the belief that you'll come out on top whilst, equally, embracing challenge – relates to dieting as well. Expect results and progress, but also anticipate pain and frustration. The more you're prepared for this impending discomfort, the more resilient you'll be. The more resilient you are, the better you'll be at dieting. By shifting the narrative to one that embraces these difficulties, you'll be able to bounce back from any setbacks and failures. You'll possess the power to perceive adversity as temporary and be able to keep blossoming through pain and hardships.

Stay Positive

Just as we should prepare for pain, we shouldn't forget the positive in a situation either. Akin to unearthing benefits from challenging life events such as a break-up or losing a job, there'll always be positives in any weight loss challenges you experience. Despite some people feeling helpless in certain situations, there are others who display unrelenting reserves of optimism.

Those who can turn the 'bad' into 'good' are described as more resilient.

This is why children and adolescents in one study, who were undergoing treatment for a peanut allergy, fared better when provided with *positive* information surrounding their side effects.[58] Being told that an uncomfortable reaction signalled the 'building of strength', compared with the control group who were told that their symptoms were an 'unfortunate consequence that had to be endured', significantly reduced their worries about treatment and diminished the reporting of future symptoms. Those primed with positive information also showed marked improvements in *physiological measures,* with greater levels of antibodies – that prevent a full-scale allergic reaction to peanut protein – being detected via blood tests. Positive interpretations of negative events can, clearly, have far-reaching consequences.

Of course, this isn't an invitation to become an all-singing, all-dancing advert for euphoria at life's trivial moments. It's been shown that being *too* optimistic makes people less likely to engage in healthy behaviours.[59] Shifting the 'negative' label of a situation to a 'positive' will, nonetheless, enable you to improve. If you've had one too many drinks at the office party, don't worry; you'll be able to rehydrate following the raging hangover. Couldn't get to the gym in the evening? Don't stress; you can use the time to prepare lunch for tomorrow. If you overate at the weekend and it put you on the edge of feeling like a huge failure, don't worry; you didn't put on ten pounds.

Keeping things in perspective, rather than catastrophising, will enable you to think clearly. The more you can view each situation as a positive, as you maintain commitment to your fat loss journey, the more you'll aid your overall well-being and continue tackling the long-term goal. The ability to cultivate positive emotions during stressful situations enables you to propagate productive coping strategies.[60] Whether that be an eagerness to try again, or to find meaning in certain events, positivity will improve psychological and physiological resilience. While your friends may canvas their social media feeds with pictures of junk food, accompanied with the hashtag #dietfail, you'll remain confident you can turn a similar situation around. Those who stay positive stay resilient.

Seek Help And Community

Just as choosing a number of universities to study at will bestow you with options to fall back on should one fall through, having more people around to pick you up – whenever those weight loss demons start to emerge – will improve your resilience.[61] Possessing an emotional parachute of people who can intervene, and safely guide you back down to earth, will help you keep focused on the task at hand. They'll listen, care, and offer advice. And if one can't do so, another one will. Your resilience is dictated not only by your mindset and personal characteristics but the strength of your social milieu as well.[62]

While the methods of many weight loss support groups are flawed, there's no denying their raging loyalty throughout the weight loss industry. While it's probably not the 'sins' or 'points' that keep people returning to them, the gratification of sharing the journey with a group of like-minded individuals has power and appeal. Those who undertake challenges *together* often experience enhanced resilience. When the going gets tough – through failure, despondency, or lack of commitment – the salve of social support is often the answer. You may not need many fellow-supporters, but accessing stability from a calming voice or two will enable you to stand firm through rocky times.

It's for this same reason that personal trainers tend to be underrated. While images of megaphones and cries of, "Ten more burpees" seem to be the norm, hiring a militant commander or taskmaster is often far from the truth. Personal trainers and online coaches act as safety nets, when motivation, positivity, and resilience weaken. They're there to keep the weight loss journey on track and help build a pliancy to any fragile mindset. The act of keeping accountable to a trainer or coach goes well beyond ensuring they're present to just give you 'two more reps'.

Effective coaches understand what people are going through, and will put systems, tactics, and plans in place, to ensure their clients are still striving towards whatever goals they have. Acquiring that branch of accountability and support will do more for your dieting success than any superfood fad, or 'fat-burning programme' will. The more you perceive yourself to have a strong network of people around you, the more you'll believe you're able to deal with life's challenges.[63]

Learn To Display Grit

Researchers have described the trait of 'grit' as a form of resilience that embodies a passion and perseverance for long-term goals – along with a willingness to endure long-term discomfort, to get there.[64] In her book, *Grit,* Angela Duckworth explains how the secret to achievement isn't talent, but is, instead, this unique blend, of "passion and persistence".[65] She believes that grit is developed from a combination of four focuses or behaviours: Discovering an interest in what you do, nurturing a strong sense of purpose, focusing on improvement – no matter what gets in the way – and holding onto the belief that you're able to overcome the challenges you face.

'Grittier' students perform better at spelling bees, 'grittier' cadets are more likely to complete their first summer of army training, and 'grittier' salespeople experience more likelihood of keeping their jobs. Duckworth says, "Grit is sticking with your future day-in-day-out, not just for the week, not just for the month, but for years and working really hard to make that future a reality. Grit is living life like a marathon, not a sprint."

Grit will shape your weight loss journey. If you can establish an unfading passion for changing your physique, you'll be able to persevere amid tribulations, or episodes of demotivation. We're not saying you must be passionate about being hungry and tired all the time, but more so about the process of growth that we know fosters results. If you're able to display unrelenting reserves of stamina over time – through *wanting* to improve your exercise and nutrition skills, along with your habits and desires – you'll be more likely to stay the course. It's this that differentiates between resilience and grit; while resilience often refers to short-term struggles, grit is a devotion to improvement, strength, beneficial behaviours, and an improved lifestyle, *over a long period of time.*

Grit has been shown to facilitate exercise behaviours, too. When thoughts of getting under the bar to push out another set of lunges make you want to hide in the changing rooms, displaying grit will help in grinding out gym session after gym session. Those who possess this influential trait not only train harder, but also exercise *more frequently,* than those who don't.[66] It's no coincidence that the people who are willing to weather hardship with their exercise behaviours – to pursue a transformed physique – also tend to see more weight loss than those who quit at various hurdles. Turning up to the gym, session after session, week after week – despite any lack of motivation or desire – forges an essential component of the ultimate dieting mindset.

We can take members of The National Weight Control Registry as a good example. These individuals have displayed unabated levels of grit. To join, they must have lost thirty pounds or more *and* kept it off for at least a year. That's no mean feat. They've been reported to make weight maintenance a priority and have stayed focused on the end result of weight control.

They've all reached the group's requirements in their own ways – whether following a high-carb and low-fat, or low-carb and high-fat diet; the common theme has been endurance, with commitment to the long-term goal. It was never about dieting for a photoshoot or summer holiday, but maintaining new behaviours for a lifetime. They have all managed to make the necessary changes to their lifestyle – for example, prioritising sleep, maintaining an exercise schedule over the weekend and on holidays, and training for an average of 300-minutes per week. The difference was that they learned to adopt those behaviours to continue *forever*. Developing the passion for a top-level goal, and striving to follow through, is compulsory to garner the trait of grit; it's essential for any dieting goals you have.

Chapter Summary And Taking Action

- Failure comes in many forms, but allows us to differentiate between setbacks and triumphs, losses and victories, and slumps and progress. It allows us to view where we've fallen short of an intended goal or objective. The terrifying nature of failure means we often shirk away from experiences and challenges. Failure is inevitable, however, and so, instead of avoiding it, we must find value in it, and learn from the lessons it teaches us.

- People often fail when dieting because they impose rigid restrictions on themselves (e.g., "I mustn't ever have bread again") and attempt to suppress negative thoughts (e.g., "Don't think of the bread on the table; you're stronger than that"). They constantly diet (e.g., "I'll start this new diet on Monday") and strive for perfection with every skill and behaviour (e.g., "If every day of the week isn't perfect there's no point in continuing").

- When dealing with the inevitable failures these problems bring, they engage in 'what-the-hell' behaviours (e.g., "Screw it, I'm going to eat the whole pack of cookies instead of the two I just ate") and they catastrophise certain moments (e.g., "this one hiccup on a Wednesday afternoon has ruined my whole week and weight loss journey"). They give up hope (e.g., "I guess it's just not meant to be") and start rationalising poor decisions (e.g., "It's Valentine's Day, so I'm allowed to eat everything in sight").

- Instead, we should embrace failure, practice excellence, adopt an iterative mindset, engage in flexible behaviours, and employ an acceptance-based approach to dieting. Think about, and make a note of, how you'll welcome your next failure (e.g., "Failure will teach me to grow as an individual"), how you'll strive for excellence (e.g., "Making mistakes is normal, so striving for perfection is flawed"), and how you'll iterate for future occurrences (e.g., "I'll be able to learn from this mishap and put a different plan in place for next time").

- Engage in flexible behaviours (e.g., "If I overeat, I'm able to practice the skill of reducing portion sizes for my next meal") and accept your negative thoughts (e.g., "Having these cravings is normal; I don't necessarily have to act upon them").

- Resilience is the belief that adversity will always precede positive adaptation. We require this important characteristic to learn from failures, develop as individuals, and keep striving towards our longer-term ambitions. The trait of resilience can be enhanced by welcoming challenges (e.g., "I'll be able to bounce back from any inevitable failures") and staying positive (e.g., "It's great that I made this mistake; I now know how I'll avoid this pitfall next time").

- Seek help (e.g., "I'll employ the guidance of a fat loss coach") and display and practice grit (e.g., "I have the passion and perseverance to always keep going, despite the discomfort and failures I'll experience") to further develop resilience.

CHAPTER 5
You Won't Start On Monday: It's Time To Stop Procrastinating

In 1934, architect Frank Lloyd Wright was commissioned by wealthy department store owner, Edgar Kaufmann, to design a weekend home for his family in the Laurel Highlands.[1] Despite struggling financially and being regarded by many critics as 'past his best', Wright ended up designing a masterpiece. With its cantilevered balconies and striking, horizontal floors, all hanging suspended over a 30-foot waterfall, the finished construction – aptly named Fallingwater – continues to be celebrated as one of the great pieces of modern architecture of all time. Its fusion with the surrounding landscape and watercourse makes it one of the most recognisable house designs across the globe. Wright still holds the title of 'world's greatest architect' by some.

The building's conception didn't surface from extensive planning and meticulous design, however. Legend has it that, after receiving the commission for Kaufmann's latest architectural pursuit, Wright did *nothing* to further the project for nearly a year. Despite there being no internet to mindlessly peruse, nor nearby spice rack to reorganise for the fifteenth time, days passed with little progress. Wright continued to procrastinate – hard. It was only a phone call from Kaufmann, who declared he'd be paying the architect a surprise visit to check in on his plans, that spurred him into action. Wright had however long it would take his employer to drive the 140 miles from Milwaukee to his office in Taliesin, to fashion his designs. Which, according to Google Maps, isn't much time at all.

Did he manage it? Wright's apprentice, Edgar Taffel, said that Wright "…briskly emerged from his office, sat down on the table [which was] set with the plot plan and started to draw. The design just poured out of him. Pencils being used up as fast as we could sharpen them. Erasures, overdrawing, modifying. Flipping sheets back and forth."

There seems to be agreement that the whole planning process – which somehow contrived to integrate the house with the waterfall, and enable the running stream to negotiate its stone walls and overhanging terraces – took just *two hours*. Having been non-existent for almost 12 months, Fallingwater, now a modern design icon, a National Historic Landmark, and once listed among Smithsonian's 'Life List of 28 Places to Visit Before You Die,'[2] was born in the same amount of time it would take for you to watch a blockbuster movie. This really was a case of 'last minute dot com'.

Wright isn't the only revered artist famous for his proclivity to shelve important projects. American author, Herman Melville, repeatedly had his wife chain him to his desk while he was struggling to finish his epic novel *Moby-Dick*, while Douglas Adams, creator of the *Hitchhiker's Guide to the Galaxy,* would supposedly soak for hours in a bathtub to avoid putting pen to paper.[3] It's evident there are different reactions to the potential for piercing through moments of procrastination; some, if sufficiently motivated – or troubled by it – harness everything in their power to avoid procrastination, while others positively encourage drawing it out.

Leonardo da Vinci, the artist and sculptor, was also partial to frequent bouts of excessive idleness. While generally regarded as one of the greatest painters of all time, da Vinci's number of *finished* pieces is often viewed to be in the range of only 15 to 20. It took him fifteen years to complete the Mona Lisa, after all.[4] It's widely accepted that the Italian would ruminate on science and helicopters, by doodling and sketching in his acclaimed notebooks, whilst never organising, editing, nor publishing his drawings. He soon wore the title of being 'unreliable'.

Whether viewed as creative geniuses or simply chronic procrastinators, starting *and* finishing did not come easily to these notorious talents.

Unfortunately, we all have our own Wright, Melville, or da Vinci buried inside us. Why do it today, when we can do it tomorrow? Why go to all that effort now, when it can wait just a little longer? Why bother starting, when we've got months and years ahead of us? We all struggle with delaying, avoiding, and procrastinating on tasks that we deem essential. Time passes, deadlines suddenly emerge, and we're suddenly forced into action – often hurriedly and recklessly. While the Wrights and da Vincis of this world have success to show for their efforts, it's not always that simple. Procrastination is more harmful to creating the ultimate dieting mindset than we might like to believe.

Have you ever wondered why you start dieting just four weeks before your holiday? Or you try on your suit or dress a week before your cousin's wedding and subsequently feel the need to starve yourself for the next seven days, to avoid having to shell out for a new outfit? Or you tell yourself you'll start meal prepping tomorrow, to only find yourself back at the café on a Monday lunchtime, wondering what on earth happened? You'll 'be fine', you convince yourself. Until that holiday, wedding, or deadline abruptly appears on the horizon, of course, and you then have to go to extreme measures to achieve the tasks and look you desire – often resulting in unsustainable and damaging methods to get there.

We're going to take a closer look, therefore, at why people avoid starting their weight loss journey and the necessary, fat loss actions for success. Why does anyone feel the need to continually adopt that infamous, "I'll start on Monday" mindset? Why procrastinate at all?

What Is Procrastination?

Procrastination is simply defined as putting tasks off, either intentionally or habitually.[5] People have trouble persuading themselves to do the things they should, or want to, do. Instead of pushing themselves towards goals, projects, and deadlines, they end up performing trivial tasks instead.

Don't fear, though; finding yourself down a rabbit hole of internet tabs and social media posts – that have nothing to do with anything – is not old news. Ancient Greek philosophers like Socrates and Aristotle developed a word to describe this type of behaviour: *akrasia.*[6] It's the state of acting against your better judgement. There's a clear conflict between what you feel you should be doing and what you're actually doing.[7] You *know* you should start exercising regularly, or even head to the greengrocers today, but, instead find yourself at the pub, unearthing small remnants of misplaced peanuts inhumed inside the creases of your top. Again.

Procrastination is that silent force, preventing you from following through on ambitions and worthwhile pursuits. Not only does it mean you're often rushing around at the last minute trying to complete certain tasks, or struggling to claw back a host of poor eating decisions, but chronic procrastination has also been found to increase the chances of anxiety, depression,[8] and cardiovascular disease[9] – as well as to lower life satisfaction. To make things worse, it's even been found that procrastination can be genetically predisposed.[10] Whatever the root cause – and sometimes managing to repeat and reinforce a family trait – the postponement of significant responsibility can be more crippling than merely engaging in a last-minute panic to get the job done.

Procrastination doesn't bring us lasting joy. While sitting on the sofa, instead of going to the gym, may bring you happiness in the short-term, rarely are you pleased with your decision in the long-term. Despite feeling content in that moment, the nagging thought, chipping away at your conscience – telling you that you should be at the gym – only serves to create feelings of stress and anxiety.[11]

The 'giving in to feel good' effect doesn't last long.[12] Guilt and unease experienced, when you're not taking action, are often far worse than the actual time and effort required, should you execute those healthy behaviours. In reality, being at the gym is never as bad as you fear and eating that healthy lunch doesn't taste as bland as you think it will. A desire to seek short-term comfort means you can fail to get started. Not only does that exacerbate feelings of stress and anxiety, but results in you then possessing less faith in yourself that you'll start next time. This increases your chances of putting off those tasks at the next opportunity because, hey, you procrastinated before, so you'll probably do it in the future as well. You've primed the path of avoidance, resulting in procrastination manifesting as a deadly behavioural pattern. Ironically, completing – not delaying – those tasks will make you happier.

Procrastination isn't laziness, either. If you were lazy, then you'd be satisfied with not striving towards any goals you have. The fact you're reading this book shows that you *want* to change. If you didn't, you wouldn't continually be researching ways to lose weight or still be paying out for a gym membership every month; nor would you have previously embarked on numerous diets. You're determined to acquire that physique; you just happen to favour short-term rewards over long-term gains. You're not a bad person, nor do you lack time management – which is how the act of procrastination is often perceived. But you, like everyone else, may be tempted, quite simply, by the powerful lure of gratifying emotions. It's a vicious cycle, whereby immediate relief prompts a feeling of reward and, as we crave that swift feeling of pleasure, we're likely to seek an instant reprieve yet again.[13] You become conditioned to learn that stopping off at the corner shop on the way home from work, to grab a packet of crisps, will bring more short-term gratification than waiting until you get home to grab a high-protein yoghurt. This is how procrastination matures into a chronic habit.

Procrastination is, therefore, an *emotional* problem.[14] It surfaces from a footing of adverse feelings. If we're able to deflect negativity in favour of short-term mood repair, we're likely to entertain it. Fear of failure, task aversion, perceived lack of control, and other detrimental emotions, all lead to greater levels of indecision. If we're able to assuage those unfavourable feelings and sensations – such as boredom, anxiety, regret, and self-doubt – with a small, short-term hedonistic burst, we're more likely to avoid them.[15] As the saying goes, 'Procrastination is like a credit card; it's a lot of fun until you get the bill'.

People will display various coping mechanisms to deal with their procrastination. From self-justification (for example, "Crafting the perfect gym plan in my neatly-colour-coordinated, Excel spreadsheet is a must") to denial (for example, "Looking up pictures of a fried halloumi salad is the inspiration I need to make something healthy"), such strategies only reinforce faltering behaviours. Procrastinators will even use valorisation (for example, "I work best under pressure") to justify their propensity to avoiding starting a project or diet. While seemingly helpful, this kind of reasoning rarely propels people into action.

While negative feelings will always surface when dieting, there are, thankfully, also positive experiences associated with losing weight, including: increased self-confidence, greater energy, improved physical and mental health, and the security of knowing your knees won't collapse every time you go to haul yourself off the sofa. The problem is, those negative feelings can often weigh heavily against those positive emotions. The thought of waiting a painstaking twelve months, to observe a physical and mental transformation, can be far more powerful than the idea of shopping for a smaller clothing size. Self-doubt is more potent than the desire for greater confidence. We'll tend to do everything in our power to circumvent negative sensations. Why deal with discomfort now, if we can delay the feeling and confront it later? Why experience struggle, when you can relax with a nice cold beer, in the luxury of your deep-rooted comfort zone?

When such demotivating and hindering factors can continually outweigh our self-control, there'll always be a disparity between how we *want* to act and how we *actually* act. It's usually only when the willingness to endure unpleasant changes eclipses the inclination to stay stagnant that people can take on the crucial behaviours that will breed results.

The problem with dieting is that it's a big ask. It's not like changing that lightbulb, or meeting a work deadline. It involves a combination of money, effort, and troves of precious time. There are often more opportunities to stay inactive, focusing on the present, than worrying about the future. This 'consideration of future consequences'[16] means that, while we can envisage what we'd like our life to look like eventually, we're often fairly content with the present moment. This is known as *present bias*.[17] Things are easy and rewarding *now,* which means that the chocolate mousse feels of greater value than the visions of a slender set of biceps that may or may not happen *later.*

Our 'Present Self' is in a constant battle with our 'Future Self'. And whilst our Future Self really would like that nice photo on the beach, our Present Self would also really like to stay at home and look at nice photos of other people on the beach, instead. This constant tug of war between two seemingly different people – the person who *wants* and the person who *does* – results, typically, in nothing being done.

Procrastination is, therefore, a dagger to the heart of progress. It obstructs your ability to make improvements to your dieting mindset. It's easy, of course. But, when we want nothing more than to start our weight loss journey and finally see results, it inevitably causes problems. Why, then, do we neglect putting in the work now in favour of 'starting again on Monday?'

Why Do You Always Want To 'Start Again On Monday?'

You Don't Know Who You Are Or What You Want

We know that aspiring to be – or act like – a certain type of person will influence our behaviour. If you desire being an influential role model for your children, then eating a healthy meal as a family becomes a priority. If you want to be strong to help your parents as they age, then regularly lifting weights becomes the natural outcome. The principles in your life that are most precious to you serve to create a clear path for your actions. They represent what you want your life to embody. When you haven't discovered who you are, or what you want, then procrastination parades as the easy option.

Without a higher purpose or a clear 'why', you'll lack direction. Experiencing the pain of having to make yet *another* healthy lunch on a Sunday, or go for *another* long walk after you've put the children to bed, becomes a lot more unattractive when you don't know how you want to live your life. If you're unwilling to experience short-term anxiety and self-doubt, to work towards traits and values that are important to you, it becomes easy to put off those pertinent dieting behaviours. If you're ignorant to the fact that becoming strong for your parents means more to you than playing video games, then sitting on the sofa can be a far more attractive proposition than going to the gym to stand on the lifting platform again. If you're unaware that you crave a leaner physique because you hate how critical you are of yourself, then avoiding the bottle of wine in favour of a Diet Coke becomes incredibly challenging.

If you're unable to expose the intrinsic reasons you want to look and feel better, then short-lived gratification becomes the norm. One study found that people will watch cat videos online, to make themselves feel better – and, in doing so, are more likely to procrastinate in the future.[18] Without discovering what you ultimately want from your life, it's likely you'll continually succumb to those momentary dopamine hits, because you're reluctant to experience discomfort. Becoming acquainted with your identity and ambitions will enable you to manage short-term, negative emotions, however, and feel content with any twinge of discomfort that emanates with certain responsibilities. You won't chase quick-fix positivity, because you'll appreciate that the bigger result will forge more pleasure in the long run.

We know that changing your identity is hard. Even if you're cognisant of the type of person you want to become – but aren't yet fully committed to change – procrastination will continue to surface. The more your ambitions endanger your current identity, the more likely you'll deflect the most appropriate behaviours towards fulfilling weight loss goals. Anything that touches on your desired values and new character may even be avoided entirely.

Procrastination then becomes evidence that you're the type of person you believe you are, not who you want to become. Any awkward feelings you experience when pursuing something new ensure you're more likely to withdraw from those situations. This type of change is charged with an emotional backlash and doesn't fit with how you feel about yourself. Of course, self-control, motivation, and energy all still matter, but only when you're resolute in acquiring new beliefs about yourself will you be willing to make the gym – or other, fitting fat loss behaviours – a priority.

Future You Is A Liar

Every action you perform when losing weight is geared towards something happening in the *future*. Overlooking the takeaway food for a nutritious, home-cooked meal won't get you abs the following morning; you just hope they'll appear eventually. Doing a few sets of bicep curls in the gym won't get you t-shirt-splitting arms later that week; you'll just hope that, someday, someone will accidentally squeeze your arm and compliment your muscles. The fuzzy chasm of time between the present and future wreaks havoc with people's willingness to make changes *now*.

Instead of the comforting fantasy of an 'Immediate Return Environment' (that home-cooked meal immediately creating the look of popping abs the next morning, for example), we must deal with the hard reality of a 'Delayed Return Environment' (those bicep curls forging big arms, months or years down the line). The problems you face, or goals you'd like to achieve, can't be solved now; you must allow for a sustained period of effort for them to materialise. Rewards that take time to surface might not seem so appealing.

This tends to create problems for dieters, as the thought of delayed gratification fills them with anxiety. Why start dieting for next year's summer holiday, today, when they've got eight months, four weddings, two children's birthday parties, and one Christmas to overcome, first? Why say 'no' to the Haribo, now, if shopping for a smaller jumper will happen only in a few months' time? In an attempt to soften those trying feelings of uncertainty, they'll procrastinate. If the current situation is unreliable, then they'll fail to even start the tasks that will help them lose weight in the future.

As an example, we can take this modification of the famous marshmallow experiment (it wouldn't be a self-help book without a hat tip to the marshmallow experiment, would it?).[19] Researchers chose to split a group of children into two groups. The first group was exposed, initially, to a series of *unreliable experiences*. They were provided with a small box of crayons, with the promise they'd eventually be brought a bigger one. They never received the larger package, however. The second group were administered a series of *reliable experiences*. They, too, were promised a bigger box of crayons, but, this time, they dutifully received one.

In this experiment ("You can have more marshmallows later if you don't consume the one placed in front of you now"), the children who were placed in the unreliable experiences group failed to delay gratification. They couldn't help but consume the single marshmallow, instead of waiting for more. Those placed in the reliable experiences group did manage to delay gratification, however, and waited, on average, four times longer than their peers in the other group.

Those who received what they were promised were taught that delaying gratification was worth it. They also learnt that they possessed the ability to wait ("I previously received the bigger box of crayons I was promised, so there's no reason I shouldn't receive more marshmallows if I wait a little longer"). Those who failed to obtain what they were promised had no reason to believe that delaying gratification was rewarding; they didn't accept that they possessed the ability to wait ("I didn't receive the bigger box of crayons I was promised, so there's no guarantee I'll receive more marshmallows either").

Dieters fall into that second category. The more times they fail to lose weight, the more they'll then fail to believe that their decisions will allow them to reap the sought rewards later down the line ("Why eat healthily this time if I'm only going to end up in the same, unhappy position as before?"). That uncertainty and lack of self-trust causes people to often delay carrying out the activities that will get them the lean physique. Procrastination occurs because the future is uncertain.

There's another glaring issue with relying on our future selves to make decisions; we like to think of that self as somebody *different*. Idolising and imagining 'Future You' as someone who will complete the tasks you can't quite manage in the present moment causes you to put off the essential jobs today. The idea of Future You – that person who exists some way off in the future – lures you into believing that, come tomorrow, the day after, or even next week, they will be more energetic, have more time on their hands, and possess more willpower. Unfortunately, those vows are nothing more than the works of Pulitzer Prize fiction.

By procrastinating, you get to enjoy the immediate benefits of your choices (for example, seeing friends, instead of crushing a heavy set of deadlifts), because someone else (that's still you, by the way) will bear the consequences (deadlifting tomorrow, instead). We're willing to burden our future selves with our current levels of idleness.[20] Why bother now, if they will take control of things later on? We even get annoyed that our future selves will glean the benefits from our current discipline and self-control.

It's for this reason that you tell yourself you'll exercise tomorrow instead of today. Or, why you'll be in a better frame of mind to diet after Christmas, instead of at the beginning of December. It's also why you're convinced you'll become leaner when you're not as busy, stressed, or struggling for enthusiasm.

By transferring the discomfort of the present onto the unclear future, you tend to feel an immediate sense of relief.

This is obviously flawed logic. It means you'll continuously fail to realise that you'll still experience precisely the *same* thoughts and beliefs in the future as you do now, unfortunately. When you conceptualise your future self, you'll scarcely ever see that individual as *you*. As time is ever moving, you'll find it difficult to correctly imagine what you'll be like – and how you'll act – in the future. You lack a sense of connectedness to that individual and can forget that you'll probably feel that same dread, anxiety, and self-doubt as you do now – especially if you continue to procrastinate. You'll *still* want to avoid those deadlifts.

You Don't Believe In Yourself

While hearing about other people's weight loss success stories can have its benefits, there may also be times when it acts like a lofty blockade, preventing you from taking action. It thwarts people's ability to believe they, too, can achieve a long-lasting transformation. We know this thinking emanates from a *fixed mindset*. Convincing yourself you'll never shift the weight, because you don't possess the ability, genetics, or mental attributes – like others – leads to procrastination. If you believe your efforts are completely futile, it makes logical sense to put them off for as long as possible.

This reason for procrastination is paired with a shortage of self-efficacy.[21] If you lack confidence in your ability to master an eating skill, or exercise movement, the motivation and desire to take action will decrease. Why begin now, if you don't believe you're able to follow the required gym programme? Why should you attempt to concoct a healthy meal, if you overcooked the chicken last time? Just as many people believe they can't shift the weight, they often conclude that they don't possess the ability to execute the individual tasks required anyway. That diminished self-efficacy encourages the desire to take a break – or even avoid starting in the first place.

Individuals procrastinate because they lack sufficient confidence and, subsequently, burrow down under feelings of helplessness.[22] If they can protect their self-presentation through avoidance, they're no longer fearful of failing, or getting something wrong. Failure exposes vulnerabilities, so those who don't believe they can change will tend to avoid anything that threatens to unmask them. If a task looks challenging, those with a fixed mindset and low self-efficacy will refrain from trying, so they can avoid making mistakes.

People's judgement of their own self-efficacy will also influence their choices and effort levels. They'll pursue tasks that they're confident they can master, and display more resilience with activities they're confident in. If they believe they're good at pull-ups, they'll repeat them. If they imagine they'll be terrible at kettlebell swings, they'll avoid them. Of course, while seeking out tasks they're confident in will breed progress, it won't produce as much as attempting the tasks they're not so self-assured with. It's often the ones they avoid that they should be facing head on.

The absence of self-efficacy is where remarks like, "I'll start after the Christmas holidays are over" or, "I've got a big party on Saturday, so the diet starts on Monday" radiate from. There's a discrepancy in what people want and what they believe they can achieve. They lack the confidence to navigate busy and stressful times, and will wait for an optimal moment to focus on their diet – one that, of course, never arrives.

This ends up with external circumstances suppressing people's internal desires. They don't carry the belief that they can conquer the external reality of Christmas, or the weekend. In always waiting until life 'quietens down', or until they can 'really focus on themselves', the journey never starts. The expectation that we'll be better set, and have more time to start in the future, arises from a 'Pause-Button' mentality.[23] Stopping the process – and taking the time to regroup and resume when the turbulent journey of life mellows out – seemingly makes sense. Yet, unfortunately, each 'mini sprint' only leads to short-term results and may possibly amount only to wasted time. As life with obstacles is the norm – not the exception – there'll never be a moment when you have a fully clear run at trying to achieve your goals. If you don't believe you can do it now, the chances are high that you'll *never* believe you can do it.

The concept of self-efficacy is also closely linked to being hopeful. If you hold a positive outlook on the situation (for example, "I *will* be committed enough to diet successfully"), then you're more likely to reduce procrastination.[24] If you're also confident you can handle your emotions and behaviours in the face of upcoming challenges, you'll be less likely to drag your feet ("I *will* be able to overcome the inevitable impatience I'll experience once I'm three weeks into my fat loss phase"). This form of self-regulation is vital for managing failure and aligning actions with values.[25] Without it, you're more likely to let unpleasant emotional states influence your decisions. If you don't believe you're able to avoid procrastinating – probably because you've procrastinated before – then you'll put off tasks that you would otherwise have completed with ease.

You Think You Have More Time Than You Actually Do

Procrastination is, at its core, an emotional issue, yet people still often fail to value their time. There's still a whole eight months ahead until your daughter's wedding, you tell yourself. "Starting a couple of weeks later won't hurt, right?" Undervaluing the significance of time manifests as procrastination. Before you know it, those eight months will have passed, and, without a prompt start, you may soon be no closer to your dream physique than when you scoffed down that triple chocolate and banana ice-cream bowl.

Time is limited. Neglecting to realise that every second you waste is gone forever will only serve to delay your attempts at transforming your physique. We know people possess optimistic predictions over the amount of time it takes to complete a task[26]; couple this with a propensity to deny that time matters in the first place, and you'll own the blueprint for a hefty bout of procrastination.

This undervaluing of time stems from a concept called *delay discounting*. If the completion of a task will occur at some point in the future, its value in the present is reduced considerably. The further away the deadline is, the less tempting it is to start today. One study showed that receiving $100 three months from now was worth the same to people as receiving $83 immediately.[27] These people were willing to *lose* $17, rather than wait a few months to obtain a larger reward. It's easy to see why postponing the gym is easily done.

Another group of researchers reached a similar conclusion with exercise.[28] Training – in this case, modifying the speed of a treadmill to find the most pleasant exercise intensity – *can* bring pleasure (contrary to popular belief, I'm sure). The way people viewed this enjoyable experience was similar to having food and money, in that these can be gratifying, but their value diminishes rapidly over time.

A delay in the reward of exercise tends to lower its desirability. If you have to wake up to get changed, hop into your car, travel to the gym, and *then* experience the enjoyment exercise brings, the picturing of those pleasurable feelings may be significantly reduced. If we must wait to encounter pleasure then it maybe doesn't seem as worthwhile as pressing the 'snooze' button. If we devalue future tasks and their related accomplishments because they seem so distant, it's unlikely we'll ever start today.[29]

This may go some way to explaining why seven-day diets, and reading self-help diet books, tend to be so appealing. The 'rewards' may seem almost or entirely immediate (despite the overall, actual reward being non-existent; the illusion of progress originates from taking this 'fake', or substitute action). Having to wait a lengthy period of time for something to surface tends to reduce motivation. Given that we can even become quite agitated when an internet tab takes longer than three seconds to load, it's no wonder the thought of having to wait months – if not years – for that new physique to surface feels somewhat distressing.

You Indulge In Too Much Information

Deciding what takeaway to order when we're at a friend's house is often a dispiriting and distressing situation.

"What do you fancy?"

"I don't mind."

"Thai? Chinese? Italian? Indian? Turkish?"

"I'm easy."

"OK, you choose."

"No, you choose."

"No, you choose."

Thirty minutes later and, with hunger and irritability having increased tenfold, no decision has been made. I'm sure this isn't a unique situation. Despite the countless choices available, we often fail to reach a decision, which then ends up with at least one person storming out of the room. This isn't because we're a group of friends or family who don't get along, but more so because there are just *too many* options to choose from. While the opportunity to analyse each cuisine's long list of pros and cons seems helpful, it can often turn out quite the opposite. This 'analysis paralysis' is caused when a multitude of possibilities cause stress, anxiety, and – clearly – arguments, so that a conclusion can't be reached.

At the time of writing, if you were to Google 'What diet should I do?' you'd be hit with 6,350,000,000 results. Pop the hashtag 'dietplan' into Instagram, and you'll be privy to 3.2 million posts. From low-carb to high-carb, and from every-carb to no-carb, there are more diets, protocols, rules, and nuggets of advice to choose from than pastries at a hotel breakfast buffet. Such an imposing selection is intimidating – and trying to settle on just one choice is draining.

Despite having more avenues to dieting information than we've ever had before, this hasn't made dieters' lives easier. Rather than empowering people to make better choices, it has intensified people's *fear* of selecting the wrong option.[30] Getting the diet. or training programme wrong, can have damaging consequences. There's not only the unease of wasting all that time and effort, therefore, but also the fear of making a potentially damaging physiological and psychological decision from the outset.

Psychologist, Barry Schwartz, coined the phrase 'Paradox of Choice', to describe the anxiety, indecision, and eventual paralysis we experience when faced with a diverse portfolio of choices.[31] Indulging in too much information leads to procrastination. Even physicians were found to be less likely to prescribe a type of medication at all, when deciding between two different types of treatment, than those who only had one option to choose from.[32] The difficulty in deciding between numerous pharmaceuticals led some physicians to recommend just not starting treatment at all. It was only *one more* option that led these doctors to put off deciding upon an outcome, such as taking a patient to surgery.

This 'analysis paralysis' isn't just confined to the depths of what diet you should embark on. From what training programme to follow, to which personal trainer you should hire – along with what type of high-protein yoghurt you ought to have for breakfast – overthinking prompts inaction. Being compelled to make the perfect decision, and feeling overwhelmed with all the available options, only aids people to put off the tasks they should be implementing. It's easier doing nothing at all than having to trawl through a long list of alternatives – and potentially making a wrong choice.

The more decisions you have to make, the worse your outcomes tend to be, over time.[33] This is why deciding what to cook in the evenings becomes such a challenge, following a busy, stressful day. If you've had to make decisions such as, whether to fire someone, what font to use on the monthly report, or whether to grab a chocolate bar on the way home or not, making another, conscious decision can feel like more effort than it's worth. You'll almost inevitably end up choosing the takeaway, because it's the easy option. This same logic is why you're more likely to also miss your training session in the evening. A host of further, stressful decisions – deciding when to go to the gym, how to get to the gym, what to do at the gym, and what you'll eat after the gym – means another round of choices you'd rather not toil over. It's just easier to stay at home.

It has even been found that judges are more likely to grant parole to offenders earlier on in the morning, or even after a food break.[34] The more decisions those judges had to make, the less 'favourable' they became towards the end of a session. This kind of 'decision fatigue' stymies the ability to think clearly and leads to poor outcomes.

How To Avoid The 'Starting Again On Monday' Mentality

Imagine discovering a leak in your bathroom. Aside from throwing a few choice words around, your first port of call would likely be to mop up the flow of water that's running worryingly close to your brand-new carpet. This doesn't fix the initial problem, of course, so you find the pipe that's damaged and place a bowl underneath, to cease the flow. This deals with the water on the floor but, again, doesn't tackle the root of the issue; water is still seeping from the broken pipe. Only when you fix the pipe *and* the problem with the storage tank in your attic, will the issue come to a halt. You can then finally sleep safe in the knowledge that your carpet isn't at risk of ending up smelling like a milk spillage that's been left to mature for a week.

A similar situation applies with procrastination. While we may be able to fix the issue of putting off responsibilities with low-level fixes – solutions that paper over the cracks – they won't address the issue at heart. Scouring the internet for weight loss hacks, motivation boosts, and even crash diets will fail to solve procrastination at its core. These quick fixes are like placing bowls underneath burst pipes; you'll still procrastinate, whatever the situation. The bigger the leak, the bigger the problem – and, the bigger the problem, the bigger the solution required.

We've established that procrastination is a high-level, emotional issue. Which means we need to stop trying to mop up the problem and head straight to the storage tank. Understanding where the complication originates from will not only save you time in the long run, but also ensure that you're able to make that start *and* keep going. It's no wonder that strategies like using stopgaps, cutting out certain food groups, and starting on Monday, lead to failure and procrastination; they aren't addressing the real issue at hand.

The good news is that by tackling these emotional issues *first* and then working on lower-level behavioural strategies, you can prevent procrastination.[35] The crucial, cognitive strategies you initially confront will enable you to focus on your long-term goals and future self. Those will deal with where the 'leak' starts. The secondary behavioural strategies involve prompting specific actions that reduce procrastination in the moment. As procrastination surfaces, like any other habit, it is possible to change the process to suit your needs; you just have to start at the bottom of the pyramid, rather than the top.

Face Your Thoughts And Emotions

Procrastination is not a character flaw. You're not weak, inadequate, nor lazy, if you put off the critical tasks to diet successfully. It's merely a sign that you're suppressing uncomfortable thoughts and emotions – ones that need to be addressed to make progress. By simply observing your unease – rather than punishing yourself for procrastinating – you can accept your feelings for what they are and reframe the situation to allow you to take action.

Just as we can dictate how we'll feel and act, when our partner leaves their socks strewn across the bedroom floor *again* (asking calmly if they can pick them up, or resorting to beating them with a slipper, depending on our mood), we can also dictate how we'll feel and act when we're facing a distressing choice over a nutrition or exercise behaviour. Start by noticing the thoughts you have when you don't feel like starting something. 'I don't want to cook; I'm not very good at it', or 'I'm too busy to go to the gym' – even, 'I won't be able to eat healthily this weekend'. Such thoughts influence your emotions and, by observing and accepting those first, you'll be better set to enforce helpful solutions. This will mean you have more control over how you feel about the situation and can, subsequently, act immediately.

The thought, 'I'm not very good at cooking' – which may lead to anxiety and overwhelm – can be replaced with, 'I'll be able to master this one meal now, so it will no longer be as demanding next time around' – which leads to optimism and confidence. A thought that causes panic and distrust, such as, 'I won't be able to eat healthily this Sunday' can shift to, 'Starting as soon as possible will teach me how to navigate future busy weekends' – resulting in grit and self-respect. Noticing and reframing your thoughts will shape your emotions and how you then act upon them.

It also helps to think about re-examining the task in hand, to focus in on the benefits. No longer is the thought going to be, 'I'm too busy to go to the gym', but, instead, 'If I go now, despite being busy, I won't have to get up at six tomorrow morning'. Similarly, a thought like, 'I'll wait till the summer holidays are over', can be exchanged for, 'If I start now, I'll be able to make even more progress when the kids go back to school'. It is important to always address the emotional issue at hand – and perhaps call upon predefined values to aid the process. Additionally, identifying the *advantages* of starting sooner, rather than later, will prove invaluable.

One study asked inactive young adults to imagine a hoped-for 'future self', who had just exercised and enjoyed excellent health and energy.[36] That simple awareness of the future increased their *current* willpower. By visualising your 'future self' feeling happier and more accomplished, having completed a task *now*, you're more likely to follow through with it. The researchers even found that those adults' awareness of the future led to them exercising more frequently later down the line. The wisdom, therefore, is to acknowledge the benefits of completing or starting *today*, rather than considering the consequences of *not* completing the task.

Learning to face your thoughts and emotions will prevent avoidance. No longer are you trying to evade those uncomfortable feelings, but are willing to confront and accept them. Even forgiving yourself for procrastinating has been found to support productivity.[37] You'll elevate your strength to deal with the presence of negative emotions and the absence of positive emotions; instead of concealing any discomfort, you'll be able to push forward. Remember to take a moment to step back and ask yourself, "Why am I procrastinating?"

Whilst we may often think that procrastination is making us happy, it's really only driving comfort for a fleeting moment. As we know, comfort doesn't always equate with success. Just like avoiding an uncomfortable conversation with your boss could extinguish your chance of a promotion, shelving any troublesome feelings and tasks needed to lose weight can quell your chances of acquiring that desired physique.

We all need to experience a certain degree of difficulty to achieve peak performance. Those who acquire their coveted physique accept discomfort as inevitable – and they complete the task anyway. Those who struggle to achieve anything worthwhile, however, may view – or even welcome – discomfort as an excuse to avoid the task at hand. Seeking relief only creates more distress, ironically, due to the strain felt from not accomplishing anything worthwhile.

As the character Walter White says, in the hit television show, *Breaking Bad,* "I have spent my whole life scared, frightened of things that could happen, might happen, might not happen. Fifty years I spent like that, finding myself awake at three in the morning. But you know what? Ever since my [lung cancer] diagnosis, I sleep just fine."

Once we avoid trying to fight each situation and, instead, accept it for what it is, we're able to move forward. Grappling with our human wiring for pleasure-seeking is challenging, but necessary for taking action. Just like for Walter White, accepting feelings such as anxiety, self-doubt, and stress opens up new opportunities. Once we welcome the negative emotions a weight loss journey will inevitably generate, at certain points, we're able to 'sleep just fine'.

Find Meaning In Your Weight Loss Journey

We know that, in our typical thinking and behaviours, short-term reward frequently trumps long-term patience. Scrolling through old photos on your phone beats making a fruit salad – and going out for dinner outshines creating high-protein snacks for the week ahead. When we lack a clear understanding of our purpose and values, it's very easy to forget *why* we want to make the fruit salad and bake high-protein snacks in the first place. Becoming wrapped up in our daily lives can mean that valued ideals and traits are quickly replaced by ephemeral moments of joy. A lack of meaningful focus can lead to procrastination.

When we uncover the purpose behind our desire to diet, everything else falls into place, however. Studies looking at brain scans have shown that people are less likely to procrastinate when they associate a task with a high-value incentive.[38] When coupling a current task with a bigger, purposeful outcome, we're much more likely to complete the behaviour at hand.[39] Suddenly, we're not making a fruit salad for the sake of just making a fruit salad, but to live by the value of commitment. The more committed we are to our goals, then the more likely we are to follow through on the smaller tasks – like spending ten minutes hacking through a pineapple.

Every time you feel like delaying a task, whether for an hour or a couple of weeks, it's important to explicitly remind yourself of your purpose. Take a moment to ask yourself whether putting off that task will be a vote *upwards* or *downwards*, for the kind of life you want to lead. Will it, in turn, create the body you want? Even students who were, twice a day, sent texts that asked them to reflect on certain questions, such as, 'How would successful people achieve this goal?', or, 'How will I feel if I don't complete this task?', were less likely to procrastinate.[40] The repeated exposure from continually reminding yourself of your 'why' will help you in starting the required task.

There may, of course, be a handful of dull activities that seem harder to link to the bigger picture, such as drinking enough water, or making another protein shake. No matter how trivial any of these tasks feel, however, there's *always* a link between those and the broader view. Take doctors and nurses, for example. They value patient care. Whilst completing their necessary admin, at the end of each day, is about as enjoyable as trying to bath a cat, when they link those mundane tasks to the deeper value of patient safety, they don't become as prosaic. Data input is suddenly less boring; it's then about forging a foundation to improve another person's quality of life. Similarly, tidying the office isn't tedious; it transforms into an opportunity to save someone else's life. Every responsibility can be paired with a greater purpose.

Once you've connected with your deeper self and recalled your reasons for change, you're able to dig further into the procrastination problem. Figure out *when* you put off those important responsibilities. Do you find yourself avoiding the gym more in the mornings or in the evenings? Do Fridays always seem like an opportunity to take your foot off the gas because Monday's just around the corner? Or does the problem arise when you find yourself fearful of missing out on the chocolate after dinner? Such awareness creates a short interlude between short-term desires and long-term purposes.

Think about *how* you procrastinate. Do you grab an extra thirty minutes in bed? Do you get three takeaways and a family-sized pack of Celebrations, in preparation for 'Starting again properly next week?' Once you've understood the nature of the problem and how you handle it, coupling your meaning with solutions to 'when' and 'how' will enable you to focus more on behavioural strategies. If you can't get out of bed in the morning, then try setting an alarm on your phone to remind yourself of your subconscious 'why'. Or, schedule five minutes in your diary to input your calorie intake in a food tracking app for the following day. Attempting to fix an issue without reviewing the real underlying issue will only cause the same problem to happen repeatedly.

Prioritise The Important Tasks

Warren Buffet – the self-made multibillionaire, highly regarded as one of the best investors in the world – once asked his personal pilot if he had dreams greater than transporting his boss around all the time. His captain confessed that he did. Buffet proceeded to take him through a simple three-step process that would eventually help him reach those ambitions.

He told him, first of all, to write down a list of twenty-five career goals. Secondly, to reflect on those goals and circle the five, 'highest-priority' objectives. Thirdly, to examine the twenty goals *not* circled and avoid those at all costs. Those are the goals that distract you; they corrode precious time and energy. It now becomes an 'avoid at all costs' list.

Focusing on your five, highest-priority goals will narrow your focus and enable you to execute the behaviours that will take you closer to your end goal. If losing weight is the aim, but the deluge of tasks you must complete feels overwhelming, homing in on the most relevant habits will kickstart your momentum. When Thursday hits, and you still feel like you're trying to claw your week back after a dodgy curry on Monday night, it can be intimidating trying to overhaul your life. Because you believe there are fifty daunting habits for you to revamp, you may find you don't know where to start. You'll end up attempting one task, but quickly get distracted by another. And another. The pattern repeats itself until you end up in a slump, wishing you hadn't started at all. Instead of fixating on *everything* left to complete, however, it's time to prioritise one or two simple tasks – ignoring the rest.

Instead of worrying about going to the gym, preparing meals, going for a long walk, getting to bed earlier, meditating (alongside a cup of oolong tea), and researching what smoothie-maker to purchase, you now select just one or two of the most important tasks that you must complete tomorrow, and ignore the rest. You'll instantly narrow the amount to be accomplished.

To keep on overcoming any intimidating feelings, also follow the 'Small and Easy' principle. By focusing on something *small* and *easy*, you'll already be one, tiny step closer to the end goal. It could be as simple as purchasing a new recipe book, writing a new gym plan, or downloading a food tracking app. Remember, *anything* that will take you one small step closer to your end goal – no matter how inconsequential – is *something*. And by doing something, you'll be taking action. Nothing can replace the momentum of 'doing'. Stacking those 'small and easy' tasks on top of each other will mean they soon accumulate into something much larger; before you know it, you'll already be one jeans size smaller.

Of course, *continuing* to execute these numerous small actions is vitally important. Standing back to admire the recipe book you've just bought is not enough; you will need to actually open it. You must avoid 'structured procrastination'; that is, salvaging your self-image by accomplishing tasks that appear useful but, in reality, take you no closer to your goals than if you hadn't performed them in the first place.

We know that encountering numerous, tough decisions leads to analysis paralysis, whereas, asking yourself which task is the *most* important will make the process more straightforward. Through prioritising the most influential actions, a huge weight will be lifted from your shoulders (except while at the gym, of course). Don't get distracted by the blinding light of all that's left to complete. No matter how much you want to meditate with a cup of oolong tea by your side, maybe your only priority is to go and lift some heavy weights. While it might seem that everything is necessary, anything that doesn't align with the day's priority tasks can be ignored. Equally, commit to nothing, and you'll be distracted by everything – but, commit to one thing, and you'll be distracted by nothing.[41]

Reward Yourself

How much would I have to pay you to visit a scientific lab and perform a 'painful' task, such as immersing your hand in ice-cold water? £10? £100? £1000? Whatever restaurant you might now be thinking of visiting with your newfound cash prize, I doubt you'll have considered your *current* emotional state – whether you're angry, happy, sad, or stressed. Yet, your emotions will ultimately influence your response.

One study examined this very same question and found that university undergraduates 'priced' their pain depending on prior experiences.[42] Students who'd just experienced the effects of ice-water immersion demanded the most money to do it again, while those who'd never experienced that pain demanded the least amount of money to perform the task. Similarly, those who'd experienced the pain before, but not recently, still asked for more money but not as much as those who'd *just* experienced that glacial-induced misery. We feel and act differently in the heat of the moment. Our current emotional state will always determine whether we take action or procrastinate.

Brain scans have suggested that our brains are not activated in the same way when we make decisions that seem hypothetical, or 'in the future'.[43] When we're faced with a 'hot' choice – for example, when feeling angry, fearful, or tired – the brain's reward centres become more active. If you suddenly catch a glimpse of yourself in the mirror and become fraught with feelings of unhappiness, you're more likely to think you'll head to the gym the following morning – charged up by those feelings of discontent. You're less likely to follow through when the next morning rolls around and the alarm clock goes off, however, because that unhappiness is no longer at the forefront of your mind. You'll likely hit the snooze button and vow to go 'tomorrow', instead. The cycle continues, and stagnation ensues.

The best way to combat this *empathy-gap effect*, is to ensure you're 'fired up' when it's time to go to the gym, or to avoid the snacks at the office party. The more emotionally stoked you are, the less likely you are to procrastinate. One simple way to master this is through adding a reward. Commonly known as 'Premack's Principle,' if you couple a behaviour you enjoy with a behaviour you don't necessarily relish completing, you're more likely to perform the latter.[44] To avoid procrastinating on essential tasks, therefore, you must pair a reward that inspires enthusiasm with a habit you have trouble implementing. You'll receive the short-term gratification of the reward, as well as the long-term benefits of the necessary task. More commonly known as *temptation bundling,* utilising your 'hot state' in a situation encourages actions that pay off in the long-term.

There is refinement needed, however, in utilising celebration as a reward. Promising yourself that, if you hit the gym, you'll scoff down a large slice of chocolate cake, is missing the point. Rewards must be sensible, immediate, intense, and personal. Celebration needs to be *directly tied* to the behaviour, as compensating yourself hours after executing the necessary habit seldom stimulates long-lasting change. Similarly, selecting a prize you know you'll be rewarding yourself with, anyway, won't elicit the introduction of a new habit. The payoff must produce that 'hot' state in your brain's reward centre. By bringing the desired enthusiasm closer in time, you're more likely to act on it.

Chapter Summary And Taking Action

- Procrastination is the act of putting tasks off, whether intentionally or habitually. People have trouble persuading themselves to do the things they should do, or even want to do.

- Procrastination isn't laziness, nor does it bring us the lasting joy we think it's bringing us. It's a method of dealing with an emotional problem – the act of avoiding negative thoughts and feelings (such as self-doubt and anxiety), by experiencing a short-term, pleasurable reward (such as watching television or eating a cookie).

- People will put off their diet or implement healthy behaviours because they lack a higher purpose, or a clear 'why'. They're often unwilling to experience short-term anxiety and self-doubt, to work towards traits and values that are important to them.

- People also procrastinate because they believe their future selves will be more motivated, and possess more self-control to complete the same tasks later (e.g., "I'll have more energy tomorrow"). They believe, similarly, that they'll have more time than they think they do (e.g., "Eight months until the holiday is a long time"). Neither of these is true. People also lack belief in themselves (e.g., "I've failed before, so what's the point in trying now?"), and suffer from analysis paralysis (e.g., "There are too many protein powders to choose from; I'll decide later").

- To deal with procrastination, you need to address the emotional side of the equation first. Keep asking yourself *why* you think you procrastinate. Figuring out your 'why' – and continually reminding yourself of it – will ensure you follow through with the important behaviours (e.g., "I'm meal-prepping *now,* because I don't want to have to cancel any more dates for fear of being judged"). Think about setting up a system (e.g., an alarm on your phone, repeating mottos, etc) that keep your higher purpose in mind.

- Working on accepting and reframing your thoughts and emotions will be more beneficial than attempting to suppress them (e.g., "I probably won't be able to eat healthily this weekend, but I'll start today because it will allow me to practice for when this situation occurs again"). Aim to slow down, pay deliberate attention, and take control of thoughts and emotions.

- Think about focusing on a 'small and easy task' (e.g., putting the protein powder in the shaker), prioritising the important tasks (e.g., tracking your food when out at a restaurant) and rewarding yourself suitably (e.g., complimenting yourself or taking a moment to appreciate your recent success).

CHAPTER 6
I Can't Do This:
Control What You Can, Accept What You Can't

Growing up in a Woolwich tower block in East London – an area notorious for its gang violence and drug issues – Reggie Nelson found himself at a crossroads. Having just lost his father at the age of 17 and deciding that his dream of becoming a professional footballer was over, he knew he had to start thinking about providing for his family. Living on a council estate with a troublesome record at school, and recent run-ins with the law, he was painfully aware of the limited opportunities at his disposal.

One evening, while watching an episode of the American reality series *How'd You Get So Rich,* a plan started to form in Reggie's head. He reasoned that, as he wanted to be rich, speaking to rich people to find out how they achieved their wealth would be the answer to his problems. If these people could manage it, then why couldn't he? He took to Google, and promptly searched for 'richest areas in London'. Stumbling upon Gloucester Road in Kensington, he set off on a bold journey that would change his life forever.

Dressed in jeans and a hoodie, and armed with nothing but a smile, he began knocking on Kensington residents' doors, greeting anyone willing to share their time and knowledge with one question: "I just wanted to know what skills and qualities you had that allowed you to live in a wealthy area like this, so I can extrapolate that and use it for myself."

Being young, black, and fearless in his approach, he was often met with individuals reluctant to help. Some would simply shut the door in his face; others would scantily reinforce how 'working hard' and 'acquiring a good education' were vital. While grateful for their time, these generic responses did little to open his eyes about how to attain the wealth he sought. That was until he knocked on Elizabeth Price's door; moved by his smile, motivation, and courage, she welcomed him inside for a cup of tea.[1]

Together with her husband, Quintin Price – a senior executive in charge of a then-\$944 billion, strategies investment group – they set about shaping Reggie's future. Discussing the 18-year-old's plans, Price invited him to an Undergraduate Insight Day at his company, *BlackRock,* to acquire a taste for business life. Motivated by the idea of finally being able to wear a suit, Reggie – under Price's wing – embarked on a quest that no one thought possible.

He went on to undertake numerous internships at finance companies across London, gained an Economics degree at Kingston University, studied Mandarin (alongside his university work), and finally acquired a job as a graduate analyst at an investment management company. He has since formed the social mobility enterprise K3D and now helps mentor other young people to reach their dreams. He has also worked closely with the Cabinet Office, to address ethnic disparities in higher education – and even met the former prime minister, Theresa May.

A far cry from the strife of council estate life, Reggie – with the courage to take matters into his own hands – managed to turn his life on its head. He said, "[I thought] How can I do something different? What can I do different enough for me to see results that no one else will think of doing?"[2] Heading down the preordained path seemingly written for him wasn't enough; he knew he had to take control of his intimidating situation and forge his own future. The simple act of mustering up the courage to knock on strangers' doors, and carving out his own destiny, was enough to uproot himself from challenging circumstances and pilot his life towards a different destination. He has become known as the young man who went from 'East London to the city'.

This story isn't about luck, or taking chances. Or the benefit of speaking to people who own Aston Martins. It's about *control.* What do you possess control over that, despite overwhelming circumstances, aligns with your dreams and aspirations? What situations can you seize, alter, and make work for you? Your perception of the amount of control you have over a problem will dictate both your physiological and psychological well-being.[3]

As you diet, you probably won't face the incredibly limited opportunities that Reggie confronted. Recognising, however, that those who believe they have control of a situation tend to experience greater optimism, sustained attention, and persistence in the face of setbacks, will enable you to continue building that distinguished mindset. Do you attribute success and failures to moments you possess control over, or to forces outside your influence? Do you believe you can change the situations you encounter to reach your fat loss pursuits? The more impact you imagine you have over your actions – in the face of both internal experiences and your environment – the more chance you'll have of ditching any excess weight for good.

Control What You Can, Accept What You Can't

Ask anyone undertaking a diet what their struggles are, and you'll be met with the typical responses. From 'I just can't say no to the snacks' to 'I always overeat at the weekends,' these replies crop up repeatedly. They're fair; coupled with what's been coined an *obesogenic environment* (an environment that encourages high energy intake and sedentary behaviour)[4] along with our hard-wired desire for highly palatable, calorific foods, it can make saying 'no' to the snacks and garnering the motivation to 'stay on track over the weekends' all the more challenging. Instead of bashing our heads against a wall, trying to comprehend the latest 'low-carb, fat-free, organic-rich, craving-reduced diet' to combat these seemingly inescapable problems, it's time to simply shift our focus. We can now live by a new motto; *'Control what we can, accept what we can't'.*[5]

Just like Reggie Nelson taking command of his future, learning to manage the aspects of our journey that we *can* control will shape a new dieting path for us to negotiate. From handling our portion sizes, even if we're dining at a restaurant, to still planning our meals in the face of a stressful week at work, and declining the chocolate bar even if our thoughts and emotions are telling us otherwise, we can train our mind to make good choices in the face of difficulties. *We* are now the ones knocking on doors. Adopting a mindset that acknowledges that certain behaviours are still within our control – despite any unavoidable challenges and obstacles – will make the dieting process much smoother. We're controlling what we can.

It has even been found that we're more likely to have a positive view of ourselves when we simply *feel* like we have control over our lives. By openly changing our belief over what we can control,[6] and not necessarily by having to change our thoughts or broader environment, we'll not only improve our cognitive welfare,[7] but, increase our chances of maintaining any weight loss, as well. This *internal locus of control* enables us to take responsibility for our actions, while an *external locus of control* is associated with blaming outside forces for circumstances.[8] Students who fail an exam will condemn either their inadequate effort, or their teacher. Sportspeople who lose an important match will attribute the defeat to either insufficient training, or the referee. Dieters who struggle to lose body fat will blame either their ability to plan and execute, or the fact that someone brought another chocolate cake into work.

It's important to note that this is not an either/or situation. Most people lie on a continuum between the two, flitting between taking responsibility for their actions, and blaming external forces. And, while internal control doesn't always equal 'good' and external control doesn't always equal 'bad', people's success is often contingent on how frequently they exercise internal over external control. Can you recognise what's under your influence and what's not?

For all the desire to take responsibility for our actions, there will, invariably, be moments of our journey that we simply cannot control. From that obesogenic environment, to your mind tempting you with the urge for takeaways, challenges will always remain. Unfortunately, when we emphasise incidents and hurdles that we can't control, we're more likely to experience limiting emotions, poor decision-making, and failure in important tasks. The challenge is not in striving to regulate these indomitable moments, however, but in *accepting* that they will always arise. The next step is in making alternative decisions that align with our long-term ambitions – the behaviours we *can* control – to defy those struggles.

The willingness to recognise the internal experiences and external moments that we can't necessarily manipulate – and still be able to make good choices – is vital for long-term progress. While we may have to accept the anxiety and cravings we experience, or that another Starbucks has popped up nearby, we don't automatically also accept the *resulting* behaviours that accompany those developments. We're still able to choose a piece of fruit, despite hankering for the sweets; we can still stick with our home-made black coffee, instead of downing another Caramel Frappuccino.

Eric Weinstein, managing director of Thiel Capital, conceived the term *High Agency,* to describe the concept of controlling our behaviours. An individual finding a way to get what they want, in the face of circumstances that don't run parallel with their aspirations, has High Agency. They're taking control. Speaking on *The Time Ferris Show* podcast, Weinstein asked, "When you're told that something is impossible, is that the end of the conversation, or does that start a second dialogue in your mind? How are you going to get around whoever it is that's just told you that you can't do something?"[9]

Those who lack the trait of High Agency concede to the story bestowed upon them. They're unwilling to make decisions that align with their goals because of external circumstances, and thoughts that they tolerate as the norm. They immerse themselves in reactive language, often reinforcing the ideas that 'There's nothing they can do' and 'It's just the way they are'. These are the people who claim they couldn't stay on track because they were at a birthday party, or couldn't train at home because they didn't have enough space or equipment.

Those who display the trait of High Agency *don't* surrender to the story handed to them. They believe they're able to bend their decisions to align with their goals, despite external circumstances and emotions blocking their path. They utilise proactive language, underlining that they can 'Look at alternatives' and 'Choose an appropriate response'. These are the people who still stay on track despite going to the birthday party, and still perform squats and press-ups at home despite the lack of space and equipment. They control what they can and accept what they can't.

I'm reminded of two pictures placed side by side, each showing a man stranded on an island. The first illustrates an individual with Low Agency, who gathers sticks to write the message, "HELP" in the sand. The second depicts a man with High Agency, who, instead assembles the *same* sticks to create a paddle and raft to pull away from the island.

Same situation; different response.

Those with High Agency are willing to undertake challenges and display perseverance when circumstances don't fall their way. They accept what is out of their grasp and engage, instead, in the actions that'll propel them forwards. They're able to swim away from uncomfortable situations and head towards their goals. They make life happen, as opposed to life happening to them.

The Benefits Of Controlling What You Can And Accepting What You Can't

Humans love exercising control. It's one of the fundamental needs we carry from an early age.[10] This is why, as we get older, we revise for exams, prepare for job interviews, follow the weather forecast, and frantically press the button at traffic lights multiple times, as if our eagerness will cause the lights to bow to our desire to get to work on time.

In one study, researchers gave one group of elderly care home patients control, by providing them with a plant to look after – compared with another group who were told that their nurses would water and tend to the plant for them, instead.[11] At the end of the study, the responsibility-induced group reported greater levels of happiness and physical activity, along with the perception of their mental alertness, compared with the comparison group. The simple act of gaining control over *something* improves our health and mental well-being – even if it does come in the form of looking after another orchid.

How, then, do people lose their perception of control? Why do they give in to external circumstances and suffer from inaction? Just as we established, from the concept of learned helplessness in Chapter Four, whenever we experience events that don't conform to our expectations (for example, 'Being diagnosed with cancer isn't meant to happen to *me'*), we lose confidence in our ability to control ourselves, or our environment – creating psychological distress in the process.[12] Similarly, the more we age, and subsequently encounter endless, challenging life events – for example, unemployment, health issues, damaged relationships, and our football team losing despite us sporting our lucky underwear – the more prone we are to believing we lack control over our lives.[13] We, therefore, give up, mentally and emotionally. When we conclude we can't control *anything,* we allow life to pass us by and accept situations that we could otherwise govern and change.

It has even been argued, recently, that we don't *start* with control and learn to become helpless, but more so, that we start *helpless* and must learn to take control.[14] The more power we practice, over the years – or even perceive we hold – the more likely we are to take command and stay positive in the face of difficult circumstances. Conversely, if we're never able to experience control – through adopting a fixed mindset with academia, sports, and finance, for example – we'll never be able to implement change into our lives. This is not so much learned helplessness, as learned *hopefulness.*

In a bid to completely revamp his original 'learned helplessness' theory, American psychologist, Martin Seligman, said, "Animals learn that they can control aversive events, but the passive failure to learn to escape is an unlearned reaction to prolonged aversive stimulation." People become comfortable with relinquishing responsibility. They're happy to let life control them, as opposed to them controlling their lives. Being passive is the default response to life and, if we're unable to learn how to take – or even perceive – control, then we remain in that inactive state.

It's easy to see how people can let external situations dictate their internal thoughts and choices, and not the other way around. The more difficulties we're unable to overcome, the less chance we have of learning to exercise control. This causes problems as we, subsequently, succumb to the environment and thoughts we experience when dieting. We don't believe we can stay on track whilst on holiday, for example, because we have no positive experiences of staying in control while away from home. We fail to avoid cravings, because we've previously found it easier to give up in the face of uncomfortable urges. If we're unable to practice High Agency, then we can't utilise it in the future. This relationship is cyclical; the more anxiety we feel around avoiding those urges, the more we're likely to ruminate over those moments. Given that we then reflect more, there's a higher probability we'll succumb to those urges, resulting in feeling even less power.

Those who can successfully regulate control of their desires, their motivation, and their effort, experience a host of psychological and physiological benefits. From better health, life satisfaction, wealth, and cognitive performance, they're more likely to achieve their goals and desired outcomes. Those individuals believe they're not only able to avoid and cope with negative outcomes, but also obtain and savour positive results.[15] Even those who can find meaning in aversive situations display something called *interpretive control*.[16] By framing a troublesome problem as poignant, or defining, they're more likely to accept it, and work on solving the problem.

When people experience a sense of control, they inhabit a clearer mind. Doubt and unease dissipate, which leads to better decision-making and clarity of thought. Those who control what they can, and accept what they can't, realise that it's no longer about 'falling prey to the temptation of the crisps' or 'failing to lose the weight again'. Instead, they put achievable actions in place, thinking more along the lines of, 'I can control what I put in my mouth, despite these temptations', and, 'My efforts will lead to fat loss, despite these difficult circumstances'. Those who believe they possess authority over their responsibilities make better choices.

When we feel like we possess command over events, possessions, or ourselves, we're empowered. We're immersed in positivity and hold more optimistic views of our ability to deal with stressful events.[17] This is why patients with positive opinions of their illness are more likely to overcome their problems, and deal with the negative emotions associated with their condition.[18] Counter to the fact that we become unhappy – and even depressed – if we lose control, the perception of having an impact on situations gives us meaning.[19] If we're able to influence events, there's a purpose to the choices we make.

The perception of control leads, ultimately, to greater action.[20] Believing you're making the right decisions, will incite movement – as well as believing that your efforts dictate your chances of success. If you hold the belief that you can make favourable choices, while everyone around you devours the all-inclusive buffet, you're more likely to make decisions that align with your goals. For the same reasons, those who posit they possess control over their lives are more likely to exercise.[21] If we can influence our memory, goal-related behaviours, and well-being, it makes sense to improve all of this by engaging in physical activity. As we know, results don't arise without action.

Those who believe that the choices they make have an impact on their weight loss journey also tend to exhibit greater motivation and confidence.[22] What trumps knowing that every decision you parent will nudge you one step closer to that dream physique? When faced with a tough situation, those who can shift the setting from something out of their control, to a position within their command, will feel inspired to stay on track.

As with everything in the health and fitness industry, we don't want to veer too far to the other end of the spectrum. Just as we struggle when we believe we don't possess any control, so problems arise when we feel as if we can control *everything*. This 'illusion of control' means people overestimate their ability to direct certain life events.[23] It leads to damaging diets, unrealistic expectations, and spending more money on lottery tickets than their bank balance appreciates. While the illusion of hope is beneficial in relation to persistence and self-efficacy, the perception that we can control everything may lead to more costs than benefits. From greater risk-taking, to insensitivity to feedback, being struck by the illusion of control isn't always helpful.[24] More useful is to diligently ascertain what you can control, as well as what you need to accept. What can you attack with High Agency, and what can you simply let *happen*?

What Should You Accept?

Internal Thoughts And Emotions

While the lesson lies in shifting our mindset to focusing on the things we *can* control, there's beauty in embracing the aspects of our weight loss journey that we *can't* control. From the urges to devour all the cake, to rationalisations about skipping a gym session, our bodies' internal workings often can't be contained. How we handle our responses to those thoughts (for example, do we eat all the cake and skip the gym or choose a piece of fruit and go to the gym instead?) dictates whether we move closer to our physical goals, or further away from them.

If we can focus on embracing irrepressible feelings, we'll not only be more content with our weight loss efforts, but also able to keep moving forwards in the face of adversity. Studies have shown that accepting your thoughts and feelings as normal – rather than as things that necessarily need to be changed – predicts greater life satisfaction, as well as reducing stress and sadness.[25] So, whilst we can change our *behaviours* in response to our thoughts, it's essential to accept such common thoughts and emotions for what they are. They're not bad or negative, nor do they make us lazy, or ill-disciplined; they're simply natural. Maturity arises in how we respond to them.

Stoicism practices this same belief.[26] One of the most important teachings that has arisen from this branch of philosophy is differentiating between what we can change and what we can't. One of the great stoic philosophers, Epictetus, said, "The chief task in life is simply this: to identify and separate matters so that I can say clearly to myself which are externals not under my control, and which have to do with the choices I actually control. Where then do I look for good and evil? Not to uncontrollable externals, but within myself to the choices that are my own…" Trying to overcome parts of your mind that you have no power over is like trying to avoid the anger and frustration when you can't connect to the Wi-Fi. It just won't happen.

It may appear paradoxical; why would *accepting* negative emotions reduce them? Surely it would compel them to become more pronounced. But, by removing judgement from any thoughts you have, you will actually dampen their effect. In this instance, replacing control with acceptance will *improve* your well-being. We know that trying to control motivation often leads us to hating what we're doing, and stifling thoughts leads to significant rebounds. We benefit from substituting the notion of 'I need to control my thoughts' with 'My thoughts are just thoughts'. Instead of thinking, 'I need to control my emotions', we can remind ourselves that 'It's normal to have positive emotions and also normal to have negative emotions'. Acceptance liberates us to fulfil a different path.

The regulation of our thoughts is not about judging our internal emotions as good or bad, positive or negative, nor beneficial or detrimental. It revolves, instead, around simply being open to them – and still acting in calibration with our goals. If we're craving chocolate and desperately want to inhale a family-sized Dairy Milk in under thirty seconds, exercising acceptance may not come through thinking, 'It's OK that I'm feeling this way and, therefore, I can inhale a family-sized Dairy Milk in under thirty seconds.' Acceptance that works in tandem with maintaining goals is in thinking, 'It's OK that I'm feeling this way and, therefore, I can choose to consume a piece of fruit instead.' You can still observe certain emotions and take actions unrelated to them, instead. You can be tired and still train. You can encounter anger, and still choose the salad. You can feel defeated and still say 'no' to your mother-in-law's carrot cake.

Acceptance is the first step towards being willing to experience uncomfortable thoughts, feelings, urges, and other internal experiences, and still choose to engage in healthy behaviours. It has even been found that those who previously engaged in this type of behavioural treatment for obesity were twice as likely to maintain a 10 per cent weight loss at 36 months post-treatment.[27] It's the act of being mindful and respectful of the parts of our lives that we can't control which, subsequently, sharpens our dieting mindset.

External Situations And The Wider Environment

Many people striving to lose weight often wish they could possess control over external situations and their wider environment. They usually want more time, more resources, and to be able to manipulate extraneous conditions to their advantage. "If only my gym were around the corner, I'd be able to go all the time," they say. Or, "If the oven wasn't broken, I could have avoided the takeaway." Or, "I'll be to refocus when the kids go back to school." Even, "Why me?" They'll imagine that being offered pre-warnings to situations, or even being granted a different stab at life and its rollercoaster of hardships, will enable them to stay on track with ease. They endorse an 'if only' mindset.

Life isn't usually that kind, unfortunately. And no number of expletives will change the fact that the oven isn't working. No matter how hard you try, you probably won't be able to knock down the gym, gain planning permission for a new one, fund the development of the site, and fully equip the new building so that it's a mere triple jump away from your house. Accepting and embracing those – sometimes literal – immovable objects, however, will enable you to craft alternative solutions and forge an impassable weight loss mindset. Acceptance stems from within, not from trying to change uncontrollable facets of life.

It's important to note that acceptance isn't tantamount to either resignation or passivity. We're not surrendering to our long-term ambitions, nor buckling to superficial threats. We're merely recognising that some situations can't be changed – and aiming to keep our emotions, purpose, and outlook consistent, to move forward. We're not succumbing to self-defeating conditions. Reggie Nelson accepted that he couldn't change his past, nor bring his dad back, but he could still take charge of the aspects of his life that he could control.

This has been labelled the *art of acquiescence* – the act of accepting, rather than fighting, each situation.[28] Accepting an external event for what it is, and not seeking to change it needlessly, will not only provide you with greater insight but permit you to inspire change. Acceptance will displace the burden of an uncontrollable situation and enable you to alter the outcome instead. How can we erase judgement from each situation? How can we accept when there aren't any salads in the salad section at Pret a Manger and – instead of losing our cool – have the intrepidity to decline the bacon and egg roll and head elsewhere else, instead? In doing so, we're able to hold dominance over how we react and, subsequently, conjure up varying plans and solutions. This is nothing to do with trying to change an unyielding obstacle thrown our way.

The acknowledgement of acceptance provides you with an opportunity to grow. If the gym isn't a quick drive from your house, you'll have learnt how to prioritise your time. If the oven stops working, you'll have mastered how to make decisions in the face of difficult circumstances and limited resources.

If there's no salad at Pret, you'll have discovered you need to stop procrastinating and peruse the shelves earlier than 3 pm. You'll have learnt more about your psyche than if you'd have been able to display complete command over the event. While you may not appreciate the lack of control you have in the moment – you desperately wanted that salad, after all – you're able to recognise you'll reap the rewards later on.

What Can You Control?

Your Response To Internal Thoughts And Emotions

On November 4th 1972, sixty-six Americans were taken hostage by revolutionary, Iranian students who managed to seize the U.S. Embassy in Tehran.[29] Outraged at the fact that their former leader – who had fled the country earlier that year following a public insurrection – had stopped over in America for cancer treatment, the students demanded he be returned for trial.[30] The hostage crisis was described as the '9/11 of its day'.

John Limbert, the newly appointed Foreign Service Officer at the time, was one of those Americans taken hostage. Following his release, he described how some prisoners, including himself, suffered hunger, torture, and isolation.[31] Some would be made to endure 'mock executions', he said. They'd be woken in the middle of the night, forced to strip to their underwear, and marched to a room in the basement, where they were made to believe they were to be executed. The guards, upon firing their unloaded weapons, simply laughed. Why did they do it? Limbert said it was because 'They thought it would be fun'.

On January 20th 1981, the remaining fifty-two hostages were finally released, after being held as prisoners for a total of 444 days. The psychological damage was fatal. Many reported the loss of control of their daily lives as the most painful experience of all. There was a sliver of hope for others, however – including Limbert.

Those who fared best, psychologically, established astute ways to recast their focus on anything they could control – no matter how small. Limbert said, "They became my guests…I created the unmistakable sense that this was my space, my territory, and it did wonders for my well-being."[32]

While only a seemingly slight adjustment to his mindset, the way Limbert framed his time spent under capture allowed him to emerge as triumphant. Instead of letting the situation slip away from him, he managed to regain control of the conditions he weathered. They didn't hold domination over him; he held domination over *them*.

Once we've accepted the thoughts we can't control, we can respond to the ones we can. While you probably won't face the unbearably harsh circumstances hostages face, being able to manage your outlook and understanding of certain thoughts will enable you to establish control over your life. You're accepting of the fact you'll experience cravings, anxiety, and fatigue during your fat loss journey – you can't necessarily control or suppress those things – but you can control your response to them.[33] You're now willing to think positively, welcome determination, and harbour optimism.

You're not necessarily 'fixing' your uncomfortable emotions, but merely receptive to their presence – and searching to alter your perspective to emotions you can control. You're still prepared to feel unhappy with your body, but also determined to make better food choices at dinner. You continue to be willing to feel tired when faced with the gym, but get excited at tackling a new exercise in your programme. You appreciate you're going to feel uncomfortable experimenting with new recipes, but are encouraged at the possibility of honing your responsibility and open-mindedness. You're able to replace your *response* to those uncontainable forces with one that helps propel you forward – anything you can seize upon that brings a sense of your own authority back to your life.

Your Actions In The Face Of External Situations And The Wider Environment

Isaac Lidsky was a promising young actor. Having appeared in countless commercials as a young boy, and cast in NBC's *Saved By The Bell: The New Class*, he was destined for big things. In 1993, at the age of just thirteen, he was hit by news no teenage boy would dare believe to be true; he learned he was beginning to go blind.[34] He was told he'd completely lose his sight, through a retinal degenerative disease, by the time he turned twenty-five. Devastated, he was sure this was an end to his early success and dreams for the future.

Determined to not be restrained by a hurdle he couldn't control, however, Lidksy embarked on a new journey that would allow him to thrive, where, perhaps, he wouldn't have before. At just nineteen, he graduated from Harvard College with an honour's degree in Mathematics and Computer Science, went on to found an internet advertising technology start-up that was eventually acquired for $230 million, became the first blind person to serve as a law clerk for the U.S. Supreme Court, and turned a failing construction subcontractor into a highly profitable business. He's since written a book, hosted TED talks, and is on numerous charitable boards. It has been quite a response to a seemingly devastating and crippling situation.

He said, "There's absolutely no question that losing my sight the way that I did — this sort of bizarre, progressive way that I lost my sight — turned out to be among the best things that ever happened to me in my life. There's no doubt about it." Losing his vision granted Lidksy the faith he could control certain aspects of his life. He was able to do everything in his power to avoid falling prey to common assumptions about what could be achieved and what couldn't. He was still able to live a fulfilled and successful life, by fixating on the journey he was still able to take.

Once we're accepting of the situations we can't control, and manage to take command of the things we can, we reach a higher level of intellect and understanding. Directing our energy towards moments we can take charge of revives opportunities for growth and happiness. If we're able to *still* take steps towards our dreams, despite being struck by an outbreak of unexpected moments and extreme emotions, we're more likely to shed that excess weight. This mindfulness-based technique, used for coping, is formally known as *willingness*.

Willingness is the concept of still engaging in fat loss behaviours, even when we're met with situations we can't control – including when it's challenging, uncomfortable, and every inch of our body is telling us it's too difficult to follow 'the plan'. Willingness is the inverse of abandoning situations that demand hardship. It's bringing out the Isaac Lidsky in us.

If there's food served at the wedding that doesn't align with your goals, willingness means accepting that disheartening factor, and still feeling confident enough to reduce your portion sizes. If your partner is desperate for a takeaway, willingness is in recognising the discomfort from missing out and still consuming your pre-made, protein-rich meal that's sitting in the fridge, instead. If you've had a busy week at work, willingness is welcoming the distress of having to wake up at seven on a Saturday morning to hit the gym if that's the only time you can go. Willingness agrees with what already exists. This affability then provides you with more energy to focus your attention on the tasks that matter.

Control always starts and ends in the present moment. Taking a step back, asking better questions, and controlling the way you think and act, in accordance with your current predicament, will lead to better decision-making. Taking the time to understand the consequences of any action you take will determine future success. It's always possible to control what you can.

How To Improve Acceptance

Let The Float Float

Just as when we'd stand on the float in the swimming pool as a child, and it would inevitably propel itself back up out of the water – avoiding our precious faces, if we were lucky – so, trying to keep the things we can't control underneath life's own, powerful surface will also end with them launching back up towards us, potentially bruising our nose – and ego – in the process. Standing on that float expends time, effort, and energy, as does trying to quell the aspects of life we can't control. From our friends not acting how we'd like them to, to our thoughts about eating healthily, fighting and suppressing the moments we have no authority over is an unproductive and hollow task, often resulting in suffering (and maybe the occasional concussion).

Improving acceptance starts with letting the float *float*. It's about noticing our refusal to feel hungry, tired, or lazy – and welcoming that restraint. By admitting the truth, we free up space to act congruently with our goals. Once you've figured out the aspects of your life that you'll struggle to regulate, you won't then lack preparedness for when those moments do surface. You'll avoid wrangling with your thoughts that will, unfortunately, occur no matter how hard you try to suppress them. As author, Byron Katie, says, "When you argue with reality, you lose, but only 100% of the time."

Preventing acceptance of the moments we can't control – as with many of the things we've covered so far – is derived from fear. It's the fear that distressing, destructive crises will manifest if we don't take control. If we don't avoid the takeaway, we'll miss out on the pleasure from a deep-crust, New York-style pizza. Or, that, if we accept feelings of discomfort, we'll ruin our identity; and, if we let ourselves feel hunger, we'll keel over in a worrying state of malnutrition. The majority of the time, those thoughts and feelings just aren't true; they're nothing but wild fantasies fabricated from creative and visionary minds.

Often to our detriment, we think we know what's best for us, including that our happiness is dictated by whether we have the pizza or not. Or that we'll wilt away if we don't attend to those hunger pangs. Once we cultivate trust in ourselves, that our bodies and minds will still function normally should we surrender to these uncontrollable moments, we'll no longer require these beliefs. We won't then feel the need to micromanage our lives. When we appreciate that we *don't* always know what's best for us, we can improve our adherence and self-control, along with our ability to lose weight.

Through accepting and avoiding changing certain feelings, we take back control. Instead of liking, or surrendering to, the situation, we follow through regardless. Doing so has been likened to holding a cactus in our hands.[35] Were we to imagine our pleasant thoughts as placing a feather in our cupped hands, it would feel comfortable. We'd be able to hold it gently without difficulty. Were we to hold a cactus – or those unpleasant thoughts – in our hands, it would be uncomfortable. Despite that discomfort, however, we'd *still* be able to hold it gently. Willingness is letting that cactus – or those undesirable thoughts and feelings – rest without struggle.

The stronger your goals and values, the easier it will be to let that cactus rest. It can be easier to endure short-term hardships if you are sure about the type of life you desire overall. If you value self-development, you'll be willing to choose the tuna salad over the burger and chips – not least because it provides you with an opportunity to develop your strength and flexibility in the face of adversity. If you value staying energised in order to play with your children, you'll be willing to accept your mid-afternoon cravings, knowing it requires too much mental power to push them away; this choice means you free up energy for your kids later. If you value caring about others, you'll be willing to accept the discomfort of going to the gym. Embracing the torment of another set of Bulgarian split squats will allow you to understand what discomfort your friends and family experience, improving your compassion in the process. If you start *wanting* these sorts of undesirable feelings, instead of rebuffing their presence, you'll soon find it a lot easier to adhere to your weight loss journey.

Surf The Urge

Just like a surfer rides the waves in the ocean, we're similarly able to surf the urges we experience. We're not looking to speed up, slow down, carve the water, or repair our compulsions, but simply allow a craving to rise, crest, and fall. We're more accepting of a natural feeling and willing to withstand its power, without feeling the desire to fight, or act upon it. This technique, labelled 'surfing the urge', is a valuable tool in practicing acceptance and staying on track.[36]

We know that cigarette smokers, briefed on how to pay close attention to their thoughts and sensations when craving a cigarette, significantly reduced the amount they smoked.[37] They were able to feel 'bad', whilst still avoiding giving in to a quick cigarette. By accepting their cravings, rather than trying to bulldoze sensations and desires away, they were able to let the lust for a hit of nicotine rise in intensity and then dissipate. By teaching their brain that it doesn't always have to act on impulses, they gained control over the situation.

The same method can be applied to our inevitable desire for certain foods. By surfing the urge, when that habitual, mid-afternoon or post-dinner pining for 'something sweet' hits us, we're able to accept the feeling and stay in control of our subsequent behaviours. By acknowledging and observing the thoughts we have (for example, "I'm currently having the urge for a chocolate-covered Hobnob") and being open to it, ("It's perfectly acceptable to encounter this urge"), we're able to let those impulses appear, then eventually fade away. We know that suppressing any nagging thoughts only heightens their strength; by respecting them, we're able to face their charm instead of fighting it.[38]

Think about scoring the intensity of your craving on a scale of 1-10 (for example, "My desire for that Hobnob is now a raging 9"). Don't feel the need to censor or reduce it; simply notice the thought and how it's affecting your body. You'll soon see the craving start to dissipate ("My desire for that biscuit is now a 4"). Staying with your physical sensations – such as your breathing and the desire to reach for the biscuit tin – will allow the urge to rise, crest, and fall ("What biscuit?").

Accepting the thoughts that we can't control brings power back to ourselves. We're no longer left trying to fight those urges – and subsequently failing – but are able to differentiate between what we do and don't need to act upon. This act of mindfulness has been found to consistently help with changing self-destructive behaviours.[39]

How To Improve Control

Practice Committed Action

Think back to the qualifications you needed to become employed in your current, or last job. No matter the level of expertise, earning that mastery probably wasn't easy. There would have been moments when any of attending classes, completing assignments, revising for exams, and gaining hands-on experience was the last thing you wanted to do. It would have been incredibly challenging. When those obstacles arose, doubts would have started to creep in as to whether you were heading in the right direction.

"Am I even making headway into gaining these qualifications?"

"Are these moments of exasperation worth the career in the end?"

"Will I even get a company car?"

Were someone to look at you from the outside in, however, they'd have seen you were still making progress. You were still attending those classes, still revising for exams, still completing assignments, and still gaining hands-on experience – despite feeling unsettled, or like you were treading water. They'd have seen you continuously striving to make small steps forwards, regardless of all the challenges thrown your way. This is known as *committed action* – the result of taking effective action in line with values and goals, in defiance of imperfect conditions.[40] Committed action is about staying the course, even when difficult moments emerge – including when you can't see or feel the progress you're making.[41] It's something that's required at school, with your job, and in life in general – and includes dieting, too.

We're now aware that we must accept certain conditions that aren't always going to help our cause. Whether it be unfavourable emotions, or a damaging environment, there'll always be reasons to not act in line with our values. Committed action allows us to accept those moments for what they are, however, and still take responsibility for our behaviour. We're stronger and more devoted than those situations may seem to want us to be.

People will often assume that, once they've accepted thoughts and situations for what they are, the work is done. Acceptance is, unfortunately, only a small piece of the puzzle. Our job is in accepting emotions but not accepting *situations*. We still need to execute the pertinent behaviours in service of our values, even when some of them may want to make us cry inside. Remember, it's not the thoughts or emotions that can prevent us from moving forwards, but our reactions to them.

Committed action can mean feeling tired and still going for a long walk. It includes experiencing thoughts that you'll never shift the weight but still making home-made lunches for the week. Committed action is having to look after two kids, work long hours, and deal with a leak in your bathroom, but still going to bed on time to achieve a regular sleep schedule. Such action outlines the characteristics you'll live your life by and creates strategies to boost commitment to your values and goals. You'll break through that mental pain barrier to achieve what you want.

It's crucial to start, therefore, by remembering your values and detailing the behaviours that run parallel to the related character traits. Remember, we never fully accomplish those meaningful values; they're simply directions that guide our behaviour, not fixed achievements.[42] Think about the sensations and feelings that will inevitably arise from striving towards those personality traits. From a lack of motivation, to anxiety at the habits left to yet master, aim to pre-empt the behaviours you'll be committed to, regardless of the situations you'll encounter and emotions you'll feel. Are you prepared to accept those inevitable sensations and still engage in the relevant behaviours? Are you willing to experience discomfort to achieve that physique you desire? In accepting the challenge, you will strengthen your ability to control the situation – and, subsequently, drop that clothing size.

The way we communicate with ourselves will also aid our committed action. From helping sports performance[43] to reducing anxiety[44] and even enhancing exercise adherence,[45] positive self-talk can induce serious behaviour change. When we're faced with complex thoughts that prevent us from moving towards our goals, our conversations – and the language we use – will still enable us to make progress. While we're not necessarily focusing on *replacing* a negative thought with a positive one, by guiding our self-talk to be helpful we're able to display higher levels of thinking and awareness.

Most responses to challenging circumstances start with 'only if', as in:

"I'll go on a long walk *only if* I'm not tired after work."

"I'll be able to track my food *only if* I stay at home to cook."

"I'll be able to stick to my calorie budget *only if* I've done my weekly food shop."

From flipping those 'only if' statements to 'even if' statements, we can take back control. We imply we're committed to our aspirations, regardless of external circumstances:

"I'll go on a long walk *even if* I'm tired after work."

"I'll be able to track my food *even if* I order a takeaway."

"I'll be able to stick to my calorie budget *even if* I haven't done my weekly food shop yet."

We're now comfortable with the uncomfortable.

Even a simple word switch from, 'but', to, 'and', elicits the same response.

No longer is it, "I need to go to the gym, but I'm tired", but, instead, "I need to go to the gym, *and* I'm tired". We can switch from, "I need to track my food, but I'm eating at a restaurant tonight", to, "I need to track my food, *and* I'm eating at a restaurant tonight". This simple substitution intimates that your behaviours aren't governed by fleeting thoughts but are controlled by committed action, instead.

We can assess our internal dialogue to ascertain whether it's helpful or unhelpful – not whether it's 'good' or 'bad'. Are the words we employ helping us to work efficiently towards our values and goals? Are they enabling us to act towards what matters? We accept our initial thoughts for what they are and look to promote self-talk that inspires committed action.

Reframe Certain Moments

During Prehistoric times – when it was much easier to buy your first cave, and children wanted to be hunters instead of vloggers – trusting our brains would have been useful. Especially when they would alert us that, if we didn't flee from the wild animal eyeing us up as a three-course meal, we'd end up with one less arm or leg. These days, through the trust we've gleaned over the years, our brains sometimes tend to mislead our behaviours. Suddenly, we're surrounded by irrational thoughts that, while seeming trivial, start to reinforce certain behaviours. This is all because your brain helped you escape a leopard that one time. It's not that your mind is purposely lying to you; it just can't distinguish between survival, and wanting to eat cake.

This causes problems. When we get stuck in traffic and our brain whispers, "Well, you're certainly not going to have time to make dinner; you're going to have to stop off at Burger King", we trust its soothing words. When our colleague offers us her birthday cake at work and our brain claims, "Well, it would be rude not to have a slice", we're placing our faith in its seemingly reasoned argument. When we analyse a situation and assume we lack control, we're mistakenly trusting our brains. We believe that every thought is true. We jump to the conclusion that we must act upon every negative emotion, and blame ourselves for moments we have no rule over. Our brains lead us to surmise we lack control.

There is hope, however. We can learn to reframe those thoughts and feelings and act in alignment with our overarching goals. People who are only occasionally fazed by such mental distortions can identify – and then swiftly correct – their erroneous thinking patterns. They can pinpoint their flawed thinking and work to extract other, positive and beneficial thoughts.[46]

Reframing the way in which you view a belief or situation will enable you to exhibit greater control. By dissecting those unhelpful thoughts, and rebuilding them in a more balanced way, you're able to make better choices. Through discerning a negative thought (for example, "Burger King is the only option here"), questioning it (for example, asking yourself, "Is this thought true?"), and generating alternatives (for example, "I could make a quick egg-omelette and have a protein shake at home instead"), we're able to reduce stress and craft better decisions. Even answering each emotion or circumstance with a "So what?" response will allow you to detach yourself from a thought that probably isn't true. You can then begin to expose the aspects of your life you can control.

The act of automatically believing unhelpful thoughts is entwined with feelings of being externally controlled – when we regard ourselves as helpless victims of fate. We assume there's nothing we can do, for example, to avoid eating poorly or cancelling a gym class. Re-evaluating the situation and transforming those thoughts into feelings of control, instead, will lead to greater success. While slightly different to the process of acceptance, we're merely noticing the thoughts that spark negativity or difficult urges, and looking to shape new, more beneficial ones in their place.

Diets arrive, for most people, with negative connotations and feelings of despair. Migrating, from words like 'dieting' and 'cutting out', to 'sustainability' and 'way of life', has been shown, however, to successfully predict people's chances of not only exhibiting greater control but, also, maintaining results.[47] It has been found that people who avoid the word 'diet' and, instead, focus on terms like following their 'food plan', or 'training programme', exercise more control over their thoughts – and their subsequent actions.[48] Being 'on' a diet implies that something is controlling you. Embracing a way of eating that advocates enjoyment, however, while still acquiring the physique you desire, implies you're now the one in control. No longer do you need to gulp down thankless daikon and kombucha smoothies, but can enjoy the occasional piece of chocolate – guilt-free – and still make progress. While you may have more intense periods of concentrated fat loss throughout your journey, the encircling aim should be to reframe those negative experiences associated with dieting, flipping them into more positive and sustainable ones.

As we know, society will often corner certain foods into being 'good' or 'bad'. White bread and cake are 'bad'; fruit and kale (for some reason) are 'good'. When we indulge in 'bad' foods, we feel guilty, as if we have no control over the situation. We're overrun with feelings of resignation, which, in turn, reinforce feelings of failure or indiscipline.

Food is neither good nor bad; it's simply food. Some have defined eating as simply 'fuelling their system' – and not feeling the need to celebrate it; others have viewed food as merely a 'means to an end'.[49] There's no right or wrong way in how you view your eating habits. As long as you reframe your belief system to control what you can, and accept what you can't, you'll increase your chances of maintaining weight loss. If your definition of food allows you to eradicate morality from each item, and reframe it as something that will enable you to apply authority over your decision, you'll have successfully undertaken the process of challenging your thoughts. When you begin to question the veracity of those feelings, and shape a mindset to one of control, you'll believe you have command over certain situations, resulting in greater progress.

Focus On What You Can Have, Not What You Can't

There's the common belief that we must cut out, remove, or banish certain foods from our diet, to drop a jeans size. It's the underlying mindset of many – often unsuccessful – diets. While the reduction in some harmful foods and habits is inevitable and, of course, necessary, the belief you must completely 'stop this' or totally 'eliminate that' is flawed. It only serves to reinforce those negative feelings surrounding dieting. It creates a *scarcity mindset*.

A scarcity mindset angles the mind towards unfulfilled needs – focusing on what you don't or can't have. This only serves to espouse a negative attitude towards dieting. If you're convinced that a mouthful of carbs will lead you to gain ten pounds of weight, overnight, you'll become consumed with thoughts of deprivation. If you believe you must eliminate all the usual takeaways from your diet, you'll likely end up miserable and unpleasant to be around.

Describing the most nutritious options on a menu in less appealing terms – such as, 'fresh', 'mild', 'lighter', 'sugar-free', and 'wholesome' – perpetuates the belief that healthier foods are not flavourful or indulgent; this, subsequently, undermines an individual's choices of dining options.[50] We've been influenced to perceive 'health' as synonymous with restriction, boredom, and lack of satisfaction. By shifting the focus to what you *will* or *can* have, however, you'll not only exhibit greater control over your behaviours, but inspirit greater fulfilment. It's been found that those who emphasised the quality of their food – and how much they *could* eat, instead of focusing solely on restriction – improved eating behaviours and reduced their cognitive restraint.[51]

With this approach, it's no longer about curbing the number of takeaways you have, but focusing on all the nutrient-rich meals you *can* cook yourself. Rather than cutting out the daily ice cream from your routine, you're now focusing on the one or two days when you *can* consume a scoop or two. It's not about having to force down vegetables you loathe, but focusing on the recipes you *can* create, and the herbs and spices you *can* add to each dish. It's in this same vein that individuals offered vegetables with indulgent descriptors – such as, 'twisted, garlic-ginger butternut squash wedges' – significantly increased consumption compared with basic, or healthy descriptions – like 'butternut squash', and 'butternut squash with no added sugar'.[52] Reframing each moment, from feelings of insufficiency to abundance, turns a negative into a positive.

This positivity, or *abundance mindset,* allows you to fixate on the limitless opportunities and decisions available to you. It transforms the typical dieting mentality from feelings of despair and longing to those of freedom and control. Instead of being governed by the emotion of desire, you're satiated with feelings of excitement about taking action. Ending prohibition breeds more power, not less of it.

An abundance mindset doesn't just derive from the foods we're able to consume, either. It also relates to the progress we're able to make, the opportunities we possess, and the effort we can exert. Shifting the focus away from everything you still have left to achieve, to the habits and lessons you've learnt, will promote greater adherence. Start focusing on what you've achieved so far, as well as what's out there for you to reach your aspirations. Believing there'll always be opportunities, and potential to grow, will enable you to take back control of certain situations.

Chapter Summary And Taking Action

- We must learn to control what we can, and accept what we can't. We can't control our hard-wired thoughts or broader environment, but we can control our behaviours and actions in response to them.

- Those who demonstrate High Agency, or the disposition to control what they can, bend responses and decisions to align with their goals and values. Generating this responsibility leads to greater happiness, empowerment, decision-making, and – ultimately – progress.

- Some people lose their belief in their locus of control through learned helplessness. They've not only experienced moments that abate their faith in what they control, but sometimes haven't been fortunate to practice taking control in the first place. Those people lack motivation, succumb to external circumstances, and fail to take action.

- We must learn to accept our thoughts and emotions. It's the first step towards being willing to experience uncomfortable thoughts, feelings, and urges – and still choosing to engage in healthy behaviours (e.g., "I'm feeling the urge for a piece of chocolate, but I'm willing to accept this thought as unhelpful and have a piece of fruit instead"). We must also learn to accept external moments we can't control (e.g., "The salad I wanted for lunch has gone off, but, as there's nothing I can do about it, I'll look to make another, good choice instead").

- We're able to improve acceptance through willingness (e.g., "I'm accepting the discomfort from avoiding the pizza with my friends, and am willing to choose the tuna salad instead. This is because choosing the latter option aligns with my value of living a healthy lifestyle") and by surfing the urge (e.g., "I'm currently desiring a chocolate biscuit, but I know I can't control that thought and I'm aware it will dissipate, eventually").

- We must control our response to our thoughts and emotions (e.g., "I still possess power over the subsequent behaviours I can control"), as well as our reaction to unexpected moments (e.g., "I'm at a restaurant that doesn't have a healthy option, but I'm still able to control whether I eat slowly or not").

- We're able to improve control by practicing committed action (e.g., "I'm feeling tired *and* I'm still going to go for a long walk, to hit my required step count"), reframing certain moments (e.g., "Ordinarily, I'd assume Burger King is the only option for me, right now, but this will be an opportunity for me to make something healthy when I get home, despite it being the last thing I want to do"), and focusing on what you can have, as opposed to what you can't (e.g., "I don't have to cut out carbs; I can have protein-rich foods instead").

CHAPTER 7
Is She/He Better Than You:
How To Use Comparison Effectively

Johanna Fernihough's children's book, *The Crow And The Peacock*, tells the story of one Crow's quest to discover the happiest bird in the world.[1]

Having just sat, preening his coal-black feathers, the Crow flies down to the pool of the Prince's palace and discovers the beauty of the Swan. "I am so ordinary", he thinks. "I wish I had brilliant white feathers like her".

Upon greeting the Crow, the elegant Swan responds, "I did think I was the happiest bird in the world, until I saw the Parrot in the Prince's garden. Surely he must be happier than me".

Intrigued by the apparent joy of the Parrot, the Crow sets off to the Prince's garden. The Parrot, displaying his red and green feathers, ponders, "Yes, I am happy, but if I had *three* colours, like the Golden Pheasant, I would be even happier".

Once more charmed by the potential beauty of a different bird, the Crow locates the Golden Pheasant. "You are so lucky to have such a beautiful plumage. Surely, you must be the happiest bird in the world?" he asks.

"I thought I was", the Golden Pheasant replies, "until I saw the Peacock! His plumage possesses so many colours; I can't even begin to describe it".

Off the Crow flew again, this time to find the Peacock. As he observed him strutting proudly along the edge of the lake, he watched as the Peacock's tail began to open, widening into a fan of brilliant gold, green, yellow, and blue. "Wow", gasped the Crow as the Peacock drew near. "You must be the happiest, most admired bird in the entire world".

"It's true", said the Peacock, "it does make me happy to be admired. But you, Crow, you can do what you like when you like. You can leave here and go anywhere you want to. Us palace birds can never leave; there are high walls and cages to contain us here". The Peacock explained how the Crow's feathers still possessed as many colours as his; they were just hidden deeper. "There's no need to envy me, Crow, because I think I'd rather be you", he said.

As the Crow flew back to the top of the tall tree in the forest, where he started his journey, he thought about the Peacock's wise words. Settling down on a branch, he began preening his 'purple-black', 'blue-black', and 'green-black' feathers. "I must be the happiest bird in the world after all", he said. He then cawed loudly, "Can you hear me, world? I love being me!"

The comparison trap. We promise ourselves we won't be sucked into its fissure of emotion and turmoil, yet find ourselves continually being spun in its constant, washing machine-like cycle. Just like the Crow, we're always searching for someone, or something, to measure ourselves up against.

Whether it be our weight loss progress, current physique, exercise ability, alleged happiness, eating behaviours, or how many Instagram followers we have, comparison runs deep in the human mind. It's our modus operandum. We're always scouring the gym, the internet, and social groups, to assimilate our supposed successes and failures with. When we seek out the Swan, we discover the Parrot. When we seek out the Parrot, we discover the Golden Pheasant. The journey never ends.

Many people fail to realise they are, in fact, the dictators of their own comparison mindset. Were they to take a step back and recognise their own beauty, their skill set, and their ability to improve, they wouldn't need to embark on such an endless journey. They tend to never come full circle, however, and, instead, become mired in a hollow and toxic endeavour. Body dissatisfaction, unrealistic expectations, envy, and damaged self-esteem ensue. Even eating behaviours are affected. One study showed that those who perceived themselves to have consumed a larger slice of pizza, compared with others (despite being given exactly the same size), ate more cookies afterwards.[2] They assumed they'd 'broken' their diet, having supposedly eaten more than the others, and saw no reason to continue with their restrained approach. The effects of comparison are inescapable.

It's not all bad news, however. Comparing fitness levels and feelings of 'thinness' to others has been found to increase health-related behaviours, such as reducing alcohol.[3] Even desiring favourable social impressions amongst others has been found to lead to reduced eating.[4] When people create vision boards of photos of people's houses, or the physiques they want, those photos have been found to be motivating and inspiring. Sometimes we *need* comparison to improve ourselves, as well as enhance our ability to diet successfully.

The world of comparison is, therefore, far more complex than it appears on the surface. Is it really *that* good or really *that* bad? Can we, in fact, use it to *help* build the ultimate dieting mindset? This chapter won't implore you to stop comparing yourself to others; any such remark is about as useful as me telling you to just 'stop eating the chocolate'. It likely won't happen. Through unpacking the origins of comparability, however, and discovering *what* we compare and *how* we do so, we're able to craft a mindset that frees us from the confines of social pressures, external validation, and values that don't align with our own. While many people may continue to spout the popular adage, "Comparison is the thief of joy", we're going to take a closer look at the idea of stacking ourselves up against others, and discover its true meaning, instead. Is it actually robbing us of happiness, or can we alternatively implement its pervasive nature effectively?

The Origin Of Comparison

Let me introduce you to Dave. Dave is a friendly hunter-gatherer, who has travelled all the way from Prehistoric times to share his story with you. Dave is his tribe's chief, wooden spearman, whose significance to his people's hunting expeditions is akin to the 'autosave' feature on your laptop; he's rather important.

His indispensable skill set shines bright on his LinkedIn page. His hunter-gatherer friends know he's the go-to man for securing any well-earned kill, so they entrust him with such crucial assignments. While others in the group may possess superior tracking, or cooking, skills, Dave holds the title of 'renowned hitman' amongst his peers. His friends measure their hunting abilities against Dave's and, on realising their competence pales in comparison, they leave the task to him. They wouldn't want to ruin any potential meal by disrupting a kill, so they step back, allowing him to take care of his responsibility. Dave dutifully obliges and continues to slay his tribe's prey successfully.

This works both ways. Dave also needs to know that his abilities still hold rank amongst the group, so he marks his competence at killing, against others. In doing so, he assesses his worth against that of his companions and ensures he can preserve his spot as captain of the tribe's hunting team. Comparison, in this case, is essential.

It's easy to see how the concept of social contrasting has developed. And, while its ideology has altered over the years, the benefits of comparing our abilities and talents with those of others are unmistakable. Why ruin your chances of survival, when a counterpart is better than you at a crucial, life-saving skill? Why waste energy trying to compete with Dave, when your tribe's ability to thrive depends on you measuring your competence and knowledge against someone else?

Comparison clearly holds some prestige. None more so than when we were forced to utilise every skill we owned, just to remain alive. Noting who we could seek assistance from, or whose traits we could exploit by assessing others' expertise and success, represented evolutionary convenience.[5] Nowadays – mainly through us not having to rely on wooden spearmen to do our weekly food shop, to survive – comparison has transformed, unfortunately, into a firepit of danger. It leads people down troublesome paths, both mentally and physically. We no longer use comparison to our benefit, but, instead, let it deplete an otherwise robust mindset.

Though not everyone uses comparison in the same way, nor experiences the same positive or negative effects from its existence, the idea of 'keeping up' has passed the test of time. For most people, it requires a marked amount of effort and focus to avoid its failings. As a result, only a handful of people use comparison effectively. If we know this is an innate function of the human mind, how can we deconstruct its significance? How do we compare ourselves with others, when dieting, and use parallels productively, instead of becoming disheartened every time we catch a glimpse of 'that person' at the gym? What do we use to measure ourselves against, when looking to drop body fat – and how can we use that to better ourselves?

How We Compare Ourselves To The Person At The Gym

By Defining Ourselves

Social Comparison Theory was first presented by psychologist Leon Festinger, who proposed we make comparisons to define and evaluate ourselves.[6] The notion that we determine our own social and personal worth hinged upon how those constructs match up to other people. From, 'How well am I performing at work?' to 'Do others also think it's acceptable to have the sticky toffee pudding *and* a brownie for dessert?', we possess this fundamental need to define our abilities, opinions, performance levels, and even physical attributes. As we struggle to judge these facets of our own minds and bodies accurately, the only way to draw conclusions is in reference to something else. That 'something else' arrives in the form of other people.

When staying alive was life's principal goal, it meant comparing our survival skills to other members of our tribe. These days, it's now about comparing the weights we're lifting in the gym to the guy next to us, or what size jeans we buy compared with our sister. We're inclined to draw judgements about ourselves by observing how we stack up against others.

Festinger also asserted that we evaluate our abilities and opinions to reduce uncertainty. If we're unsure of a belief we hold, or a particular performance level, we seek out the beliefs and performance levels of others, until we can distinguish where we stand. We're likely, subsequently, to favour making objective comparisons first (for example, 'I can squat more than him') – typically noting something that can be clearly measured. When such definitive comparisons aren't available, however, we turn to subjective observations instead (for example, 'I'm better looking than her'). Social comparison occurs primarily within dimensions where there are no categorical answers, nor objective benchmarks. We can, therefore, only rely on the beliefs, thoughts, opinions, and social media pages of *others* for our own records. It's no wonder the world of comparison is an ominous and toxic place to navigate.

We're taught from an early age to adhere to society's prevalent metrics. Getting the best exam results. Making the most money. Looking the best you can. While some achievements are useful – and, of course, essential – many are worthless. And, as we're unable to define ourselves independently, we seek approval and appreciation in the form of doing, looking, and feeling better than our friends and family, as well as, occasionally, the guy or girl we encounter at the gym. How we process these social comparisons dictates what we see around us and how we feel – it also, ultimately, influences the success of our dieting journey.

By Comparing Upwardly And Downwardly

Psychologist Thomas Wills hypothesised that there are two primary forms of comparison: downward and upward.[7] Downward comparison involves comparing yourself with someone you identify as 'worse off' than you; upward comparison involves comparing yourself with someone you identify as 'better off' than you. It's important to note that downward comparison isn't necessarily 'good' and upward comparison isn't necessarily 'bad'; both can bring about positive and negative outcomes. This is part of why our utilising comparison effectively – and not completely disregarding its existence – will boost that dieting mindset.

People will often engage in downward comparisons to make themselves feel better. 'At least I don't look like him', for example, or, 'Wow, my morning smoothie looks much more colourful than hers'. This often occurs when people feel their self-esteem has been exposed, or their identity is under threat. Not only does it reduce anxiety, but stimulates a quick burst of happiness as well.[8] Soothing your ego and belief system – because no one makes a morning smoothie quite like you – ensures you feel comforted with both your current and potential situation.

It isn't always smiley faces and swift shots of elation with downward comparison, however. Knowing your situation can decline, or that you could also end up 'worse off' can equally elicit negative emotions. For example, cancer patients who discovered that others with the same illness had deteriorated were reminded that they, too, could regress in their recovery.[9] Similarly, people who've lost a lot of weight may avoid comparing themselves with others who've regained all the weight they lost, for fear of suffering the same fate.

Downward comparisons may also incite dishonesty about the current situation. This can then lead to avoidance of the changes you need to make. If, for example, someone is defined as 'clinically overweight', but perceives their body shape or size as acceptable compared with others 'worse off', they may be less tempted to change their lifestyle – thereby potentially putting their health at risk. Just because other people aren't acting in alignment with your goals and values doesn't mean you should emulate those same actions.

Most people are predisposed to compare upwardly, though. We want to know how we're performing in reference to those whom we perceive as doing better than us. These upward comparisons are heightened when we can make them privately and are not at risk of being judged as inferior. Unfortunately, however, this often impairs an individual's chances of dieting successfully. From longing to look like their best friend, to comparing their body shape to someone they follow on social media, upward comparison repeatedly nourishes unrealistic standards, unsustainable reserves of motivation, and dangerous attempts at aiming to look or feel like someone else. A constant reminder of inadequacy can lead to depression – and even to the sabotage of others' achievements.[10] It may well be this phenomenon that underpins why a certain friend will always tempt you to have that extra glass of wine, or share a dessert with them at dinner.

People quickly forget the long list of reasons – genetics, opportunity, untenable timeframes, health-sapping restrictions, and Photoshop – that means someone may look a certain way and why striving to look like them is, subsequently, flawed. The status war zone we're currently cemented in leaves us feeling as though anything below supposed perfection is regarded as a failure. 'Acceptable' has become expendable.

There are benefits to possessing this upward drive, however. Comparing yourself with others who are perhaps 'better off' may provide hope and inspiration. Those who exercised alongside someone working 'harder' than themselves were more likely to mimic the exercise behaviour of their partner[11] and those who posted pictures of 'thinner' people on their refrigerators were motivated to reach the same goals.[12] This type of comparison must, of course, be utilised within the confines of logic and sound reasoning, given its propensity to elicit negative emotions so easily.

In addition to the direction of comparison, other influential factors determine who we examine ourselves against. Festinger noticed that the *closer* our opinion and ability level is to someone else's, the more likely we are to make comparisons. Even personal characteristics, such as gender and hair colour, will influence who people draw parallels with.[13] This is why we rarely compare our income or status to Richard Branson or Bill Gates – or to the guy scrounging around the bin outside the supermarket; we compare these supposed markers of success with those of friends or family members. The more we view an individual's importance to us, the more likely we'll compare ourselves to that person. This, in turn, leads to the confirmation of those people's beliefs and opinions. We want to be like others because we view them as influential to our lives. We, subsequently, start acting and thinking like them, which further strengthens the confidence we have about our own thoughts and abilities.

While friends and family are often the primary sources of comparison, some celebrities and social media influencers can also emerge as unreasoned idols. If you spend time watching or reading about certain people, it can *feel* like they're part of your peer group, even if you've never met them. Notice how you start comparing yourself with the people on that reality television show, quiz, or sports event you're watching? Once you view yourself as 'that type of person', you begin identifying with that group and strive to be just like them. We also tend to feel good about ourselves when we believe we're in the 'top third' of a certain group. Problems arise, however, the moment we establish that we fall into that category; we then seek the next 'best' group. The cycle never ends.

We will recognise, occasionally, that we're making unhealthy comparisons – and stop. We realise the detrimental effects on our mindset and decide to be bigger, better versions of ourselves. Go us. Of course, it's not that simple. When we stop comparing ourselves to that fitness model on Instagram, for example, feelings of animosity will likely emerge. 'She's too obsessed with the gym' or 'Their eating habits are bordering on unhealthy' or 'They don't even look that good', we reason with ourselves. That subtle pulse of resentment towards others' successes means that we start to turn against them. If we can't handle the negative feelings surrounding comparison, we then trade them for apparently more useful ones – to undermine another's achievements. While we may firmly believe we're warming our ego, it's, in fact, doing the opposite.

It is clear that comparison is a double-edged sword. On the one hand, it appears we *need* it; we lack the structure upon which to live our lives with its absence. It serves, in a positive way, to lift us to achieve more – and acts as a platform to gauge our opinions and progress. On the other hand, comparison can coat us with feelings of hostility and other negative emotions. We may feel inferior and worse off when we consider our body shape and size – and our progress – against that of others. We are not so much defining comparison as 'good' or 'bad', however, as showing how it's reliant on our *perspective* of each situation. This is about *how* you use any comparison and act upon it.

By Evaluating Our Self-Concept

We've already identified that how you view yourself plays a significant role in defining the type of person you are. These evaluations and ideas about your likes, dislikes, relationships, values, and who you are – known as your *self-concept* – buttress your identity. They allow you to make sense of the world you live in and maintain or enhance that sense of self. Are you outgoing, rich, generous, lazy, or good-looking *in comparison with others*? The adjectives of 'self' create the story you tell yourself, about yourself.

Comparison is inherently neutral, neither positive nor negative. You can determine whether you're taller, stronger, or faster than someone, by simply drawing these comparisons. As you're able to develop and modify the subjective ideas within the stories you tell yourself, you're able to turn those comparisons into positive or negative emotions. 'I'm objectively stronger than him, which makes me feel happy', you might think, for example. This furthers your proclivity to draw parallels with others. You're simply looking to reinforce those admissions about who you are, whether they include believing you're the one who can never seem to shift the weight, or who can never keep up with others in the gym. You're not comparing yourself to others from a blank slate, but more so from a place that underlines the beliefs you already hold about yourself.

You may tend to constantly seek feedback to confirm your self-views – from whom you compare yourself with, to how you interpret social comparisons. If you want to reinforce the type of person you believe you are, you're more likely to seek out others' similar achievements, as well as similar opinions about yourself. This type of self-evaluation enables you to potentially improve the feelings you possess surrounding yourself.[14] This, in turn, controls and directs your actions, even if you're unaware of it. As such, it can also go the other way. For instance, in a study where images of Michael Jordan were subliminally presented to subjects, participants were significantly more likely to rate themselves as less athletic, even though Michael Jordan was not an obvious reference point for athletic achievement.[15]

It's been proposed that we engage in four types of self-evaluation motives when comparing ourselves with others. The first, known as *self-assessment,* is simply seeking an accurate view of the self.[16] Are we doing the right thing? Do we fit with society's norms? Am I as fit as I think I am? We want to know whether we're as knowledgeable as we think we are, or as dedicated as others who share the same goals. We compare ourselves to reduce uncertainty about our self, regardless of whether it results in positive or negative feedback.

We also tend to amplify our self-image. When we pinpoint versions of others to boost our self-worth and esteem, we use them as forms of *self-enhancement.* In this instance, we don't necessarily care for accuracy; our motive is that we're more concerned with making ourselves feel better, along with protecting any weaknesses we perceive we possess. This is why we compare ourselves with others whom we conclude aren't doing as well, or even avoid comparing ourselves with others who are supposedly more successful than us. It's also the mechanism in place when we believe we're smarter, cleverer, and more attractive than our friends,[17] or, even, better drivers than they are.[18]

Although *self-enhancement* is useful for maintaining a positive perspective of ourselves – and for boosting motivation to improve specific skills or performance levels[19] – it will eventually dig up vulnerabilities, leaving us anxious, stressed, and fearful about everything we're doing. Comparing ourselves to others to synthetically boost our ego, or temporarily immerse ourselves in feelings of superiority, will often, inadvertently, leave us feeling dejected.

On the other hand, whenever we use comparison to better ourselves, we use it as a form of the third motive: *self-improvement.*[20] If scanning others' achievements and situations propels us forward, it helps us become better versions of ourselves. 'How can I use her hip thrust technique to help mine?' for example, or, 'What can I do to achieve her standards?' and, 'How can I ensure I stay at the top of *my* game?' Using this feedback to enhance our own being is helpful. It's why this familiar type of comparison is often viewed as favourable.

If you're dieting and you compare yourself with others to keep making progress, you free yourself from the negatives of undesirable observations. If your gym partner is forcing you to work harder, or the influencer who's cooking and posting pictures of healthy meals on social media inspires you to expand your own culinary skills, comparison can be viewed as a *good* thing. Using others to embody the effort, skill, and commitment that you, too, should be displaying is advantageous. This form of assessment is essential.

The final form of self-evaluation is that of *self-verification.*[21] It's the concept that we'll continuously strive to construct, refine, and defend our identity. This is why, when we use comparison, we're not looking to create new ideas about ourselves, but merely justify our current ones. This means we can find ourselves in risky territory again. If you believe you lack willpower, for instance, you'll continually seek comparisons that reaffirm this view. All that ends up happening is people compare their ideas about themselves with the ideas that others have about themselves. 'My friends are so much better at saying no to the biscuits than me', for example. Those beliefs – or snippets gleaned from social media – aren't necessarily representative of people's actual lives; they're purely the opinions they hold about themselves.

We aren't too smart when it comes to comparison, unfortunately. Instead of realising we're comparing prior beliefs about our identity and self-concept with someone else's ideas about theirs, we tend to believe we're falling behind. That we're not as fit as others, or we don't look as good – or we're not as successful. In reality, all everyone is doing is just comparing ideas to other ideas. This is what creates those unrealistic standards and damaging mindsets – not necessarily the truth, but positive and negative self-views. Whether it be 'fitspiration' (i.e., fitness inspiration) or 'thinspiration' (i.e., motivation to become thinner) we seek, we're caught in a perpetual cycle of comparing our perceived 'worst' to someone else's apparent 'best'.

This is why we shouldn't take the majority of our comparisons too seriously. We spend a significant amount of time comparing ourselves with others, whilst failing to realise that we've already decided who we are and what we're capable of. Were we to recognise that, then we'd be able to sidestep the darker side of comparison and be free to utilise it differently.

The Effects Of Comparing Ourselves To The Guy/Girl At The Gym

Society disparages comparison. "Don't do it", we're told. "Get off social media if you want a happier life". It seems like sage advice. Who wants to feel bad about themselves, after all? Who needs to continually strive for unattainable physical standards and fitness levels? But is avoiding comparisons really the answer to an evolutionary predisposition that's been continuously propagated over the years?

Of course, there are negatives to comparing ourselves to the other person at the gym. We may feel sick with jealousy when we stumble upon another, 'Just ran a 20-minute 5k!' status on Facebook – or experience crippling anxiety when flicking through another, quick-fix diet magazine. There are forgotten positives to take, however, from contrasting our situations with others. Disregarding these precious lessons only feeds the comparison fire. Taking a deeper dive into the negatives *and* the positives of drawing parallels with others allows us to utilise comparisons productively. Rather than be consumed by the flaws of any comparison, which may ultimately damage our dieting mindset, we can assemble a mentality that pushes us to, finally, lose weight successfully.

On Self-Esteem

Self-esteem reflects the thoughts, beliefs, and feelings we possess about ourselves and is an indication of how much we value ourselves. It's based on how we feel about the moments we can control in our lives and can be either favourable or unfavourable. Those with high self-esteem are self-assured of their values and principles. They have complete trust in their ability in certain tasks, display greater emotional stability, and view themselves – and their bodies – in a positive light. Those with low self-esteem feel, however, that their opinions aren't important. They doubt their chances of success, and frequently experience negative emotions in relation to their lives and physiques. It's no wonder that comparison can further affect those positive or negative feelings.

When we're able to compare ourselves favourably with others (for example, 'I look better in that Gymshark outfit', or, 'I can dance better on TikTok'), we feel good about ourselves. This helps to explain why people will often veer towards downward comparison to boost their self-esteem. It's also why students who were applying for a job felt better about themselves when they were made aware of other pupils applying for the same position, who weren't perceived as so competent.[22]

On the other hand, when we compare ourselves to those in a seemingly better position (for example, 'They can run a faster 10k than me', or, 'They get more likes on their gym-selfies'), we then frequently feel worse about ourselves. This leads to diminished enjoyment in the process, which can mean some people even give up altogether. It helps to explain why we may encounter feelings of depression, or anxiety, when we use upward comparison to boost our self-esteem.[23] One study even found that comparing higher earnings of neighbours was associated with lower levels of self-reported happiness.[24]

It creates a vicious cycle; we feel worse about ourselves when we compare upwardly. The resulting low self-esteem means we're then more likely to make further comparisons with those seemingly better off than us, leading to further undesirable feelings. We may start adopting that *fixed mindset* and assume there's no point in trying when we view photos of fitness models in magazines and on television. The perception of how much control we have over our ability to change will influence whether we improve or damage the impression of our worth, when making comparisons.[25]

It's worth noting that the effects of drawing parallels with others also hinges on the *current* state of your self-esteem.[26] If you possess a wealth of confidence, then, making upward comparisons may benefit you. If you lack self-assurance, then, making upward comparisons may lower your psychological well-being even further. It's been found that, when those with low self-esteem viewed others on social media, they felt the need to edit their photos to appear more socially appealing.[27] It's why you may differ in the way you react to comparisons – ironically – compared with others. Truly believing that no one else has more value than you, for example, will remove the anxiety and worry you'd otherwise experience when focusing on everything you've not achieved or can't attain.

Importantly, there are various ways in which we can cushion and improve the impact of social comparison on our self-esteem. We know that, when we use upward comparison without acknowledging the complete picture, we're traversing a slippery slope. Were we to, instead, appreciate that we're unaware of the journey and situation behind the scenes of others, we'd promote mastery rather than achievement. While the guy or girl from the gym may possess the physique you desire, you're blind to how it surfaced. Did they sacrifice relationships to get there? Did they engage in harmful methods to attain that six-pack? Did they pour energy into that endeavour only to leave other aspects of their life behind? You simply don't know.

Comparing the middle of your journey to the final product of someone else's, similarly, serves little purpose. Just like attempting to drive on the motorway on your first driving lesson because your friend, who's already passed their test, currently does, would be reckless; trying to boost self-esteem through replicating others' already finished endeavours is a car crash waiting-to-happen. Why would you expect to look, cook, or train like someone else, who's spent years honing their skills, when you've only just started? Comparing the heart of your journey to the end result of someone else's damages feelings of confidence in your abilities and worth. It's why admiring someone's transformation photo, without recognising the hard work and commitment required to get there, can be off-putting and detrimental to your own motivation.

It's worth thinking about placing self-esteem on a continuum. One end of the scale implies that self-esteem is influenced by how we match up to others; the other indicates that we feel better about ourselves when we're true to our values and core selves.[28] Were we to think, 'Yes, the person at the gym may well have a desirable physique, but, in turning up every day I'm practicing the perseverance and self-development I want to master', we'd then be elevating favourable levels of confidence. Staying true to ourselves will influence our ability to handle inevitable comparisons.

On Mental Health

At the start of 2021, there were approximately 4.33 billion social media users around the world.[29] That's more than 55 per cent of the total, global population – and a whole lot of Tweets to scroll through. When each platform provides us with ample opportunities to gawk at, scrutinise, and interpret a glut of photos, statuses, and captions, it's no wonder we're ensnared in the middle of a comparison crisis. There has never has there been such a mammoth opportunity to measure up against others of similar ability, physical shape, and healthy – or unhealthy – habits.

Social media has been found to, largely, have negative effects on mental health.[30] From depression,[31] to negative self-perception,[32] to lower body image and disordered eating,[33] the impact of double-tapping reels and browsing what others 'eat in a day' is commonly perceived as damaging to our mindset. The ease at which we can now compare our lives, successes, failures, physiques, and gym-selfies begets more problems than benefits.

Given the scope of heavily-filtered images and posts that we're exposed to, it's no wonder that people perceive others as happier, and leading 'better' lives[34]

– especially when it comes to physical appearance. It's been found that female university students feel more concerns about their bodies, because they constantly compare their appearance to their peers on Facebook[35] – and even browsing Instagram for as little as thirty minutes a day can lead to increased self-objectification.[36] Uploading that group photo at the bar is more telling than we ever thought. When we regularly, upwardly-compare ourselves with others, we're only serving to threaten our mental health. Feelings of inferiority and inadequacy torment us, as the comparison games become more competitive than ever.

In the past, social comparison amongst friends and family has typically involved the individual and just a handful of others. Social media, on the other hand, now provides an almost limitless stage on which to compare ourselves. There's always *another* person to look up to, or down at. From lowering self-worth and self-confidence, to heightening feelings of sadness and jealousy,[37] it's hard not to assume we're failing, doing something wrong, or unable to acquire the same levels of respect, success, and physical stature as other people. The act of comparison, when swiping through social media, is dangerous – especially when we seek out another bikini-laden, glute workout to follow.

The information we're exposed to on social media platforms teaches us lessons about ourselves, especially when we're locked, permanently, inside our own, algorithm-fuelled echo chamber. The messages we obtain aren't always correct, nor beneficial to our mental well-being, unfortunately. If you're already submerged in negative feelings surrounding your self-concept, you'll inadvertently seek negative feedback. If you believe you're overweight or unattractive – for example – you'll pursue photos and videos that reaffirm that adverse assessment. As painful as it is, looking at another influencer's semi-naked photoshoot by the pool, reinforces our beliefs about ourselves via *self-verification* (our desire to be known through *our* self-views, as reflected through *others'* self-views). The constant desire to look up to others contributes to unrealistic ideals of how we'd like to look and act. Not only do we find ourselves measuring up against a constant state of 'beauty and glory' (how often do you view an unfiltered, uninspiring picture, after all?), but also buckling to the loaded world of 'fitspiration'.

When we're exposed to those photos of topless men and women, with unprecedented levels of low body fat and increased muscle mass, along with memes shouting from the rooftops to 'just get on with it' – and videos of exercises that would be better suited as the opening act at a circus – we're drowned in a host of problems. From lower perceived attractiveness,[38] to body image concerns,[39] and feelings of missing out,[40] we chase elusive goals and ideals in the hope of repairing such problems. We know that, when individuals follow fitness boards on Pinterest, they're more likely to engage in extreme weight loss behaviours.[41]

Our screen-centric culture often inflicts distress and complications on our dieting mindset. Seldom should you use the carefully-crafted videos and photos of others to help determine your own decisions and choices. While taking a social media detox (and telling everyone about it) is often implausible, it's wise to always be wary of the material and information you're privy to. Are the arenas of 'thinspiration' and 'fitspiration' helping, or harming you?

The influence of social comparisons and social media on mental health is not all doom and gloom, however. There's a body of evidence to show that some internet applications can have beneficial effects on well-being.[42] It's been found that perusing images displaying body positivity on Instagram can *enhance* satisfaction with one's own body[43] – and posts that exposed 'real' images as fake, disrupted the social comparison process, and actually reduced body dissatisfaction.[44] Even feelings of envy can sometimes inspire people to focus on self-improvement.[45]

There's still debate as to what comes first, just like the proverbial chicken and egg. Does social media cause people to be depressed, or are depressed people more likely to use social media? When studies completed over eight years tell us that there's actually no connection between the time spent on social media and mental health issues, we must take a closer look at things.[46] It's clear that the link between social media usage and well-being – whether enhanced or degraded – is not bound to an either/or framework, but shaped by both positive and negative influences.[47]

Much like with self-esteem, it's important to note that social media affects people differently, depending on pre-existing conditions and personality traits. Those who are more optimistic, for example, tend to experience fewer harmful effects of upward social comparison than those who possess lower optimism.[48] While the overarching nature of comparison on mental health is negative, it's not to say you'll experience identical effects to one of your friends, in following the same people. Always be wary of how you react to flicking through your social media apps, nonetheless.

On Self-Improvement

For all its failings, comparison can provide benefits. We may not realise what potentials exist without the ideal of others' achievements, after all. Who knew it was possible to lose that amount of body fat, lift that amount of weight in the gym, or contort your underwear in such a way as to make that selfie look even better? Comparison allows us to expand our sense of what we can imagine for ourselves. When we use it as inspiration and self-improvement, comparison can be a constructive facet of our dieting mindset. For instance, it's been found that comparing recipes can expand food choices,[49] and certain exercise-related, social media posts can inspire others to exercise more.[50]

Canvassing the achievements and progress of others can prove advantageous when we use it to shape our actions and beliefs. When people view self-improvement as attainable, compared with others, it often triggers a form of 'levelling-up motivation' – which improves subsequent performance.[51] As a separate example, in one study, people making upward comparisons around job uncertainty, and career planning, were more likely to strive towards reaching job-related goals.[52] A short-term boost of motivation is never a negative. By searching for others in seemingly better positions, we're able to focus on improving our short-term goals, whether through our exercise habits or creating a healthy meal for dinner, for instance.

Using the accomplishments of others to inspire our own efforts slots into the definition of the *growth mindset*. If we see others succeeding with their dieting endeavours, then it has the potential to motivate us, too. Instead of feeling threatened by others' triumphs – the definition of the *fixed mindset* – we believe that we, too, can remodel our own lives and behaviours to achieve the same level of success. Other people's physical achievements no longer force you to tackle your own shortcomings, thereby making them harder to deal with; instead, adopting a growth mindset prompts you to learn from that same person. Dieting is not a zero-sum game. If someone else wins, it should encourage you to believe that winning is possible – within your own playing field – for you as well.

Comparing your situation to others allows you to anticipate potential hurdles and the steps to overcome them. While your work colleague may possess a figure you desire, you could quickly realise that their fancy, low-carb regime turns them into a cranky mess every day – meaning you decide to give that one a miss. While your cousin has achieved superior fitness levels, perhaps you discover that they keep getting injured while following their gym programme – and decide that imitating their path to success would be careless. When you use comparison to regulate decision-making, it then becomes an asset.

Whenever you feel a twinge of unhealthy comparison arise, however, it's imperative to flip the switch. Rather than end up besieged by feelings of jealousy, or wonderment, you become determined to use the lessons learnt from their journey, to better yours. Analysing others to ascertain what's possible – and not possible – alongside focusing on how you can reach the end goal, are untapped corners of the comparison world. As we know, there's a fine line between using comparison as a form of self-improvement and becoming consumed with feelings of envy, but drawing the benefits from others' situations can breed our own successes.

It's important to remember that you're not comparing others' triumphs with yours, so much as the *process* of their achievements. If someone shows you their transformation photo, you learn from *how* they got there, rather than the end result. If someone posts a picture of their beautifully home-made meal, the aim is not to draw comparisons with the finished dish but the creation behind the end product. What skills did they cultivate to reach that level of expertise? What failures did they have to overcome to be able to display the finished outcome?

It may seem tough. But it's part of reminding yourself that your efforts and mindset require practice – and hard work. Through cultivating this self-reflection, you're focusing on what matters (the process) and what doesn't (the finished product). Comparison, when used for the art of self-improvement, is one of the most profitable tools you possess in crafting the ultimate dieting mindset.

On Gratitude And Happiness

Comparing yourself with That Person From The Gym – who has three kids, a high-profile full-time job, and not only manages to exercise five times a week but flaunts a physique that frequently gets heads turning – may result in negative emotions due to their supposed 'better' situation. You're also able to compare yourself with The *Other* Person From The Gym, however, who appears to find themselves in a '*worse*' position. Because they sporadically attend the gym, aren't as seemingly 'fit' as you, and always struggle to lose weight, this can boost your self-evaluation – leading to potential, self-enhancement benefits and positive emotions. You're now grateful for your situation. We know these effects should only be utilised in the short-term. Dwelling on The Other Person From The Gym's situation won't actually improve yours, but, through making small and effective downward comparisons, you're able to practice gratitude – thus forming positive effects.[53]

Interestingly, when you utilise a 'What could have been' mentality – turning a potentially upward comparison into a downward one – you're able to improve happiness. One study, examining competitors at the 1992 Summer Olympics, showed that, somewhat counterintuitively, bronze medallists were actually *happier* than silver medallists.[54] Those who finished second focused on how close they came to taking gold – and, negatively, what they'd missed out on; those who finished third, compared themselves with others who didn't even make the podium, and, instead, what they'd achieved. When we use downward comparison effectively, we're able to enhance our well-being.[55]

It has also been proposed that we're able to make 'contrastive' and 'assimilative' comparisons.[56] Contrastive comparisons highlight the differences between us and others, while assimilative comparisons reduce that disparity. Those contrastive comparisons can lead to feelings of pride, when we realise how much effort we've put in compared with others. Whether that be training hard, or working to improve our fruit and vegetable consumption, we believe we're in a better position when we increase that 'gap'. This can further motivate us to work harder and achieve more.

The reverse is true when making upward comparisons. We want to reduce the gap between those 'better off' than us, ensuring we feel like we can achieve something similar (i.e., 'If *they* can do it, so can I'). When we increase that inequality, unfortunately we're more likely to resent the individual, as the divide reminds us how far we must go to achieve the same levels of supposed success.

There are clearly benefits to making appropriate comparisons. We must ensure we're utilising them towards gratitude and happiness, not animosity and disdain for others. This is why some individuals reported greater satisfaction with their relationships when they were told to consider their bond as 'better' than that of others.[57] It turns out that believing you and your partner are exceptional at arranging date nights, compared with others, isn't necessarily a bad thing. Focusing on what skills and beliefs you have, along with the triumphs you've achieved, can improve physical and mental health.

The evidence is clear; there are both positive and negative effects from comparing yourself with others. We need to harness the benefits, however, rather than assuming comparison should be avoided at all costs. How can we profit from its positive effects? And, above all, use it effectively?

How To Use Comparison Effectively

Pinpoint Your Motivations

Persistent comparisons don't arise without numerous motivations bubbling beneath the surface. Uncovering those motivations will expose the underlying reasons for continually seeing how you stack up against others. Are you comparing yourself to The Person From The Gym to improve your own journey and exercise technique, and elevate your sense of self about that progress and ability? Or is it simply to soothe those pre-made conceptions and beliefs you have about yourself? Probing those motives will ensure you're able to take a step back and use worthwhile comparisons, instead.

By determining your comparison triggers – those little moments that spark feelings of healthy competitiveness, or delight – you'll affirm your values. Are you obsessed with noticing how much time influencers can spend at the gym, and with their children? Then it's clear that you value family life. Do you constantly feel you are competing with friends, over who's working the hardest in your gym class? It's clear you value commitment and focus, with all the activities you engage in. Once you've figured these out, you can then use the values you've unearthed to dictate how you live your life.

This simple task can, similarly, work in the other direction, too. If you find yourself comparing the definition of your abs to the movie star on the screen, you can also remind yourself that you don't necessarily value that materialistic trait – as much as you do gratitude and humility, for instance. You can, instead, focus on those moments of your life that you *do* cherish. Why bother wasting mental energy in scrutinising an aspect of your life that you don't hold close to your chest? Affirming your values and virtues will procure greater personal development, and goal achievement, with the facets of life that truly matter to you – instead of chasing trivial ambitions.

You can take hold of your comparison prompts – the circumstances and qualities in others that provoke the comparisons you make – and recognise why you're making those connections in the first place. You can, subsequently, observe the ideas you possess about yourself and others. Is it another's body shape or their strength level that matters? Is it the likes they get on their gym-selfies? Do those reveal insecurities about what you lack, or feel unable to attain? Do they even matter to you? Pinpointing your motivations enables you to pacify those subsequent feelings, before they transform into counterproductive endeavours.

If you can dig deep, and admit that the reason you compare your fitness journey with others is, for example, for external validation, self-enhancement, or to heighten your own happiness, then you can change your thought process. Instead of scouting out people to enhance your feelings, change the narrative. This means no longer viewing others' social media feeds, to let them influence your well-being, but using them to drive the things that matter to you the most. Rather than succumbing to the effects of 'fitspiration', you focus on how *you* look and feel instead.

The good news is, we get better at this as we get older.[58] Our likelihood to engage in comparison processes declines across our lives. Researchers have hypothesised that we're more likely to evaluate ourselves against our own past, rather than the current state of anyone else. This is how to use self-assessment successfully. If you're now stronger, leaner, and more confident than you were at the beginning of your journey, that's more of an indicator of success than comparing how you look in a swimsuit with others. Ignore the present and connect the dots of your past to better yourself. As Jordan Peterson, in his book, *12 Rules For Life,* states, "Compare yourself to who you were yesterday, not to who someone else is today."[59]

Move The Barometer

There exists the story of the influential Chinese philosopher, Zhuang Zhou, who was strolling along a riverbank, accompanied by a close friend. The pair stopped by the river for a moment to gaze at the water. Observing a shoal of fish, Zhou exclaimed, "Look at those fish; look at how they're enjoying themselves."

"How can you say that?" his friend asked. "How would you know? You're not a fish, so how would you know if they're having a good time?"

Zhou replied, simply, "You aren't me, either, so how would you know that I don't know the fish are having fun?"

While we're quick to compare ourselves with others, we're not only comparing what *we* consider worthy of measuring, but assume others value us by the same metrics, as well. In reality, we're blind to others' thoughts and beliefs. We're unaware of what they know, how they feel, or what their values are. Importantly, we can't change them, either.

If your idea of the perfect body is thigh gaps and hip dips, you not only measure others by their thigh gaps and hip dips, but assume that people are looking at you for the quality of your thigh gaps and hip dips, as well. If your idea of attractiveness is a slim and slender body, you compare your slenderness to others' slenderness and believe they're judging you in a similar fashion. It's important to realise that everyone possesses their own metrics – and theirs will often differ completely from yours.

Instead of attempting to halt the comparison process, we can, instead, change *what* we compare. By moving the barometer, we can take the negative emotions out of the equation and focus on ourselves. We focus on *our* journey and *our* metrics. Transforming our idea of success – and not necessarily what others have decided for us – will put us at ease with how we stack up against society. The next time you find yourself punctured by the negatives of comparison, look to accept that others measure themselves differently – and remind yourself of what *you* consider worthwhile.

Yes, That Person From The Gym lives a crazy life and still flaunts a body that looks good in swimwear, but is this truly your definition of success or worth? Or even happiness? The weight loss industry is often focused strongly on external factors; this fixation should be complemented by meaning and well-being as well. You don't know if The Person From The Gym goes home every night crying because they hate their job, feels sick with anxiety, and, despite having a body you desire, hasn't had sex with their spouse in six months. You, however, love your job, live a stress-free life, and had sex last night. Yes, losing weight is a goal you have; is it your true definition of achievement, however? For That Person, it's looking great at the gym. For you, it's about feeling great within yourself. In shifting the benchmark, you're able to haul your standards from the moments and traits that don't matter to you to ones that lead to a purposeful and rewarding weight loss journey.

The successes and perceived happiness of others are rarely as pain-free and enchanting as we might like to believe. With accomplishment often comes sacrifice and strain. When desiring someone else's life, body, or strength, you must realise what arrives with it. You can't seize their success without experiencing all that comes alongside it. You may, of course, wish for the hours spent in the gym and the deprivation that some go through to reach a certain physique. It would be reckless, however, to assume that you can reach the same status, or look, without carrying the passion and anguish from all that comes with it, as well. Yes, that physique may look desirable from the photoshoot highlights reel; are you willing, however, to endure the levels of hunger, the gruelling training sessions, and all the sacrifice that was experienced to get there?

In this fast-paced age of social media and materialistic items, we get caught up in others' lives. When it comes to dieting, we're obsessed with the amount of weight our friends have lost, or how many times they've exercised a week. While we may like to believe these are useful comparisons, they're often not. The beauty is, however, that while we *can't* change others, we *can* change our own benchmarks – and that's perfectly acceptable. Start digging into what defines success for you, or allows for your own, personal growth. Change the barometer, and you'll change you.

Celebrate Yourself And Others

There's an episode of *The Simpsons* in which Homer's cheery, next-door neighbour, Ned Flanders, opens a shop called 'The Leftorium'. Homer – bestowed with the chance to choose three wishes – fantasises that Ned's new business collapses. From imagining a shop of empty customers, to Ned turning out his pockets and begging the bailiffs, Homer delights in his friend's failings. It's only when Homer imagines a dead Ned's grave – with his children weeping beside it – that he stops himself.

"Too far", he says, quickly.

The Germans possess a word for people's propensity to delight in others' misery: *schadenfreude*. Where comparison is concerned, we know that individuals often indulge in such a sensation to elicit feelings of self-enhancement. From secretly wishing that friends would regain the weight they've lost, to rejoicing when others inform them that they haven't been to the gym in three weeks, it cultivates self-righteous joy. We also know, however, that this feeling is short-lived. It fortifies feelings of resentment and envy, ultimately, and takes away from our own accomplishments.

While seemingly counterintuitive, a trusted method to overcome the negative feelings associated with comparison is, in fact, to *celebrate* others' successes. Revel in your friend's outstanding fat loss transformation, or your sister's ability to juggle a 50-hour workweek and still train four times, in as many days. Praising the effort and success of others dampens the deafening call of bitterness and, instead, enables productivity on our end.

It's no easy task, of course. Being consumed by feelings of envy makes it incredibly challenging to praise others. But, through celebration – even if occasionally through gritted teeth – we relieve ourselves from the negatives of comparison. Celebrating others' accomplishments sets off a positive feedback loop. We praise others who, in return, praise us, which further motivates and drives us to achieve the goals we set ourselves.

It's also important to remind yourself of your own strengths. When you come across someone who begets those feelings of comparison envy – whether through them adorning clothes you wish you could fit into, or posting another transformation photo – focus on treasuring your own triumphs. What have you accomplished recently that brings about feelings of happiness? Have you successfully overcome a tough social event, or managed to get eight hours of uninterrupted sleep each night, during the past week? The process of self-affirmation, in which we focus on valued, positive attributes about ourselves, can soften the dangerous effects of comparison with others.[60]

The next time you bump into a friend or colleague who's achieved or possesses what you want, focus on your successes first. Imagine what others would like to take, or replicate, from *your* life and accomplishments. Then set about praising that same friend, colleague, or family member. Buddhists call this 'rejoicing in the good fortune of others', and, as Sharon Salzberg says, in her book, *Loving-Kindness,* "It is a rare and beautiful quality to feel truly happy when others are happy."[61] You're no longer consumed by feelings of jealousy or resentment, but able to shift the way you view others' successes. While it's undoubtedly tough to appreciate the joy of other people's transformations and fitness achievements, praising those victories will enhance your own pleasure and, subsequently, your own accomplishments.

Master Your Self-Worth

In valuing ourselves, we appreciate who we are and – ultimately – become content with that individual. Self-worth is at the core of our very being. Our thoughts, feelings, and behaviours are closely linked to how we view our worth as humans. Harnessing this power is how we can use comparison favourably.

Self-Worth Theory assumes that the biggest human priority is the search for self-acceptance.[62] This often arrives in the form of achievement. Our perception of attainment – whether through losing more weight or eating more organic food than friends or family – significantly influences our self-worth. Placing so much emphasis on our success in comparison to others is, however, a dangerous game to play. If we're unable to look as good on social media, nor fit in with society's physical standards, we assume we lack value and merit. We begin to fixate on our perceived shortcomings – 'oversized' hips or a 'lack' of discipline, for example – to gather reasons why we're not about to diet successfully, or achieve the physique we desire.

We rank our triumphs against others to measure our growth and accentuate the parts of life we don't personally value. Even students who based their self-worth on external sources, such as approval from others and academic performance, reported more stress, anger, and relationship conflicts – and, in tandem, had higher levels of drug and alcohol use.[63]

Thankfully, we're able to master our self-worth. When we no longer view ourselves as the broken, second-hand van in a long line of fancy supercars, we evaluate our abilities and achievements paired with ourselves, not with others. We value ourselves as the shiny convertible, not the damaged truck. We no longer emphasise our rate of weight loss compared with what others deem acceptable; nor do we highlight our inabilities in the kitchen or the weights room.

When we successfully determine our self-worth – and ignore the desire to inflate it – we allay the pressures of comparison. We become aware of our own strengths and weaknesses and remove defensiveness from criticism. As the American teacher and psychologist, Ram Dass, says, "The problem is you're afraid to acknowledge your own beauty. You're too busy holding onto your unworthiness. You'd rather be a schmuck sitting before some great man that fits in more with who you think you are."[64]

To master your self-worth, you must appreciate the moments that don't determine the value you place on yourself. From the number of times that you train in a week, to how many dopamine-repleted 'likes' you receive on your latest exercise video, these aspects of your life have nothing to do with how worthy you are. When we purge ourselves from such beliefs, we're less likely to succumb to the adverse effects of comparison. Why does our rate of progress matter when compared with others, given that we value our own growth and character development? Why does an individual's sun-soaked bikini photo have any bearing on how we view our own physique?

When we begin to understand ourselves and elevate self-acceptance, we recognise the moments we truly appreciate. From the feelings we have about our own dieting venture, to the internal measures we set ourselves, we become responsible for our own actions, not those of others. We now focus on the unique qualities that make up our feelings, thoughts, desires, and values, not what someone else views as failure or success. If you value the trait of perseverance, you work on developing this in the context of yourself. You keep trying to master your own exercise and eating habits – not those of others. If you value trying new experiences, you rate the enjoyment of going to the gym and eating new foods that fit with what you find meaningful – not those of someone you befriended on social media. Pursuing values that you feel are important will free you from the perils of the comparison game. Self-acceptance promotes self-improvement, instead of hindering it.

Much like an anti-inflammatory drug, you only require comparison in small doses. Too little, and you possess minimal information to inspire action and dictate what you believe is achievable. Too much, and you experience doubt, impractical expectations, and anxiety over who you should be, what you should be doing, and what you look like. There is a middle ground and you *can* find it.

Chapter Summary And Taking Action

- Making comparisons with others is an innate drive built within us. Drawing parallels with friends, family, and people on social media reduces uncertainty and enables us to define ourselves. We're able to compare our opinions and behaviours, as well as ability and performance levels.

- Downward comparison involves comparing yourself with someone you identify as 'worse off' than you; upward comparison entails comparing yourself with someone you identify as 'better off' than you. There are positive and negative effects to both. This is why comparison shouldn't necessarily be viewed as a negative, but more as something to be mastered.

- There are four types of self-evaluation motives we engage in, when comparing ourselves with others. *Self-assessment* involves comparing ourselves to reduce uncertainty about our self, regardless of whether it results in positive or negative feedback; *Self-enhancement* is used for maintaining a positive perspective of ourselves; *Self-improvement* is the act of making comparisons to improve as individuals; *Self-verification* refers to confirming previously held notions and beliefs about ourselves.

- Comparing yourself with others rarely boosts self-esteem across the long term. Failing to realise the full journey behind someone's achievements damages feelings of confidence in our own ability and worth. Similarly, drawing parallels with others on social media can lead to negative effects on mental health – from experiencing lower perceived attractiveness, to body image concerns, and feelings of missing out. Not all comparisons damage self-esteem, nor is social media always a negative; we must be cognisant of their problems, however.

- When we use comparison to shape our actions and beliefs and help us improve as individuals, we reap the positives from looking at others. Through cultivating self-reflection, we focus on what matters (the process) and what doesn't (others' finished journeys and own experience). Similarly, we must ensure we utilise comparisons towards gratitude and happiness, not dissatisfaction and disdain for others.

- To affirm your values, whilst improving the comparisons you make, work on unearthing your triggers for comparing (e.g., "I'm only comparing my current physique to his/hers because I'm currently feeling angry"). Similarly, start digging into what defines success for you or allows for personal growth (e.g., "I truly value companionship, rather than my waist size"). Change the barometer of what *you* – rather than others – define as success, and you'll change your outlook on your journey.

- Start focusing on celebrating others' successes and your own strengths, to remove the feelings of resentment that may arise from analysing their triumphs, alongside appreciating what determines the value you place on yourself. Focusing on the unique qualities that make up your feelings, thoughts, desires, and values – not what others view as failure or success – means that you'll have finally mastered the comparison game.

CHAPTER 8
Just One More:
Improving Self-Control

I bet you're an addict. I don't mean a 'devouring a litre-bottle of cheap vodka on a Thursday afternoon' type of addict, but a 'repeatedly reaching for your phone, feeling like you've lost an arm if you're unable to check your social media folder' type of addict. When boredom hits, you seek out a screen to interact with. When watching television, you're scrolling on your phone or laptop, as well. When your partner's regaling you with stories about their day, you're more interested in the fact that your friend from high school has uploaded *another* photo of their dog. You probably only have to inspect your 'phone usage' to concede defeat to the perils of the apps and programmes you're glued to.

Internet and social media obsession are real. While the term 'addict' may not be clinically correct, our phone's compulsive, compelling, and distracting nature makes for a vicious cycle. The desire to continually want *more* is akin to the highs and lows of an alcoholic or hooked drug user. The urge to check for that little red notification on Facebook, or the ping of a new email, can lead to damaged productivity, wasted opportunities, decayed physical interactions, and even the occasional divorce.

Ask people why they're permanently attached to their phones, and they'll bombard you with an eruption of excuses as to why your accusation is simply untrue. "I need to check it for work", they'll say. Or, "No, Mum, you're obsessed with *your* phone". Should they acquiesce, belatedly, to an overuse problem, the prevailing explanation that filters through is, "I just don't have the self-control to avoid looking at it". Attributing incessant phone usage to a lack of discipline is a popular self-justification. The much sought-after values of self-denial and steadfast perseverance date back to Victorian times, after all

– it's inferred we *need* willpower to be respected and admired. The ability to exercise self-control – in so far as we care about ourselves as mature, virtuous, and rational individuals – becomes central to the person we aspire to be. Therefore, the absence of restraint *must* be the reason why people can't go twenty minutes without reaching for their phone, tablet, or laptop.

Is it really a lack of self-control, though? Is a willpower deficiency common when it comes to frisking the ubiquity of social media? Or is there something deeper bubbling beneath the surface? Research has shown that blaming a lack of self-control on our deep-rooted fascination with technology is flawed.

Our love for the internet is rooted in a deep-wired human trait. The cognitive-reward structure offered by services like email, and social media, is similar to that of a casino slot machine; 'Most of it is junk, but every so often, you hit the jackpot'.[1] Studies have shown that gambling games, such as scratchcard lotteries, offer low-cost chances of winning a substantial prize, which, in turn, stimulates excessive play.[2] Our phones are no different: the budget barrier to entry being a quick peruse of your phone and the jackpot being a new direct message, notification, or opportunity to glare at another, half-naked fitness influencer performing squats on the beach.

Just like the famous study of Russian physiologist, Ivan Pavlov – training his dogs to cultivate a particular association between the occurrence of one event in anticipation of another – our relationship with our phones breeds the same exchange. We've learned to correlate that vibration in our pockets, or new, social media 'like', with a pleasurable rush of feel-good brain chemicals. Someone 'loving' your latest status provides that much-needed dopamine hit. You soon learn to associate the vibration or notification with a gratifying experience, and it becomes ingrained in your psyche to check your phone every five minutes – perhaps much to your partner's or relative's chagrin.

It *isn't* a case, therefore, of lacking self-control, but of other, subconscious, factors playing a part in your urge to scroll, tap, and swipe. This isn't about willpower, but rather, inherent physiological functions and habits – along with veiled psychological powers that are contributing to that unstoppable obsession. It is the desire to prevent boredom, the intrinsic motivation to systematically check what our friends are doing and thinking, and the effortlessness of opening another app, that reinforces unhealthy behaviours. You probably don't lack reserves of self-control when it comes to checking your phone, but are under the mystical command of other, compelling influences.

Can the same be said of sticking to a diet, then? Is a shortage, or depletion, of restraint the prime reason people fail to achieve desired results? Or is it by virtue of other psychological elements influencing our ability to say 'no'? Is willpower a mental emergency fund we either do or don't have – like a savings account at the bank? Or is the ability to evade the dessert manipulated by factors that are simply out of our authority?

Ask people the principal reason for their dieting failures, and most will state a 'lack of self-control'. One report showed that 75 per cent of New Yorkers believed this to be the case.[3] The perpetual dieter will surmise that they don't possess the willpower to avoid snacks after dinner or remain motivated to keep returning to the gym – that willpower is a physical reserve they just don't own. They'll believe this is why their friends and family do better; *others* are the ones blessed with the bulletproof resolve, while they're left to – literally – pick up the crumbs. It's perhaps no surprise, then, that people often rate themselves lower in self-control than in other character traits such as kindness, fairness, honesty, and gratitude.[4] They'll deem it's the fundamental reason they can't showcase an ultimate dieting mindset. As we now know that the constant checking of our phones isn't just down to a lack of self-control, we must uncover whether it's the same case with our eating and exercise habits, as well.

What Is Self-Control?

It's no secret that humans are captivated by impulses and desires that don't align with their long-term ambitions. Why head to bed, when the 'Go To Next Episode' box is waiting to be clicked? Why avoid the cigarette, when that immediate 'high' is one puff away? Why favour the carrot batons at the dinner party, when the crisps are noticeably more appealing? In order to accomplish the goals we set ourselves, though, we need to conquer those impulses. We must override temptations and replace them with other, more valuable behaviours. The capacity to do so is simply classed as self-control.[5]

When we exercise the power to say, "I will", towards those behaviours we want to complete, and, "I won't", to those behaviours we don't want to complete – along with, "I want to achieve", when remembering our long-term goals – we then display self-control, or, what's colloquially known as *willpower*. This is the struggle we experience when one part of ourselves prevents another from responding to desires and compulsions. Inhibiting those immediate desires, in the service of greater goals and priorities is deemed a desirable skill. It's essential for navigating life's challenges (for example, stopping yourself from spending money on another pair of shoes), pursuing long-term goals (for example, acquiring a job promotion), and overcoming dieting obstacles (for example, resisting the pretzels at the buffet). Without self-control, we'd be in disarray, consigned to a life of floundering, harmful decisions and unsolicited, awkward situations.

While, as we discussed in Chapter Six, there's a time and a place for practicing acceptance – and not necessarily suppressing our desires – there's also scope for exercising moments of self-control. Regulating our choices and utilising willpower, is a necessary alternative under certain conditions. There's evidence to show that, not only do some people possess more self-control than others, but, showcasing that additional willpower has positive effects on academic performance, relationships, career success, financial prosperity, and other important aspects of life.[6] Those with greater self-control are even more likely to avoid exhibiting the symptoms of eating disorders.[7] The more effective we are at curbing those impulses, the better we'll fair in certain realms of our life. How can we, therefore, sharpen our self-control 'sword'?

The Physiological Self-Control Process

Successful self-control usually respects the following stages, in a methodical process of awareness:

- Step One: 'I have this desire' (e.g., 'I want a Big Mac')
- Step Two: 'I don't want to indulge in this desire' (e.g., 'I know it's not going to necessarily help me craft the physique I want')

- Step Three: 'I'm going to choose something else, instead' (e.g., 'So, I'm going to cook a meal at home')
- Step Four: 'And this alternative is going to be more optimal in the long run' (e.g., 'Which is going to help me craft the physique I want')

When faced with a threat – in this case, risking long-term goal attainment – our bodies respond by igniting our fight-or-flight stress response. Respiratory and cardiovascular systems become heightened, stress hormones are released, and we're wired to act quickly. Our brains *want* us to be more impulsive. While, in the past, this was useful – for example, when being chased by a giant bear – it's not so practical now, when attempting to avoid the seduction of a quick trip to McDonald's. Our brain can't distinguish between wanting to drop a clothing size and survival and will do everything in its power, therefore, to marshal us towards the lure of the takeaway. Food, energy, and Big Macs help you to live, after all. Our survival instincts are activated, dopamine is released, and all we can think about is the reward of a juicy burger.

Clearly, the fight-or-flight response isn't exactly what's required when looking to exercise this kind of self-control. We don't need our physiological responses to speed up but, more so, to slow down. This welcome reaction has been coined a *pause-and-plan response*.[8] It's one that lowers your heart rate and blood pressure, whilst slowing breathing – you, then, subsequently, don't act impulsively. When we behave and think clearly, we can make better decisions and manifest restraint befitting longstanding ambitions. To exhibit opportune self-control, we need to protect ourselves from ourselves.

There's evidence to show that our heart rate variability – that is, the variation in time between heartbeats – may play a role in determining self-control ability.[9] Greater variability in the duration between heartbeats (sometimes they speed up; sometimes they slow down) is desirable. It means we possess a more robust tolerance to stress and are then prepared to perform and react optimally, when faced with demanding circumstances. When our heart rate decreases, but variability increases, we experience a sense of calm –

meaning we're better prepared to ignore distractions, delay gratification, and deal with stressful situations.[10]

When faced with the risks of an enticing Big Mac, we, therefore, need to recognise the threat to our dieting goals and activate a composed, self-monitoring system that diverts the danger. Alleviating stress and promoting relaxation during pressing times promotes greater self-control. We must trigger the physiological changes in the brain and body, that control and slow down our impulses – not encourage them.

The Psychological Self-Control Process

Relying on our physiology to curb immediate temptations isn't always possible. Sitting in the lotus position on the floor of a McDonald's to meditate, control our breathing, and divert those fight-or-flight pressures may not be too well received by other customers. We must call upon our mindset, instead.

We learnt, in Chapter One, that we have two parts to our brain, a 'rational' side and an 'emotional' side. The rational, or logical, side is responsible for planning and direction; it impels the brain to execute the 'harder thing'. It protects our long-term goals, and shepherds us towards beneficial decisions, whether going for a walk, cooking a home-made meal, or having a protein shake, instead of a beer. We like this side when building the ultimate, self-control mindset.

The emotional side is responsible for instant gratification and instinct. It acts on impulse and is designed to feed off our evolutionary disposition for intuition and survival. It's this part of the brain that means we make less beneficial decisions, such as choosing the sofa, ordering a takeaway, and favouring the beer over the protein shake. When building the ultimate self-control mindset, we *don't* like this side.

There is a never-ending battle, unfortunately, between those systems – one impulsive, the other focused on planning. Overcoming this constant, motivational tug of war requires the use of self-control.[11] When we practice sufficient willpower (for example, saying 'no' to the next episode, and walking past the snacks on the kitchen counter), we engage in the mental processes that can override those prominent, emotional desires for short-term gratification; they help us focus, instead, on our rational, long-term goals.[12] We're essentially able to slow down, handle our emotions, and resolve those conflicts.

To display greater levels of self-control, we need, therefore, to prioritise the pleasure that we derive from achieving those longer-term ambitions – and disregard the quick-fix nature of any shorter-term impulses. A congruence then exists between our values and desires; we're able to cope with stressful situations effectively and make choices that align with our longer-term wishes. Values such as these are subjective, of course. What you may regard as restraint might not be viewed comparably by someone else. But, when we delay gratification and commit to individualised resolutions and intentions, we display self-control. When we utilise the brain's logical side, to understand and appreciate the consequences of our behaviours, we practice discipline and – ultimately – willpower.

While we invariably need both sides to function, the ongoing clamour for victory between them does make dieting increasingly challenging. Exhibiting pertinent self-regulation, in the face of these motivational conflicts, is no easy feat. Self-control is, therefore, a mindset that we need to adopt and practice every day. The ability to flit between our two, distinct mental systems, and engage more – at the right times – with the deliberate, reflective side of the brain, increases our chances of nullifying temptations.[13] Once we realise that what we value is also what we desire, then we can practice self-control with greater ease. The way we perceive our goals and values, and apply them to our daily lives, makes those 'I want' and 'I won't' decisions more straightforward. When we can solve our internal, motivational conflicts, we can subsequently display sufficient willpower to overcome the situation we find ourselves faced with.

The self-control process appears straightforward. We seek the workings of our rational mind, initiate a pause-and-plan response, and practice a degree of emotional intelligence to curb our impulses. It's the perfect mindset.

But wait. Not quite so fast. If it were *that* easy, then no one would find themselves concealed under a sweet-smelling blanket of colourful chocolate wrappers of an evening – and making promises to start again the following morning. What is it that happens, when we focus *too much* energy on the 'planning' side of our brain? What about when we *need* to rely on emotion and make impulsive choices? What about motivation – and the effort required behind certain decisions? The inner workings of self-control are slightly more complex than they may at first appear.

Do We Really Possess Self-Control Reserves?

Let's set the scene: you've come home, exhausted from a long day at work, and, as well as being punctured with feelings of incredible irritation at the actions of some of your work colleagues, notice the kids have left the living room looking like a replica World War II bomb site. Your partner hasn't started making the dinner yet, either. You collapse onto the sofa, knowing you've eventually got to tidy up, take the rubbish out, make the evening meal, and still finish that report for your boss, by tomorrow. 'In a bit', you think to yourself.

That 'bit' soon passes, however, and you still haven't mustered up the energy – or self-control – to peel yourself off the sofa and complete everything on your never-ending, to-do list. Instead, you quickly find yourself reaching for a glass of wine and a piece of dark chocolate; you justify the decision by telling yourself you'll 'be better tomorrow'.

Why is it that you *want* to complete those tasks, but can't even reach for the remote control to change the television channel – let alone galvanise yourself to get off the sofa? Why were you able to complete all your responsibilities earlier in the day with ease, but fail to execute that same level of willpower to make sensible, healthier choices as the day passes? Where has your self-control gone?

Some academic sleuthing reveals that this was formalised originally as *ego depletion.* It was posited that discipline wanes over time, such that people exert less control, at a certain point, if they've continuously been employing control previously. Willpower was diagnosed as a 'limited resource'. In the seminal study on willpower, people who forced themselves to eat radishes instead of chocolates – thus exerting more self-discipline – quit faster, subsequently, on unsolvable puzzles, than those who didn't have to display the same levels of self-control.[14] It was argued that reserves of self-control depreciate, whenever we choose to quell short-term desires in favour of striving for long-term goals.

We were told we might regard our self-control reserves as an expendable asset, like a big mug of coffee that we sip throughout the day. When we engage in an activity that demands self-control – choosing a bowl of fruit, instead of Coco Pops for breakfast, for instance – we supposedly take a huge gulp from that cup of 'self-control'-flavoured coffee. When we're faced with decisions that demand goal adherence, social interactions, and personal introspection, we take continual sips from the mug, meaning that our 'fuel' slowly diminishes. Every act of self-control – including fighting the urge to slap a work colleague with a ruler – *weakens* our self-control stores and, invariably, impairs our ability to make other, calculated decisions throughout the day. That mug, which was brim-full of coffee when we started, soon vanishes – making it harder to stay on track mid-afternoon and in the evenings, as well as a few weeks into our fat loss journey.

Every time we choose logic over emotion, our ability to invest in rational decisions then decreases across the day. The more we dispense from our self-control reserves, the less strength we possess to utilise them thereafter. This logic helps to explain why balancing an object, whilst counting backwards from a thousand, has been found to result in less perseverance during subsequent physical exercise – such as push-ups or sit-ups.[15] It's also why smokers who abstain from smoking for 24-hours are more prone to overeating on a subsequent, ice-cream tasting task[16] – and why people who diet are more likely to cheat on their partners.[17] You might want to keep a close eye on that last one.

Research also showed that, just like the musculature in our body, self-control relies on glucose – one of the body's preferred sources of fuel – as its own energy source.[18] The more 'energy' we possess, then, the more self-control we can apply. This also means, however, that our brain weakens as we overexert this 'energy'; akin to tiring after a set of soul-crushing squats, we become mentally fatigued as time passes. It's no wonder, then, it was assumed that we're able to start the day or week making decisions that benefit our desire to diet, but then ultimately find those choices more challenging as time passes. Every time we fight the urge to grab a chocolate biscuit or skip the gym, we're expending quality, metabolic resources – and, consequently, self-control reserves.

This oft-repeated concept of *ego depletion*, formally known as 'The Strength Model', has been at the pinnacle of self-control research and theory for years. We've perhaps even come to treat it as common knowledge, amongst ourselves, that our willpower is a finite resource. We know that we possess a sort of mental fuel that powers the will, but, like the petrol in a car, it becomes impoverished with persistent use – whatever the underlying cause.

This is a book about your mindset, however – and things aren't always as straightforward as they seem. Slowly but surely, The Strength Model of Self-Control has been found to lack significant answers to other, critical, willpower-related questions. What about subsequent tasks that we're highly motivated to complete, for example? What if people subconsciously conserve their energy for activities they know they must accomplish later on? What about the fact that self-control can actually *improve,* when other self-control tasks are performed in tandem? What if we *believe* we have more willpower than we actually do?

We know that our judgement of ability levels, failures, cravings, and opinions about others will all influence our decisions and achievements. Similarly, how we consider our *thoughts* and *motivations* about self-control considerably impacts how we manage to exploit the vulnerabilities of willpower. Self-control doesn't actually deplete over time, as once assumed. It has become evident that it's not necessarily a physiological problem, so much as a *psychological* problem.

Changing Your Mindset Surrounding Self-Control

Changing Your Beliefs

Have you ever started an exercise in the gym and, after the first couple of reps (that felt, worryingly, like you were pushing a 30-tonne truck), thought to yourself, 'There's no chance I can possibly complete another repetition, let alone ten more?' Yet, despite feeling like your arms were about to fall off, you somehow completed the set, gave your mental power a nod of smug appreciation, and ended up quite pleased with yourself.

What happened? Your brain, sensing a rapidly-depleted energy supply, urged you to stop midway through your set of shoulder presses, for fear of you winding up dead on the gym floor. The fact you *could* keep going, however, suggests that the way you view fatigue has little to do with your physical limits.[19] You hadn't necessarily reached physical exhaustion; you simply *thought,* temporarily, that you had. This is the process that explains why you *can,* ultimately, push out another rep or two – or complete that extra kilometre on your run. Can the same be said of self-control, then? Do you possess more willpower than you would like to believe?

While there's a torrent of evidence to suggest that self-control is a limited resource,[20] the lens through which we *view* our reserves of restraint has been found to have a far greater influence on how we utilise that resource. Much like incorrectly believing we can't keep going during an exercise in the gym, grabbing onto the misguided acceptance that self-control is a finite asset may well be preventing you from achieving any weight loss goals you have. There's evidence to show that diminishing willpower reserves can be caused simply by the way we *think* about that concept, rather than reflective of our true, physical and mental ceilings.[21] Presupposed, self-defeating thoughts – not solely the physiological limits of self-control – affect our ability to enact restraint.[22]

Akin to the *fixed mindset,* believing your self-control is a predetermined trait – and one that can diminish throughout the day – may encourage poor decision-making. A lingering, self-justification of finite, self-control collateral provides you with a clear rationale to blame external factors and act against your better judgement. It affords you a reason to relinquish responsibility. If you endorse the notion that you've already extinguished self-control reserves by mid-afternoon, you're more likely to succumb to snacks in the evening. Those implicit beliefs about willpower cause issues when dieting. Shifting our attitude towards self-control to one of *personal strength* and *competence* is more likely to inspire adherence, than if we believe that we do or don't possess a coveted ability for moderation.

Early research hypothesised that the ingestion of glucose could enhance our self-control. Carol Dweck and her colleagues argued, however, that the effect of that energy boost was principally owed to psychological processes, over physiological ones.[23] They studied how people displayed self-control when fatigued, and were told to drink a sugar-laden lemonade beverage to provide them with that supposed, much-needed energy boost. Those people who were informed that self-control was *unlimited* didn't display any signs of supposed 'ego depletion' when performing a word/colour association task. They didn't require that energy boost to maintain a higher level of willpower. Those who were led, however, to believe that self-control *was* limited, performed poorly on the same task. They presumed they'd expended any reserves of restraint that they had and, therefore, couldn't function any better – despite ingesting that purported energy boost.

Other studies have shown, similarly, that, when people believe they have depleted their mental energy, then their performance – specifically in anagram-related tasks – diminishes.[24] Having been informed that reserves of self-control were impaired, participants felt the need to conserve their resources and, subsequently, reduced their amount of effort. We, presumably, conserve willpower when we regard our assets as restricted. Despite the leading theory stating that self-control is governed by the amount of energy we possess, it's been shown that engaging in self-control *doesn't* necessarily reduce our blood sugar levels.[25] Even artificially sweetened beverages, and not necessarily those filled with glucose, have been found to contribute the same effect as self-control 'boosters'.[26]

It appears that ego depletion may be another paradigm illustrating how belief, and not so much our physiology, can drive behaviour. It wasn't necessarily the added glucose in those studies that provided participants with a rush of extended mental stamina, but more so their trust in the process that they could overcome any supposed self-control limits. Even students informed about this 'unlimited theory' of willpower displayed better time management, less procrastination, fewer unhealthy eating habits, and less impulsive spending, over many years.[27] Changing judgements and understandings can counteract the notion of ego depletion.

Your perception of mental exhaustion, not the actual amount of work required to 'stay on track,' determines your ability to exhibit irrepressible self-control. As Menno Henselmans, in his book, *The Science of Self-Control,* states, "Your feelings of fatigue are just that: feelings. It is up to you what you do with them."[28] The next time you're faced with a situation that demands willpower, remember that you always have more restraint and strength than your brain would have you believe. You *can* say "I won't" to the tasks you don't want to engage in; you *can* say "I will" to the behaviours you want to execute – and you *can* 'achieve' those long-term goals that you desire. You're not confined to the shackles of pre-destined self-control qualities.

Harnessing Motivation, Effort, And Autonomy

On June 2nd, 1995, US Air Force fighter pilot, Captain Scott O'Grady, was shot down, enforcing a NATO, no-fly zone over Bosnia.[29] Ejecting himself from his aircraft, he landed in unfamiliar and unfriendly territory and was forced into hiding, to avoid being flushed out and killed by Bosnian-Serb forces. Despite extreme fatigue and stress, he instantly mobilised his 'survival mode'. He forced himself to lie motionless, for hours on end, face down in the brush – cupping his camouflaged, flight gloves over his head and ears – to escape being noticed.

The enemy was never far away. O'Grady avoided capture by sleeping during the day, collecting rainwater to drink using a sponge, eating grass and bugs, and moving only between the hours of midnight and 4 am. He was able to display indomitable levels of self-control, to remain hidden and avoid being caught – and potentially killed – during distressing and energy-sapping circumstances.

After nearly a week behind enemy lines, the captain was able to eventually make radio contact with American troops, who ended up rescuing him just hours later. He later received a Bronze Star and Purple Heart for his achievements and bravery during the mission. What helped him pull through? It was instinct, extensive survival training, and the self-control to stay focused, to withstand adversity, and to lie lifeless, while search parties passed within feet of him – all of which ensured he remained alive.

The question remains, however; if, as humans, we supposedly possess limited self-control capital, then surely O'Grady wouldn't have been able to display such a significant amount of willpower for days on end? He would have drained his reserves almost immediately, given the stressful and tiring situation he endured – and would have eventually had to move, being potentially found and killed. Surely, self-control isn't down to restricted resources then, but to our desire, effort, and motivation behind the tasks at hand?

The Strength Model of Self-Control assumes that displaying willpower grows harder over time. When we're mentally fatigued, or continually forced to choose between instant gratification and long-term reward, we find the brute suppression of impulses increasingly challenging. What, however, about moments when we're *forced* to use self-control? Or when we're deciding between two, equally rewarding choices? Why, even if we're tired, do we never struggle with willpower when determining between two enticing options on the dessert menu – or not require discipline when we *want* to watch television, or devour one of our mum's home-made cupcakes, after a long, mentally exhausting day? Why could O'Grady still display self-control days later, despite continually weathering such draining conditions?

Issues with self-control can be attributed to a *priority shift,* as opposed to a resource problem.[30] These contemporary models of self-control opine that our willpower isn't based upon some exceptional ability to power through adversity, but that we override temptations based on the perceived effort of a task, the opportunity costs for making a decision, our current well-being, and the overall value of the choice.

We know that self-control is required to override the growing conflict between the two distinct drives in our brain – the drive for immediate, effortless gratification (for example, eating the cupcake) and the demand for future, effortful fulfilment (for example, losing weight). Because enduring that conflict is an unpleasant experience, we eventually lose focus, grow bored, and seek activities that promote instant gratification, instead. We don't necessarily struggle with self-control, because we've used up all our mental energy, but because we experience that fatigue in the first place. Our attention and priorities shift, meaning that future-focused behaviours are halted, in favour of immediately-rewarding actions, instead.

Because, being human, we prefer rest and leisure, it makes sense to take refuge on the sofa and eat chocolate (i.e., easy, rewarding tasks) after a busy day, rather than tidying up, making a healthy dinner, and finishing that special project (i.e., challenging, unpleasant tasks). Self-control is an investment strategy.

Problems with self-control arise, primarily, when we lose concentration on what's been labelled as 'have-to accomplish' goals (for example, consuming low-calorie food items) and, instead, shift to 'want-to accomplish' goals (for example, devouring highly-palatable, calorie-abundant foods). When the rational side of our brain squanders control, our emotional side takes over. While these 'shoulds' and 'wants' are subjective, we generally lean towards moments promoting swift reward, and responsibilities that require little work. What is easier? Is it devouring three biscuits upon getting in from work (or a hectic trip) – or remaining fixated on the long-term goal of losing weight? We ultimately chase tasks that provide joy and entertainment, not those that inspirit tedium and increased industry. Our self-control powers are, therefore, governed by effort, autonomy, and motivation.

When we experience a shift in motivation towards intrinsically rewarding and enjoyable activities, our self-control stores *won't* diminish. It's why tasks of high value to certain people, such as smoking[31] or meditating,[32] counteract feelings of increased effort, and provide reward and appreciation for the time spent on the task, instead.

When we possess sufficient motivation to balance competing goals, we can display appropriate levels of self-control. Only when we perform an activity out of obligation, or increased effort, do we experience mental fatigue. Problems with self-control when dieting arise, therefore, when your brain perceives your long-term goals as only partially rewarding, relative to their required effort.

When people are provided with an added incentive to display levels of self-control, however, they're able to overcome any supposed willpower depletion.[33] In the case of one such study, being told that their results in a problem-solving task would assist in developing new therapies for patients with Alzheimer's disease, aided participant's use of willpower. When people are required to focus on the *why* and importance behind their long-term goals, they display more self-control than those who focus on their willpower resources, including when noticing how tired they are.[34] The more motivated you are, the better you'll be at curbing impulses.[35]

Similarly, if we grow disinterested in a particular responsibility, or even *perceive* a task as tiring or challenging, we then lose our ability to display self-control. You can't say 'no' to the cookie at work – not because you lack self-control, but because you already perceive it as a mentally demanding and taxing endeavour to do so. The same logic applies with the people who were told to engage in physical activity and call it a 'scenic walk', who then consumed *fewer* snacks and displayed lower levels of fatigue in subsequent tasks, than those who were told it was an 'exercise walk'.[36]

Even falsely believing that an easy task is depleting resulted in participants, in one study, displaying impaired performance on a subsequent memory task.[37] Tasks requiring sustained concentration increase the conflict between the emotional and rational sides of the brain, which makes choosing the more valuable option incredibly burdensome. When it comes to willpower, purpose, enjoyment, and fulfilment all matter whilst dieting.

People don't necessarily surrender reserves of willpower the longer they delve into a dieting phase. But, because they tend to overlook the rewards from their efforts, incentives dwindle and adherence fades. Aversion to effort increases, instead, and motivation for a pressing reward multiplies. Refusing the drinks at the work event requires effort and energy. Because people realise they won't lose a pound *instantly* from saying 'no', they adopt an intensified reluctance to the more pragmatic decision – which can result in, ultimately, capitulating and downing several gin and tonics in protest. Depletion may not relate to a finite resource being exhausted, so much as preferences and priorities fluctuating. The ongoing battle to balance current pleasure with maintaining stability for the future creates discipline issues. Fundamentally, we shun behaviours that don't engage us and seek actions – that are often damaging to the bigger picture – that do.

Emotions And Feelings Matter

It's no coincidence that, when we're faced with a nagging self-control dilemma, it's preceded by the notion that we do or don't 'feel' like doing something. We might say, for instance, "I don't *feel* like going to the gym", or, "I don't *feel* like avoiding the popcorn, nachos, and family bag of Cadbury Heroes at the cinema". Feelings and emotions seemingly motivate and alert us to when self-control is required. Regulating our emotions at the right times and in the right situations ensures we're better placed to temper our mindset – and, subsequently, our ability to exert sufficient willpower.

Negative emotions have generally been found to impair executive functions, which reduce self-control.[38] For example, amongst restrained female eaters, it was found that the threat of an electric shock – and thereby anticipating an anxiety-provoking event – led to an increase in ice cream consumption.[39] Research has shown that adults are more inclined to seek immediate gratification when they feel negative emotions.[40] The disharmony derived from the two contrariant parts of our brain rouses varying feelings, such as anxiety, frustration, and fear.[41] When these emotions – often the root of temptation – come to the fore, they serve as an alarm to forewarn us of possible goal failure, and the need to remedy behaviour. As a result, we tend to experience less desire to expend energy on attention and resolution, meaning that we're more disposed to seek gratifying pursuits. We then succumb to the behaviours we don't want to engage in.

Conversely, positive emotions signal to us that we can display sufficient willpower at the necessary times.[42] Feelings such as entertainment, competition, and compassion impel us to view an activity as rewarding – and the use of mental skills that control behaviour are no longer experienced as effortful. Participants in one study, who viewed a film clip that elicited low-arousal positive emotions, subsequently chose grapes over chocolate – compared with those who viewed a neutral recording.[43]

Take the bread sitting on the restaurant table, for example. We're faced with a persistent impasse; how will we feel *following* our decision? We imagine what life will be like with each outcome – devouring, or refusing, the bread – both positive and negative. If we conclude that our decision to abstain will result in pride and increased life satisfaction, those positive emotions will reinforce the benefits of choosing long-term rewards over momentary desires.

Of course, we're not *always* in a positive mood – just contemplate the tension engulfing the air when your partner, or other family member, discovers you haven't loaded the dishwasher properly. Besides, as it's also been found that, sometimes, even positive emotions lead to self-control failures,[44] it's not reasonable to expect our restraint to operate in perfect condition all the time. Unrestrained eaters who watched pleasant and humorous clips from the television sitcom *Friends,* for example, ate more popcorn and raisins during viewing – suggesting that positive emotions can lead to less self-control, especially in those people not necessarily attempting to control their eating behaviours.

Negative emotions can, on occasion, be to our benefit. When people can elicit future feelings of guilt and regret, for instance, they're able to steer themselves away from temptation.[45] Connecting with those emotions can facilitate self-control, through our desire to avoid behaviours that generate negative feelings. This is when utilising our 'why' can help influence the decision-making process. We should, of course, never let 'food guilt' guide the decision-making process, explicitly. The more we value – and respond emotionally to – anticipated future outcomes, however, the more self-control we can exert.

Viewing self-control through an 'emotional' lens forces us to appreciate the need to manage our feelings. Self-control ebbs and flows based on the experience, and how we judge situations. This is why, sometimes, we *feel* like avoiding temptations, and, at other times, *feel* like devouring all that's in front of us. It may be more productive, therefore, to believe that willpower difficulties can be attributed to emotions such as anxiety and boredom – which spearhead goal conflict – rather than telling ourselves that we're mentally fatigued and need to replenish flailing, self-control stores.

Emotional self-regulation is complex. Trying to suppress emotions through pure fortitude is a tough ask. By practicing skills, however, such as emotional acceptance, 'defusion' (i.e., gaining distance from thoughts and emotions), and managing our physiological responses (for example, via deep breathing), we're more likely to be able to moderate our feelings. Even 'reframing' problems can enhance self-control.

For example, in an American study, those who were asked to outline the costs and benefits of avoiding instant gratification *now,* to receive more *later,* showed greater self-control.[46] When offered five dollars today, against ten dollars in a month, many opted, illogically, for the immediate prize. However, when the question was reframed to make the trade-offs explicit (i.e., 'Would you prefer five dollars today and zero dollars in a month, or zero dollars today and ten dollars in a month?'), more people favoured the larger, delayed reward. When making food-based decisions, we can employ the same *temporal discounting* tactics. Would you prefer a slice of cake today and no centimetres lost around your waist in a month, or avoid the cake today and lose three centimetres around your waist in a month? Rather than relying on an effortful fight against an impulse, reframing the problem to fixate on longer-term rewards removes the need to conquer it in the first place.

How To Master Your Self-Control

Much like a fitness influencer will perform countless hip thrusts, should she wish to increase the shape of her glutes, it could be assumed that, to elicit the same growth, we should similarly work on strengthening our self-control. 'Self-control day' is the new 'leg day', if you will. It was previously postulated that, because willpower was a limited resource, we could train it – just like our glutes – to gain strength and size.[47] Placing a big bowl of crisps on your desk and practicing restraint, for example, would elicit greater levels of self-control in the future. However, since we now know that self-control *isn't* necessarily a constrained resource – and is, instead, a consequence of effort, autonomy, and motivation – employing tactics like that aren't beneficial. Some studies have shown that directly training willpower doesn't necessarily lead to improvements[48] – and this begs the question, *can* we improve it at all?

The answer is, ultimately, 'Yes'. But, instead of developing our self-control as we would the musculature in the body, those improvements arise from refining our *mindset*. The beliefs, thoughts, and values we possess, surrounding the tug-of-war between instant gratification and long-term reward, matter more. When the balance between indulgence and control shifts in favour of the long-term goal, self-control is improved.[49] Targeting our motivation, attention, effort, and beliefs is, therefore, the answer to unlocking robust levels of willpower.

View Your Self-Control Powers In A Different Light

In 1973, an unnamed man from Nashville, Tennessee, was diagnosed with end-stage liver cancer. He was given just months to live. After his death – exactly in the time predicted he had left to live – his autopsy showed, however, the original tumour in his liver *hadn't*, in fact, grown, and wasn't large enough to be the reason for his death. His intern didn't believe he'd died from his primary diagnosis, but from something else; something more sinister. In response to his close friend's passing, he wrote, "I do not know the pathologic cause of death. Could it be that, instead of the cancer, it was his expectation of death that killed him?" Even Sherlock Holmes would have struggled here. Much like people believing that a statin (a class of drug that lowers cholesterol) causes muscle pain, even when those people were placed in the control group – and others deeming wind turbine farms to be the cause of lung cancer, diabetes, multiple sclerosis, and even chickens failing to lay eggs – it's clear that people may be able to 'worry' themselves sick. Or, in the liver cancer case, dead.

Just as we discovered, in Chapter Three, the beauty of the placebo effect, we must also contend with the pitfalls of its sister, the *nocebo effect*. When an individual's health status worsens, due to their negative beliefs and expectations, then they're succumbing to the power of their thoughts.[50] If we believe that something terrible is going to happen, it often does. Death is, perhaps, the most telling example.

Negative expectations tend to evolve much faster than positive ones; our bodies are programmed to protect us from adverse events, after all. If we possess a negative outlook on self-control, we're more likely to display the related characteristics. If we already, firmly, believe that we lack the requisite willpower to achieve any desired fat loss goals, then we've already lost. We'll invariably succumb to such a damaging line of thinking. Telling ourselves, "I can never say no to the treat jar at home", or, "I'll never be able to display as much willpower as my best friend", reinforces the belief that pre-set boundaries influence self-control – that willpower is limited, and we can't improve it. It's the nocebo effect in play. As we now know that everyone possesses near-enough unlimited levels of self-control, our task is in learning how to implement that self-discipline, instead.

Whenever you encounter a situation that demands willpower, it's important to remind yourself that you *already* possess the requisite self-control to shift your focus, towards your long-term aspirations. Recalling that any mental fatigue you're experiencing is nothing but a subjective feeling will enhance your decision-making process. It's not about lacking willpower, it's because you're bored. It's not because you fail to say 'no', it's because you're demotivated. It's not because you're weak-willed and addicted to chocolate, it's because you're finding the task in hand effortful. Learning to harness the rational side of your brain, in these situations, will enable you to focus on forming the right choices – and overcome any supposed, self-control deficiencies.

Evidence suggests that those who believe their willpower is unlimited perform better on working memory and learning tasks.[51] Even those people who've experienced a demanding day were more likely to continue working towards their long-term aspirations, during the following 24-hours, if they believed they hadn't used up valuable willpower resources.[52] It's time to flip any self-reported beliefs about willpower, that you currently hold, on their head – and accept that lacking self-control is primarily down to your perception of the effort and difficulty of saying, "I will", or, "I won't", rather than the actual effort and difficulty of the task. Just because you spend the week refraining from all those temptations, scattered around the house, doesn't mean you can't display the same levels of self-control during the weekend; it's probably because you *believe* you can no longer elicit those same levels of self-control, instead.

There's also evidence to show that, when we're forced to engage in numerous self-control tasks at the same time, we can display increased levels of willpower. When participants in one study were forced to curb the desire to consume crisps, while their attention was free to watch a video – thus exerting less willpower – they were less likely to say 'no' to a snack than if they were forced to exercise more self-control, by avoiding looking at words that popped up on the same video.[53] Self-control begets more self-control. We're more likely to succeed in self-regulation and goal attainment when we adopt a mindset that embraces our ability to display unrivalled riches of willpower.

There's even an argument to say that we shouldn't believe in the premise of willpower at all. I bet you don't struggle with self-control when wanting to socialise with friends or chasing a desired job promotion, after all. You wouldn't be likely to recommend your best friend get rid of their dog so they could put their limited love resources towards a new, human relationship, would you? Resisting temptation isn't necessarily associated with not being able to adhere to the plan, but more so the *type* of plan you're trying to adhere to. Self-control evidently has a firm hold on our imagination. It's a self-justification; a fallback when things don't go quite our way. While saying that we don't require it *at all* is a tough concept to endorse, adopting this unique, yet effective, mindset will help you perform better.

It is time, ultimately, to start believing in yourself. You no longer find it challenging to avoid those post-dinner snacks, but can credit yourself with the mental fortitude to eschew mindless gluttony just before bed. You no longer run short on willpower reserves, three weeks into your fat loss journey, but maybe haven't tapped into the appropriate, motivational stores yet. You no longer lack self-control, but struggle to find the balance between immediate gratification and discomfort. You now shift your mindset around self-control to one of confidence and trust. You believe you have the willingness to exert effort and enjoyment towards the task at hand.

Tame Your Intrinsic Motivation

Ask successful musicians why they play their instruments, or elite sportspeople why they play their sport – or, even, contented bakers why they create batch after batch of salted caramel and apple rolls – and they'll often respond with, "Because it's fun", or, "Because I enjoy it". They don't need to force themselves to sit down at the piano, or white-knuckle their way through every gruelling, training session. When we view tasks as ventures that we *want to* engage in, we're soothing the more primitive, emotional side of our brain. We're *motivated* to engage in those types of activities. We don't need self-control.

There are two types of motivation: extrinsic and intrinsic.[54] Extrinsic motivation involves engaging in an activity because it leads to a tangible reward, or avoids punishment. It's going to university, for example, just to make your parents proud – or dieting because you're scared of others' opinions about your body. It arrives, typically, from the rational part of our brain.

Intrinsic motivation involves engaging in an activity because it's interesting and deeply satisfying. It's studying because you're curious about the subject – or dieting because you embrace the challenge of training hard and eating well, for example. It arrives, typically, from the emotional side of our brain. It's no coincidence, therefore, that when we're intrinsically motivated to do something, we don't necessarily require any self-control. When an activity provides entertainment, competition, and interest, we don't view it as an 'effort'. This helps explain why those who enjoy exercise, who view it as a challenge, and who value the outcome of greater physical fitness, are more likely to display long-term exercise-adherence than those who engage in it, simply, for aesthetic reasons.[55] They don't need to battle between 'want-to' goals and 'have-to' goals.

Working without a higher purpose is exhausting – and ultimately damaging. The big question is, therefore, can we develop our intrinsic motivation? In short, yes, we can. Fostering perceptions of autonomy (i.e., whether we feel in control of our behaviours and goals), competence (i.e., whether we possess the skills required for success), and relatedness (i.e., whether we feel as if we belong to a group or community of people) has been found to promote optimal motivation. Such supreme motivation inspires greater self-control.[56]

When we're left to our own devices to complete a task (i.e., made to feel more autonomous), the challenge feels easier.[57] We're not as fatigued, meaning we can continue with the activity for hours on end without struggle. This helps to explain why external forces – such as pressurising yourself to go to the gym because someone else said you need to lose weight, or participating in an eight-week weight loss challenge for a cash prize – will seldom lead to long-lasting change.[58] The less autonomous a task feels, the greater the mental fatigue it induces, because it increases cognitive conflict between the two competing parts of the brain. When we pursue goals of personal importance, however – such as viewing yourself as an active person, or embracing the struggle of developing strength in the gym – the subsequent behaviours become easier to implement and regulate.[59]

Simply put, it's better to view each weight loss-related behaviour as a task you *want* to pursue, rather than because you have to do it. That intrinsic motivation and sense of fulfilment provide feelings of instant reward, which we know drives beneficial, impulsive behaviours. Making food taste more enjoyable, or unearthing your 'why' for the task in hand, leads to greater self-control because of those feelings of autonomy.[60,61]

Similarly, when a skill feels easy – and we know we'll receive a subsequent reward – we're more likely to complete it. This 'law of least effort' means that skills we're competent at require little self-control. Hence, grabbing a chocolate bar from the vending machine, or helping children finish the food on their plates (i.e., simple exercises) require minimal self-discipline.

Even the *perception* of a task's effort has been found to influence self-control.[62] And making rewards contingent on competence increases self-control. This, in turn, means that assuming work is easy will ward off the effects of mental fatigue. This is why we're continually told to focus on the 'easy wins'. These small victories drive feelings of competency; as a result, we're motivated to execute tasks we're proficient at. This then also stimulates confidence and self-efficacy, leading to greater levels of self-control.

Instead of thinking of all the body fat you have left to lose, or all the times you need to drag yourself to the gym, focus on the activities you're adept at – such as, hitting a required step count, or concocting nutritious smoothies. Even conjuring up feelings of compassion, or success at competition (i.e., not just physical rewards) can drive intrinsic pleasure. The less difficulty, then the less self-control demanded, too. Of course, we can't *always* focus on the tasks we're skilled at – growth seldom prospers from comfort. But, when self-control is required, concentrate foremost on the behaviours you can accomplish with ease.

Intrinsic motivation can also be developed by deepening connections and seeking a higher incentive. It's why belonging to a team and following the behaviours of others can induce behaviour change, through increased motivation. This stems from the 'why' that we created in Chapter One; when you foster feelings of purpose, and propagate your values, the self-government of meaningful outcomes isn't as challenging.

Every time you brave a situation involving willpower, ask yourself what's required to move *towards* your long-term goals – and *why* it's relevant. When the value of acting in alignment with your far-reaching aspirations (cooking a healthy, home-made meal, for example) outweighs indulging in goal-incongruent actions (ordering a takeaway from Deliveroo, for example), you'll find it easier to exhibit self-control.[63]

As Daniel Pink, in his book, *Drive,* says, "We're designed to be active and engaged. And we know that the richest experiences in our lives aren't when we're clamoring for validation from others, but when we're listening to our own voice – doing something that matters, doing it well, and doing it in the service of a cause larger than ourselves."[64]

There is some evidence to show that extrinsic motivation *can* influence self-control. Those who exhibited depleted self-control, and were paid to drink a beverage containing vinegar, managed to drink more than those who weren't compensated as well.[65] Admittedly, this probably isn't the best strategy to rely on, because, what happens when there isn't anyone shoving a twenty-pound note in your face to guzzle down a spinach and kale smoothie? It's clear, however, that motivation – and the salience of 'want-to' goals – can reduce the lure of temptations and damaging behaviours. When we unearth and champion the reasons for our long-term ambitions, we then require little willpower. The less we feel we *have to* do something, the easier it is to align choices with future rewards.

Practice Self-Compassion

A commonly held belief running through dieters' minds is that losing weight is *meant* to be hard. In other words, if we're not chewing down our fingernails to avoid caving into those temptations, not ramming macabre green vegetables down our throats, nor pushing ourselves in the gym to the point of bringing up those very same, green vegetables, then we're not working hard enough. "Can't stick to the diet? It's not the fault of the diet but yours", you're told.

All of us have been fed the lie that we're meant to push through those perceived limits of self-control to succeed. We've been *shamed* into believing that dieting is a punishing endeavour, reserved for those with monk-like discipline and commitment. People deficient in willpower are to be held in contempt. This shame manifests as a merciless mindset that produces those 'No pain, no gain' taglines – and tortuous weight loss journeys better suited to a series of the TV programme, *The Biggest Loser.*

Relying on shame, guilt, and punishment to exhibit self-control does work – for all of about two days. As impossible as it may seem, if you don't *enjoy* the journey you're on, you're more likely to give up. Those 'want-to' goals will always trump any 'have-to' goals. We now know that, when we don't provide enough fulfilment for the more primitive, emotional part of our brain, it takes hold of the reins and seeks the temptations that fuel its desire for indulgence and instant gratification. The more we try to run on feelings of hate, exhaustion, and resentment – promoters of 'have-to' goals – the more we end up failing.

Relying on shame and suffering leads to displeasure, which ultimately circles back to further feelings of shame. We end up hating ourselves for not being able to practice adherence or say 'no' – and revert to the comforts of a big bag of crunchy Maltesers, for example, to soothe our feelings linked with the sense of failure. It's this logic that helps explain the results of the study in which, those who drank more alcohol than they were meant to, felt resultant guilt – and, subsequently, drank *more* the following day.[66] When you stop swimming in feelings of shame, however, you start liking yourself – and, when you like yourself, you halt the eagerness to deprive, punish, and chastise any poor decision you make. This all boils down to displaying *self-compassion*.

Self-compassion is being kind and understanding when confronted with personal failings. It means acknowledging that it's natural to make mistakes.[67] It *doesn't* involve punishing yourself for self-restraint failures and surrendering to cravings. It's about accepting, instead, that – firstly – it's normal to experience slip-ups, and – secondly – it's acceptable to feel guilty about such blunders. Self-compassion is the difference between experiencing negative emotions and quitting, and accepting negative emotions and displaying perseverance.[68]

This has been demonstrated where women, who were told to eat a Dunkin Donut to induce feelings of diet guilt, ate *fewer* subsequent chocolates when provided with a *self-compassion manipulation*.[69] What led to less overeating was being told that, "Everyone eats unhealthily sometimes, so there's no reason to feel really bad about it" – compared with those who weren't provided with that particular directive. The second group, who *weren't* instructed to accept and embrace a perceived failure, couldn't inhibit gluttony-inducing emotions and, subsequently, ate more.

When you replenish self-condemnation with kindness and forgiveness, you remove the shame and guilt surrounding mistakes – and *improve* self-control levels. The pain you once felt, from dieting, now becomes a reward. No longer do you punish yourself for 'Not being able to refuse the chocolate', or, 'Not being able to stay motivated to go the gym'; you, instead, permit yourself to welcome those emotions and shortcomings. That self-compassion enables you to change direction and mould better decisions, rather than dwelling on mistakes, and succumbing to the 'what-the-hell' effect. As Jean Fain says, in her book, *The Self-Compassion Diet*, "If you are a compassionate eater, you dispense with the promises and hang out with whatever uncomfortable feelings arise after one too many indulgent spoonfuls. You befriend emotional and physical discomfort and treat it like a welcome houseguest, not a housefly."[70]

Some would argue that forgiveness and compassion will only lead to greater self-indulgence. How can being *nice* to yourself lead to greater self-control? "If I'm not hard or strict enough with myself, I'll never get anything done", people conclude. They surmise that they require a hard-nosed voice overseeing their every move. We know that this control, whether internally or externally, doesn't work, however.

When you're faced with a decision that demands self-control, avoid any critical, self-punishment; accept, instead, that struggling is commonplace. When you succumb to the umpteenth spring roll canapé at the wedding, or the extra drink at the party, don't berate yourself; remember, you're human. Notice your feelings and consider the truth in any self-defeating thoughts. Are you a failure? Have you actually ruined anything? What would you say to a friend? When you avert criticism and recognise that poor decision-making is routine, you'll alleviate self-critical thought. You can remove negative feelings without allaying feelings of personal responsibility.[71] Self-compassion ultimately aids self-control.

Avoid Having To Use It

It's not easy getting out of bed, is it? Especially when we're confronted with the horrifying knowledge that we'll have to limp from the warmth of a comfortable duvet to the frosty and unpleasant chill of the bedroom. I'm sure you've heard of strategies to combat this all-too-familiar problem: place your alarm clock on the other side of the room, have your clothes ready by the bed, programme your coffee maker to start brewing the moment you wake up, have your partner beat you over the head with the pillow until you get up. These are all worthwhile strategies, and all follow the same ethos: manipulate your surroundings to your advantage to promote effortless self-control.

All your choices surrounding food and exercise are more congruent with external surroundings and physical cues than your own, precisely crafted judgements and reasoning. We bow to the power of our environment. It's no coincidence that, when high-calorie desserts are within easy reach, people find themselves succumbing to their accessibility.[72] Equally, when people see others around them eating, they're more likely to snack, themselves.[73]

Redesigning your surroundings, to pacify self-control requirements, makes the dieting process a lot more straightforward. The absence of old cues provides a window of opportunity to make alternative decisions and implement fresh intentions. In the children's book, *Frog And Toad Together,* the characters escape their cookie binge by placing the cookies in a jar, tying it up with rope, and then taking the ladder out to place the jar on a high shelf, out of reach.[74] Not such a bad idea, after all.

We know the crux of willpower is in intentionally strengthening desired impulses and weakening undesired ones. While 'effortless' self-control may appear contradictory, given this use of inhibition, it comprises a vast array of responses beyond willpower alone. When we proactively choose, or change, situations that reinforce that constrained response, we engage in, what's known as *situational self-control strategies.*[75] When we modify conditions in our lives that make temptations – and related, instant gratification – *more costly* and less attractive, and also make long-term goals *less costly* and more attractive, then we no longer have to manage disunity between 'want-to' goals and 'have-to' goals. Self-control no longer becomes an arduous battle. We're able to, not only, decide where our attention will be fixed, but, also, influence the costs and benefits of a particular decision – in line with simply restricting the number of potentially-damaging options available to us.

There are a host of methods to limit the need for continually relying on self-control.[76] We can engage in *situation selection* methods, whereby we consciously choose people to be with, or places to be, that facilitate effortless self-control – such as meeting friends who will be going to the gym, or settling on visiting the salad bar instead of the fast-food establishment. We can also engage in *situation modification* strategies, whereby we purposefully change our environment to help encourage the behaviours conducive to fat loss – such as removing all trigger foods from our kitchen cupboards, or packing our gym bag the night before. Even listening to entertaining audiobooks has been found to increase gym visits.[77]

The earlier on in the 'self-control journey' that we can direct the tides of impulse generation, the easier it then is to keep our long-term aspirations intact. Instead of relying on metacognition to make decisions (i.e., considering how we're evaluating a current situation and finding new ways to think about it), we can select and modify our environment to our advantage. This is how 'effortless self-control' – also known as *avoiding temptations* – can dictate self-control success.[78]

Transforming the context you find yourself in will enable you to make better choices, from increasing your exposure to beneficial cues – such as placing cut-up fruit in a clear box by your desk – to avoiding harmful ones – such as paying at the pump for petrol, instead of fighting the urge to purchase a chocolate bar conveniently placed by the till. Paradoxically, the most progressive self-control strategies may be the least pronounced, for the same reason that they're so effective; they reduce the discomfort of resisting immediate gratification.

Effortless self-control also derives from habits. Once a habit (i.e., the formation of context-response associations) is cultivated, it guides our behaviour when we intend to do something else. Those behaviours, and perceptions of the relevant situation, automatically activate the mental representation of the habitual response.[79] For example, chocolate lovers who had developed a habit of eating carrots continued to make healthy 'carrot choices', even when chocolate became available.[80] Willpower was no longer an issue.

Automatic behaviours can pre-empt situations where temptations abound and protect us from making poor decisions, when deliberation is hard. When we modify habit formation to our benefit (i.e., the process of response repetition, stable cues, and encouraging rewards), healthy behaviours aid progress. In one study, overweight participants who were instructed to develop predictable and sustainable weight loss routines, modified their home environments to increase cues to eat healthy foods and engage in exercise – and had immediate positive rewards for certain behaviours, as well as continuing to lose weight during the months following the end of that multifaceted, habit formation intervention.[81]

Ultimately, if we're not forced to use self-control, it makes sense that we won't struggle with the demands of quashing unwanted desires. It's also no coincidence that those high in self-control traits experience fewer conflicts, simply because they experience fewer temptations.[82] Conversely, those who try harder to exert self-control report feeling more mentally drained.[83] People with the most self-control don't necessarily exercise self-control.[84] Researchers have concluded, pertinently, that, "In self-control, the enemy is within. Nevertheless, the most effective way to do battle with our inner demons may be, in fact, by taking the battle outside of the mind."[85]

Chapter Summary And Taking Action

- In order to accomplish the goals that we set ourselves, we need to conquer impulses and desires. We must override temptations and replace them with other, more valuable behaviours. The capacity to do so is labelled 'self-control'.

- Alleviating stress and promoting relaxation, during pressing times, promotes greater self-control. We need to trigger the changes in our brain and body that control and slow down our impulses, rather than encourage them. There's a never-ending battle, additionally, between the brain's impulsive and planning systems. When we practice sufficient willpower, we engage in the mental processes that override those prominent emotional desires for short-term gratification and, instead, focus on our rational, long-term goals.

- Initial research into self-control posited that willpower wanes over time, such that people exert less control at a certain point, if they've continuously been employing control previously. However, there's evidence to show that this seminal 'resource model' of willpower may not be true, and that diminishing, self-control reserves can be caused simply by how we *think* about that concept. Presupposed self-defeating thoughts, priority shifts, perception of effort, the value of certain choices, and emotions all affect our ability to enact restraint – not necessarily the physiological limits of discipline.

- To master your self-control, view your powers in a different light. Whenever you encounter a situation that demands willpower, it's important to remind yourself that you *already* possess the requisite self-control to shift your focus towards your long-term aspirations. No longer do you lack self-control, but are struggling with the perceived effort, autonomy, and motivation of a task – and are finding the balance between immediate gratification and discomfort.

- Motivation – and the salience of 'want-to' goals – can reduce the lure of temptations and damaging behaviours. When we unearth and champion the reasons for our long-term ambitions, we require little willpower. The less we feel we have to do something, the easier it is to align choices with future rewards. Similarly, practicing self-compassion enables you to change direction and mould better decisions, rather than dwelling on mistakes and succumbing to the 'what-the-hell' effect.

- When we modify situations in our lives that make temptations – and, ultimately, instant gratification – *more costly* and less attractive, and make long-term goals *less costly* and more attractive, we no longer have to manage disunity between 'want-to' goals and 'have-to' goals. Change your environment (i.e., remove trigger foods, make beneficial habits more accessible, etc.) and you'll change your behaviour.

AFTERWORD

A strange thing started happening when I began helping each client overhaul and remodel their dieting mindset.

They started to experience even *more* impressive results.

Not only did they find many of their archetypal, weight loss struggles far less problematic, but they began *sustaining* and *improving* progress with greater ease. No longer did adherence and interest relent; instead, consistency, enthusiasm, and endurance surfaced. Whereas many people had once fallen prey to the inevitable rebounds, psychological struggles, and difficulties in advancing without accountability and help, they now emerged as more assured and rational individuals. They displayed greater confidence, showcased growth, and revealed superior levels of resilience. They now thrived where others struggled. They had built the ultimate dieting mindset. They were, now, essentially *new* people.

I'm not proclaiming that transforming your mindset ought to sit as the zenith of your fat loss journey. We can't just 'wish away' the body fat, nor 'think ourselves' thin. I'm merely arguing that it holds greater influence and meaning than it's currently reputed to do, equipping us with the mental fortitude to bring about long-lasting change.

I hope you now agree.

Low-carb, sugar-free, slimming-soap diets are sellable – and sexy. Tackling and changing your mindset might appear to not hold quite the same appeal. Even so, ignoring beliefs, overlooking your identity, neglecting a passion for growth, and squandering the opportunity to adopt a new line of thinking – along with many of the other, important topics discussed in the preceding pages – incites unwanted and additional challenges. We now know that knowledge is power – even *reading* about the impact of your mindset can shift your behaviours and have a measurable impact on your life.

Excluding a mindset transformation, in favour of a quick-fix diet, is reckless. Disregarding the opportunity to utilise failure differently, avoiding learning how to accept and react to varying and harmful thoughts, and surrendering to old-fashioned views on social comparison are likely only going to make things harder for yourself. Attempting to diet without shifting the mindset you currently occupy surrounding self-control, motivation, procrastination, and values is nothing but hopeful. It's akin to throwing your protein balls at the wall and trusting that one of them will eventually stick. I know my clients now agree.

Why, then, discount such a prominent anchor in your dieting venture? Why pretend it doesn't matter? Omitting the need to modify our mindset runs parallel to overlooking the laws of thermodynamics. If you're not willing to place yourself in an energy deficit, you won't lose and keep off the weight; if you're not ready to alter your mindset, you, similarly, won't lose and keep off the weight. It works both ways.

Cutting out carbs, abstaining from the chocolate, or – literally – running yourself into the ground, popularises the easy path. Doing so possibly requires little effort, which is why those futile attempts seldom work. Devoting time to repairing a ruptured mindset – one dragged through years of false claims, damaging myths, and undesirable societal standards – requires industry and struggle. It's work. It involves endeavour. Dare I say it also demands *grit*. Which is why not many are willing to withstand the process.

I hope, however, that, in wading your way, courageously, through this book, you now view things in a somewhat different light. Hopefully, you appreciate the importance of shifting the typical mentality surrounding dieting. You recognise the power that your frame of mind and ideology hold over your actions and behaviours. And you firmly believe that you can now build the ultimate dieting mindset.

I wish you luck on your journey. I wish you the best in working through these pages again, unearthing the gems and moments that mean the most to you – and highlighting the tasks that you know will bring you greater success. I hope you'll no longer rely solely on the physiological processes of weight loss, to get ready for that summer holiday or make just 'one last attempt' at shedding a few of those unwanted pounds. I hope that you no longer accede to the allure of another, enticing, 'sexy' diet. Instead, I hope you get there the right way – and realise that it really is mind over matter.

ABOUT THE AUTHOR

Daniel Harrod is an online fat loss coach and personal trainer based in London, England. He has worked in the fitness industry for over ten years and finished as runner-up in the *Personal Trainer of the Year* category at the National Fitness Awards in 2019 and 2021 (he, obviously, would have won it in 2020, were it not for a global pandemic). His writing on fat loss, psychology, and mindset has frequently appeared on popular fitness channels such as *Men's Health, Women's Health*, and *The Personal Training Development Center.*

You can get in touch with Daniel at danielharrod.com or @danielharrodpt.

REFERENCES

Introduction

1. Crum, A. J., Corbin, W. R., Brownell, K. D., & Salovey, P. (2011). Mind over milkshakes: Mindsets, not just nutrients, determine ghrelin response. *Health Psychology, 30*(4), 424–429. https://doi.org/10.1037/a0023467

2. Blackwell, L.S., Trzesniewski, K., & Dweck, C.S. (2007). Implicit Theories of Intelligence Predict Achievement Across An Adolescent Transition: A Longitudinal Study and an Intervention. *Child Development, 78*(1), 246-63. https://doi.org/10.1111/j.1467-8624.2007.00995.x

3. Stone, M.R., Thomas, K., Wilkinson, M., Jones, A.M., Gibson, A., & Thompson, K.G. (2012). Effects of deception on exercise performance: implications for determinants of fatigue in humans. *Medicine and Science in Sports and Exercise, 44*(3), 534-41. https://doi.org/10.1249/mss.0b013e318232cf77

4. McClure, S.M., Li, J., Tomlin, D., Cypert, K.S., Montague, L.M., & Montague, P.R. (2004). Neural correlates of behavioural preference for culturally familiar drinks. *Neuron, 44*(2), 379-87. https://doi.org/10.1016/j.neuron.2004.09.019

5. Levy, B. R., Slade, M. D., Kunkel, S. R., & Kasl, S. V. (2002). Longevity increased by positive self-perceptions of aging. *Journal of Personality and Social Psychology, 83*(2), 261–270. https://doi.org/10.1037/0022-3514.83.2.261

6. Dweck, C. S. (2008). Can personality be changed? The role of beliefs in personality and change. *Current Directions in Psychological Science, 17*(6), 391–394. https://doi.org/10.1111/j.1467-8721.2008.00612.x

7. Burnette, J. L., O'Boyle, E. H., VanEpps, E. M., Pollack, J. M., & Finkel, E. J. (2013). Mind-sets matter: A meta-analytic review of implicit theories and self-regulation. *Psychological Bulletin, 139*(3), 655–701. https://doi.org/10.1037/a0029531

8. Lowe, M.R., Doshi, S.D., Katterman, S.N., & Feig, E.H. (2013). Dieting and restrained eating as prospective predictors of weight gain. *Frontiers in Psychology, 4,* 577 https://doi.org/10.3389/fpsyg.2013.00577

9. Thomas, J.G., Bond, D.S., Phelan, S., Hill, J.O., & Wing, R.R., (2014). Weight-loss maintenance for 10 years in the National Weight Control Registry. *American Journal of Preventive Medicine, 46*(1), 17-23. https://doi.org/10.1016/j.amepre.2013.08.019

10. Pownall, H.J., Bray, G.A., Wagenknecht, L.E., Walkup, M.P., Heshka, S., Hubbard, V.S., Hill, J., Kahn, S.E., Nathan, D.M., Schwartz, A.V., Johnson, K.C. (2015). Look AHEAD Research Group. Changes in body composition over 8 years in a randomized trial of a lifestyle intervention: the look AHEAD study. *Obesity (Silver Spring), 23*(3), 565-72. https://doi.org/10.1002/oby.21005

11. Westenhoefer, J., Stunkard, A.J., & Pudel, V. (1999). Validation of the flexible and rigid control dimensions of dietary restraint. *The International Journal Of Eating Disorders, 26*(1), 53-64. https://doi.org/10.1002/(SICI)1098-108X(199907)26:1<53::AID-EAT7>3.0.CO;2-N

12. Mann, T., Tomiyama, A. J., Westling, E., Lew, A.-M., Samuels, B., & Chatman, J. (2007). Medicare's search for effective obesity treatments: Diets are not the answer. *American Psychologist, 62*(3), 220–233. https://doi.org/10.1037/0003-066X.62.3.220

13. Tribole, Evelyn. (2017). Tribole.IntuitiveEatingResearchUpdate.SCAN.2017. 36. 1.

14. Sairanen, E., Lappalainen, R., Lapveteläinen, A., Tolvanen, A., Karhunen, L. (2014). Flexibility in weight management. *Eating Behaviours, 15*(2), 218-224. https://doi.org/10.1016/j.eatbeh.2014.01.008

15. Global BMI Mortality Collaboration, et. al. (2016). Body-mass index and all-cause mortality: individual-participant-data meta-analysis of 239 prospective studies in four continents. *The Lancet, 388*(10046), 776-786. https://10.1016/S0140-6736(16)30175-1.

16. Kuk, J.L., Christensen, R., & Wharton, S. (2019). Absolute Weight Loss, and Not Weight Loss Rate, Is Associated with Better Improvements in Metabolic Health. *Journal of Obesity 2019.* https://doi.org/10.1155/2019/3609642

17. Milner, J.J., Beck, M.A. (2012). The impact of obesity on the immune response to infection. *Proceedings of the Nutrition Society, 71*(2), 298-306. https://doi.org/10.1017/S0029665112000158

18. Flint, S.W., & Reale, S. (2018). Weight stigma in frequent exercisers: Overt, demeaning and condescending. *Journal of Health Psychology, 23*(5), 710-719. https://doi.org/10.1177/1359105316656232

19. Palascha, A., van Kleef, E., van Trijp, H.C. (2015). How does thinking in Black and White terms relate to eating behavior and weight regain? *Journal of Health Psychology, 20*(5), 638-48. https://doi.org/10.1177/1359105315573440

20. Warner, A. (2019). *The Truth About Fat: Why Obesity is Not that Simple* (1st ed.). Oneworld Publications.

Chapter 1

1. Oyserman, D. & Elmore, K. & Smith, G. (2012) Self, self-concept, and identity. J. Tangney and M. Leary (Eds). The Handbook of Self and Identity, 2nd Edition, pp 69-104, New York, NY: Guilford Press.

2. Oyserman, D. (2007). *Social identity and self-regulation*. In A. Kruglanski & T. Higgins (Eds.). Handbook of social psychology, 2nd ed. (pp. 432-453). New York, NY: Guilford Press.

3. Ouellette, J. A., Hessling, R., Gibbons, F. X., Reis-Bergan, M., & Gerrard, M. (2005). Using Images to Increase Exercise Behavior: Prototypes Versus Possible Selves. Personality and Social Psychology Bulletin, 31(5), 610–620. https://doi.org/10.1177/0146167204271589

4. Ogden, J., & Hills, L. (2008). Understanding sustained behavior change: the role of life crises and the process of reinvention. Health, 12(4), 419-437. https://www.jstor.org/stable/26649869

5. Sincero, J. (2018). *You Are At Badass At Making Money: Master the Mindset of Wealth* (pp.32-43). John Murray Learning.

6. Sharot, T., & Garrett, N. (2016). Forming Beliefs: Why Valence Matters. *Trends In Cognitive Science, 20*(1), 25-33. https://doi.org/10.1016/j.tics.2015.11.002

7. Bromberg-Martin, E.S., & Sharot, T. (2020). The Value of Beliefs. *Neuroview, 106*(4), 561-565. https://doi.org/10.1016/j.neuron.2020.05.001

8. DeJong, W. (1980). The Stigma of Obesity: The Consequences of Naïve Assumptions Concerning the Causes of Physical Deviance. *Journal of Health and Social Behavior, 21*(1), 75-87. https://doi.org/10.2307/2136696

9. Bonafini, B.A., & Pozzilli, P. (2011). Body weight and beauty: the changing face of the ideal female body weight. *Obesity Reviews, 12*(1), 65-65. https://doi.org/10.1111/j.1467-789X.2010.00754.x

10. Carbone, G. (2020, January 11). Surprise, Ethan Suplee Is Ripped Now After Losing Hundreds Of Pounds. *Cinema Blend*. https://www.cinemablend.com/news/2488285/surprise-ethan-suplee-is-ripped-now-after-losing-hundreds-of-pounds

11. Williams, B. (2020, January 30). How Ethan Suplee Lost Weight, Got Jacked, and Found His Healthy Balance. *Men's Health*. https://www.menshealth.com/fitness/a30715343/ethan-suplee-workout-plan-video/

12. Michael Matthews. (n.d.). Ethan Suplee on Losing 300 Pounds and Getting Jacked. *Legion Athletics.* Retrieved April 12, 2022, from https://legionathletics.com/ethan-success-interview/

13. Hitlin, S. (2003). Values as the Core of Personal Identity: Drawing Links between Two Theories of Self. *Social Psychology Quarterly, 66*(2), 118-137. https://doi.org/10.2307/1519843

14. Lekes, N., Hope, N.H., Gouveia, L., Koestner, R., & Philippe, F.L. (2012). Influencing value priorities and increasing well-being: The effects of reflecting on intrinsic values. *The Journal of Positive Psychology, 7*(3), 249-261. https://doi.org/10.1080/17439760.2012.677468

15. Parks, L., & Guay, R.P. (2009). Personality, values, and motivation. *Personality and Individual Differences, 47*(7), 675-684. https://doi.org/10.1016/j.paid.2009.06.002

16. Hayes, S. (2019). A Liberated Mind: The essential guide to ACT (pp. 224-245). Vermilion.

17. Tajfel, H. and Turner, J.C. (1985) *The Social Identity Theory of Intergroup Behaviour.* In: Worchel, S. and Austin, W.G., Eds., Psychology of Intergroup Relations, 2nd Edition, Nelson Hall.

18. Hogg, M. A., & Terry, D. J. (2000). Social identity and self-categorization processes in organizational contexts. *The Academy of Management Review, 25*(1), 121–140. https://doi.org/10.2307/259266

19. Murphy, M.C., & Dweck, C.S. (2010). A Culture of Genius: How an Organization's Lay Theory Shapes People's Cognition, Affect, and Behavior. *Personality and Social Psychology Bulletin, 36*(3), 283-296. https://doi.org/10.1177/0146167209347380

20. Cruwys, T., Norwood, R., Chachay, V. S., Ntontis, E., & Sheffield, J. (2020). "An Important Part of Who I am": The Predictors of Dietary Adherence among Weight-Loss, Vegetarian, Vegan, Paleo, and Gluten-Free Dietary Groups. *Nutrients, 12*(4), 970. https://doi.org/10.3390/nu12040970

21. Cruwys, T., Platow, M. J., Rieger, E., Byrne, D. G., & Haslam, S. A. (2016). The social psychology of disordered eating: The Situated Identity Enactment model. *European Review of Social Psychology, 27*(1), 160–195. https://doi.org/10.1080/10463283.2016.1229891

22. Maltz, M. (1960). *Psycho-Cybernetics.* Simon & Schuster.

23. Manson, M. (2019). *Everything Is F*cked: A Book About Hope* (p. 67). Harper.

24. Shish, M., Pittinsky, T.L., & Ambady, N. (1999). Stereotype Susceptibility: Identity Salience and Shifts in Quantitative Performance. Psychological Science, 10(1), 80-83. https://doi.org/10.1111/1467-9280.00111

25. Walton, G. M., & Cohen, G. L. (2007). A question of belonging: Race, social fit, and achievement. *Journal of Personality and Social Psychology, 92*(1), 82–96. https://doi.org/10.1037/0022-3514.92.1.82

26. Branscombe, N. R., & Wann, D. L. (1994). Collective self-esteem consequences of outgroup derogation when a valued social identity is on trial. *European Journal of Social Psychology, 24*(6), 641–657. https://doi.org/10.1002/ejsp.2420240603

27. Gagnon, A., & Bourhis, R.Y. (1996). Discrimination in the Minimal Group Paradigm: Social Identity or Self-Interest? *Personality and Social Psychology Bulletin, 22*(12), 1289-1301. https://doi.org/10.1177/01461672962212009

28. Ogden, J., & Hills, L. (2008). Understanding sustained behavior change: the role of life crises and the process of reinvention. Health, 12(4), 419-437. https://www.jstor.org/stable/26649869

29. Sandoz, E.K., & Hebert, E.R. (2016). Meaningful, reminiscent, and evocative: An initial examination of four methods of selecting idiographic values-relevant stimuli. *Journal of Contextual Behavioral Science, 4*(4), 277-280. https://doi.org/10.1016/j.jcbs.2015.09.001

30. Huldtgren, A., Wiggers, P., & Jonker, C.M. (2014). Designing for Self-Reflection on Values for Improved Life Decision. *Interacting With Computers, 26*(1), 27-45. https://doi.org/10.1093/iwc/iwt025

31. Clear, J. (2018). *Atomic Habits* (pp. 36-41). Random House Business.

32. Iyer, A., Jetten, J., Tsivrikos, D., Postmes, T., & Haslam, S.A. (2009). The more (and the more compatible) the merrier: Multiple group memberships and identity compatibility as predictors of adjustment after life transitions. *British Journal of Social Psychology, 48*(4), 707-733. https://doi.org/10.1348/014466608X397628

33. Vlaskovits, P. (2011, August 29). Henry Ford, Innovation, and That "Faster Horse" Quote. *Harvard Business Review.* https://hbr.org/2011/08/henry-ford-never-said-the-fast

34. Sinek, S. (2011). *Start With Why.* Penguin.

35. Ogden, J., Stavrinaki, M., & Stubbs, J. (2009). Understanding the role of life events in weight loss and weight gain. *Psychology, Health, & Medicine, 14*(2), 239-249. https://doi.org/10.1080/13548500802512302

36. Frankl, V.E. (2004). *Man's Search For Meaning* (pp. 84-85). Generic.

37. Beer, E. (n.d.). Forget bikini bodies and big arms: Here's the real secret for getting motivated to transform your body. *Precision Nutrition.* Retrieved April 12, 2022, from https://www.precisionnutrition.com/weight-loss-motivation

Chapter 2

1. Tong, K. (2019, August 4). Cristian Ronaldo confirms that he wore ankle weights during Man Utd training. *GiveMeSport.* https://www.givemesport.com/1494616-cristiano-ronaldo-confirms-that-he-wore-ankle-weights-during-man-utd-training

2. Hayward, Ben. (n.d.). The 'little bee' who always cried – the story of young Ronaldo's path to greatness in Madeira. *Goal.* Retrieved January 4, 2022, from https://www.goal.com/en/news/2466/goal-50/2017/01/09/29353802/the-little-bee-who-always-cried-the-story-of-young-ronaldos-path-

3. Thiran, Roshan. (2018, June 11). What I Learned From Ronaldo: How He Became The World's Best Player. *Leaderonomics.com.* https://www.leaderonomics.com/articles/leadership/what-i-learned-from-ronaldo-how-he-became-the-worlds-best-player

4. Dweck, C. S., & Leggett, E. L. (1988). A social-cognitive approach to motivation and personality. *Psychological Review, 95*(2), 256–273. https://doi.org/10.1037/0033-295X.95.2.256

5. Dweck, C. S. (1999). *Self-theories: Their role in motivation, personality, and development.* Psychology Press.

6. Dweck, C. S. (2006). *Mindset: The new psychology of success.* Random House.

7. Blackwell, L.S., Trzesniewski, K.H., Dweck, C.S. (2007). Implicit theories of intelligence predict achievement across an adolescent transition: a longitudinal study and an intervention. *Child Development, 78*(1), 246-63. https://doi.org/10.1111/j.1467-8624.2007.00995.x

8. Sarrazin, P., Biddle, S., Famose, J. P., Cury, F., Fox, K., & Durand, M. (1996). Goal orientations and conceptions of the nature of sport ability in children: A social cognitive approach. *British Journal of Social Psychology, 35*(3), 399–414. https://doi.org/10.1111/j.2044-8309.1996.tb01104.x

9. Wood, R., & Bandura, A. (1989). Impact of conceptions of ability on self-regulatory mechanisms and complex decision making. *Journal of Personality and Social Psychology, 56*(3), 407–415. https://doi.org/10.1037/0022-3514.56.3.407

10. 6. Dweck, C. S. (2006). *Mindset: The new psychology of success.* Random House.

REFERENCES

11. Burnette, J.L. (2010). Implicit theories of body weight: entity beliefs can weigh you down. *Personality and Social Psychology Bulletin, 36*(3), 410-422. https://doi.org/10.1177/0146167209359768

12. Wigfield, A., & Eccles, J. S. (2000). Expectancy–value theory of achievement motivation. *Contemporary Educational Psychology, 25*(1), 68–81. https://doi.org/10.1006/ceps.1999.1015

13. Hagger, M.S., Chatzisarantis, N., Biddle, S.J. (2001). The influence of self-efficacy and past behaviour on the physical activity intentions of young people. *Journal of Sports Science, 19*(9), 711-25. https://doi.org/10.1080/02640410152475847

14. Burnette, J. L., O'Boyle, E. H., VanEpps, E. M., Pollack, J. M., & Finkel, E. J. (2013). Mind-sets matter: A meta-analytic review of implicit theories and self-regulation. *Psychological Bulletin, 139*(3), 655–701. https://doi.org/10.1037/a0029531

15. Shaffer, J. (2016). Neuroplasticity and clinical practice: Building brain power for health. *Frontiers in Psychology, 7,* Article 1118. https://doi.org/10.3389/fpsyg.2016.01118

16. Nguyen, Thai. (2017, December 6). 10 Proven Ways To Grow Your Brain: Neurogenesis And Neuroplasticity. *HuffPost.* https://www.huffpost.com/entry/10-proven-ways-to-grow-yo_b_10374730?guccounter=1

17. Ackerman, Courtney. (2021, November 25). What Is Neuroplasticity? A Psychologist Explains. *Positive Psychology.* https://positivepsychology.com/neuroplasticity/

18. Orvidas, K., Burnette, J.L., Schleider, J.L., Skelton, J.A., Moses, M., & Dunsmore, J.C. (2020). Health Body, Healthy Mind: A Mindset Intervention for Obese Youth. *The Journal of Genetic Psychology, 181*(6), 443-457. https://doi.org/10.1080/00221325.2020.1796573

19. Orvidas, K., Burnette, J.L., Russell, V.M. (2018). Mindsets applied to fitness: Growth beliefs predict exercise efficacy, value and frequency. *Psychology of Sport and Exercise, 36,* 156-61. https://doi.org/10.1016/j.psychsport.2018.02.006

20. Crum, AJ., & Langer, E.J., (2007). Mind-set matters: exercise and the placebo effect. *Psychological Science, 18*(2), 165-71. https://doi.org/10.1111/j.1467-9280.2007.01867.x

21. Ross, R., Gray, C.M., & Gill, J.M.R. (2015). Effects of an Injected Placebo on Endurance Running Performance. *Medicine and Science in Sports and Exercise, 47*(8), 1672-81. https://doi.org/10.1249/MSS.0000000000000584

22. Hagger, M.S., Chatzisarantis, N., & Biddle S.J. (2001). The influence of self-efficacy and past behaviour on the physical activity intentions of young people. *Journal of Sport Sciences, 19*(9), 711-25. https://doi.org/10.1080/02640410152475847

23. Turnwald, B.P., Goyer, J.P., Boles, D.Z., Silder, A., Delp, S.L., & Crum, A.J. (2019). Learning one's genetic risk changes physiology independent of actual genetic risk. *Nature Human Behaviour, 3*(1), 48-56. https://doi.org/10.1038/s41562-018-0483-4

24. Zahrt, O. H., & Crum, A. J. (2017). Perceived physical activity and mortality: Evidence from three nationally representative U.S. samples. *Health Psychology, 36*(11), 1017–1025. https://doi.org/10.1037/hea0000531

25. Zahrt, O.H., & Crum, A.J. (2019). Effects of physical activity recommendations on mindset, behavior, and perceived health. *Preventive Medicine Reports, 17,* 101027, https://doi.org/10.1016/j.pmedr.2019.101027

26. Lindheimer, J.B., O'Connor, P.J., & Dishman, R.K. (2015). Quantifying the Placebo Effect in Psychological Outcomes of Exercise Training: A Meta-Analysis of Randomized Trials. *Sports Medicine, 45,* 693-711. https://doi.org/10.1007/s40279-015-0303-1

27. Ehrlinger, J., Burnette, J.L., Park, J., Harrold, M.L., & Orvidas, K. (2017). Incremental theories of weight and healthy eating behaviour. *Journal of Applied Social Psychology, 47*(6), 320-330. https://doi.org/10.1111/jasp.12439

28. Briers, B., Huh, Y.E., Chan, E., & Mukhopadhyay, A. (2020). The unhealthy = taste belief is associated with BMI through reduced consumption of vegetables: A cross-national and mediational analysis. *Appetite, 150,* 104639. https://doi.org/10.1016/j.appet.2020.104639

29. Brown, Harriet. (2015, March 24). The Weight of the Evidence. *Slate.* https://slate.com/technology/2015/03/diets-do-not-work-the-thin-evidence-that-losing-weight-makes-you-healthier.html#:~:text=In%20reality%2C%2097%20percent%20of,and%20downright%20deceptive%20at%20worst.

30. Schwarzer, R., & Renner, B. (2000). Social-Cognitive Predictors of Health Behavior: Action Self-Efficacy and Coping Self-Efficacy. *Health Psychology, 19*(5), 487-495. http://dx.doi.org/10.1037/0278-6133.19.5.487

31. Ehrlinger, J., Burnette, J.L., Park, J., Harrold, M.L., & Orvidas, K. (2017). Incremental theories of weight and healthy eating behaviour. *Journal of Applied Social Psychology, 47*(6), 320-330. https://doi.org/10.1111/jasp.12439

32. Thomas, F.N., Burnette, J.L., & Hoyt, C.L. (2019). Mindsets of health and healthy eating intentions. *Journal of Applied Social Psychology, 49*(6), 372-380. https://doi.org/10.1111/jasp.12589

33. Blotnicky, K.A., Mann, L.L., & Joy, P.R. (2015). An Assessment of University Students' Healthy Eating Behaviours with the Expectancy Theory. *American Society of Business and Behavioral Sciences, 22*(1), 55-68.

REFERENCES

34. Li, C., Cao, J., & Li, T.M. (2016). Eustress or distress: an empirical study of perceived stress in everyday college life. *Proceedings of the 2016 ACM International Joint Conference on Pervasive and Ubiquitous Computing: Adjunct.* https://doi.org/10.1145/2968219.2968309

35. Scott-Dixon, K., & St. Pierre, B. (n.d.) Good stress, bad stress: Finding your sweet spot. *Precision Nutrition.* Retrieved, January 8, 2022, from https://www.precisionnutrition.com/good-stress-bad-stress

36. Crum, A. J., Salovey, P., & Achor, S. (2013). Rethinking stress: The role of mindsets in determining the stress response. *Journal of Personality and Social Psychology, 104*(4), 716–733. https://doi.org/10.1037/a0031201

37. Mills, H., Reiss, N., & Dombeck, M. (n.d.). *Types of Stressors (Eustress vs Distress). Grace Point Wellness.* Retrieved January 4, 2022. https://www.gracepointwellness.org/117-stress-reduction-and-management/article/15644-types-of-stressors-eustress-vs-distress

38. Conversano, C., Rotondo, A., Lensi, E., Della Vista, O., Arpone, F., & Reda, M.A. Optimism and its impact on mental and physical well-being. *Clinical Practice and Epidemiology in Mental Health, 6*(1), 25-29. https://doi.org/10.2174/1745017901006010025

39. Etkin, J., Evangelidis, I., & Aaker, J. (2015). Pressed For Time? Goal Conflict Shapes how Time is Perceived, Spent, and Valued. *Journal of Marketing Research, 52*(3), 394-406. https://doi.org/10.1509/jmr.14.0130

40. Smith, E.N., Young, M.D., & Crum, A.J. (2020). Stress, Mindsets, and Success in Navy SEALs Special Warfare Training. *Frontiers in Psychology, 10,* 2962. https://doi.org/10.3389/fpsyg.2019.02962

41. Lee, H.Y., Jamieson, J.P., Miu, A.S., Josephs, R.A., & Yeager, D.S. (2018). An Entity Theory Of Intelligence Predicts Higher Cortisol Levels When High School Grades Are Declining. *Child Development, 90*(6), 849-867. https://doi.org/10.1111/cdev.13116

42. Life Chances (2016, August 5). Life Chances – what are we talking about? *Life Chances.* https://blogs.ncl.ac.uk/lifechances/definitions/

43. Cockernham, W.C., Bauldry, S., Hamby, B.W., Shikany, J.M., & Bae, S. (2017). A Comparison of Black and White Racial Differences in Health Lifestyles and Cardiovascular Disease. *American Journal of Preventative Medicine, 52*(1), 56-62. https://doi.org/10.1016/j.amepre.2016.09.019

44. Puhl, R.M., & Brownell, K.D. (2003). Psychosocial origins of obesity stigma: toward changing a powerful and pervasive bias. *Obesity Reviews, 4*(4), 213-227. https://doi.org/10.1046/j.1467-789X.2003.00122.x

45. Hooper, N., Crumpton, A., Robinson, M., & Meier, B. (2018). A weight-related growth mindset increases negative attitudes toward obese people. *Journal of Applied Social Psychology, 48*(9), 488-493. https://doi.org/10.1111/jasp.12528

46. Thomas, F.N., Burnette, J.L., & Hoyt, C.L.. (2019). Mindsets of health and healthy eating intentions. *Journal of Applied Social Psychology, 49*(6), 372-380. https://doi.org/10.1111/jasp.12589

47. Rosenthal, R., Jacobson, L. (1968). Pygmalion in the classroom. *The Urban Review, 3,* 16–20. https://doi.org/10.1007/BF02322211

48. Schroder, H.S., Fisher, M.E., Lin, Y., Lo, S.L., Danovitch, J.H., & Moser, J.S. (2017). Neural evidence for enhanced attention to mistakes among school-aged children with a growth mindset. *Developmental Cognitive Neuroscience, 24,* 42-50. https://doi.org/10.1016/j.dcn.2017.01.004

49. Gross-Loh, C. (2016, December 16). How Praise Became a Consolation Prize. *The Atlantic.* https://www.theatlantic.com/education/archive/2016/12/how-praise-became-a-consolation-prize/510845/

Chapter 3

1. Sydney Opera House. (n.d.) *Our Story.* Retrieved January 17, 2022, from https://www.sydneyoperahouse.com/our-story.html

2. Flyvbjerg, B., Garbuio, M., & Lovallo, D. (2009). Delusion and Deception in Large Infrastructure Projects: Two Models for Explaining and Preventing Executive Disaster. *California Management Revie, 51*(2), 170-194. https://doi.org/10.2307/41166485

3. Flyvbjerg, B. (2005). Design by Deception: The Politics of Megaproject Approval. *Harvard Design Magazine,* Spring/Summer, 22, 50-59, http://dx.doi.org/10.2139/ssrn.2625198

4. BBC News. (2011, March 2). *Raf Typhoon: 'Bad Planning added billions to jet costs.* https://www.bbc.co.uk/news/uk-12614995

5. DW Staff. (2004, February 17). *German Government Cancels Toll Contract.* Deutsche Wells. https://p.dw.com/p/4gWS

6. Kahneman, D., & Tversky, A. (1982). Intuitive prediction: Biases and corrective procedures. Judgment Under Uncertainty, 414–421. https://doi.org/10.1017/cb09780511809477.031

REFERENCES

7. Buehler, R., Griffin, D., & Ross, M. (1994). Exploring the "planning fallacy": Why people underestimate their task completion times. *Journal of Personality and Social Psychology, 67*(3), 366–381. https://doi.org/10.1037/0022-3514.67.3.366

8. Hall, K.D., & Kahan, S. (2018). Maintenance of Lost Weight and Long-Term Management of Obesity. *The Medical clinics of North America, 102*(1), 183-197. https://doi.org/10.1016/j.mcna.2017.08.012

9. Tversky, A., & Kahneman, D. (1974). Judgement under Uncertainty: Heuristics and Biases. *Science, 185*(4157), 1124-1131. https://doi.org/10.1126/science.185.4157.1124

10. Foster, G. D., Wadden, T. A., Vogt, R. A., & Brewer, G. (1997). What is a reasonable weight loss? Patients' expectations and evaluations of obesity treatment outcomes. *Journal of Consulting and Clinical Psychology, 65*(1), 79–85. https://doi.org/10.1037/0022-006X.65.1.79

11. LeBoeuf, R. A., & Shafir, E. (2009). Anchoring on the "here" and "now" in time and distance judgments. *Journal of Experimental Psychology: Learning, Memory, and Cognition, 35*(1), 81–93. https://doi.org/10.1037/a0013665

12. Northcraft, G. B., & Neale, M. A. (1987). Experts, amateurs, and real estate: An anchoring-and-adjustment perspective on property pricing decisions. *Organizational Behavior and Human Decision Processes, 39*(1), 84–97. https://doi.org/10.1016/0749-5978(87)90046-X

13. Kahneman, D., & Lovall, D. (1993). Timid Choices and Bold Forecasts: A Cognitive Perspective on Risk Taking. *Management Science, 39*(1), 17-31. https://www.jstor.org/stable/2661517

14. Newby-Clark, I. R., Ross, M., Buehler, R., Koehler, D. J., & Griffin, D. (2000). People focus on optimistic scenarios and disregard pessimistic scenarios while predicting task completion times. *Journal of Experimental Psychology: Applied, 6*(3), 171–182. https://doi.org/10.1037/1076-898X.6.3.171

15. Tanner, R. J., & Carlson, K. A. (2009). Unrealistically optimistic consumers: A selective hypothesis testing account for optimism in predictions of future behavior. *Journal of Consumer Research, 35*(5), 810–822. https://doi.org/10.1086/593690

16. Pronin, E., Olivola, C.Y., & Kennedy, K.A. (2007). Doing Unto Future Selves As You Would Do Unto Others: Psychological Distance and Decision Making. *Personality and Psychology Bulletin, 34*(2), 224-236. https://doi.org/10.1177/0146167207310023

17. Liberman, N., & Trope, Y. (1998). The role of feasibility and desirability considerations in near and distant future decisions: A test of temporal construal theory. *Journal of Personality and Social Psychology, 75*(1), 5–18. https://doi.org/10.1037/0022-3514.75.1.5

18. Ebert, J. (2001). The role of cognitive resources in the valuation of near and far future events. *Acta Pyschologica, 108*(2), 155-171. https://doi.org/10.1016/S0001-6918(01)00033-6

19. Kwasnicka, D., Presseau, J., White, M., & Sniehotta, F. F. (2013). Does planning how to cope with anticipated barriers facilitate health-related behaviour change? A systematic review. *Health Psychology Review, 7*(2), 129–145. https://doi.org/10.1080/17437199.2013.766832

20. Peetz, J., Buehler, R., & Wilson, A. (2010). Planning for the near and distant future: How does temporal distance affect task completion predictions? *Journal of Experimental Social Psychology, 46*(5), 709–720. https://doi.org/10.1016/j.jesp.2010.03.008

21. Wilson, T. D., & Gilbert, D. T. (2013). The impact bias is alive and well. *Journal of Personality and Social Psychology, 105*(5), 740–748. https://doi.org/10.1037/a0032662

22. Gilbert, D. (2007). *Stumbling on Happiness* (p. 125). Harper Perennial.

23. Knutson, B., Fong, G. W., Adams, C. M., Varner, J. L., & Hommer, D. (2001). Dissociation of reward anticipation and outcome with event-related fMRI. *NeuroReport: For Rapid Communication of Neuroscience Research, 12*(17), 3683–3687. https://doi.org/10.1097/00001756-200112040-00016

24. The Interesting Fact of the Day Blog. (2019, May 22). *Hofstadter's Law and the Planning Fallacy*. https://www.theifod.com/hofstadters-law-and-the-planning-fallacy/

25. Min, K. S., & Arkes, H. R. (2013). When is difficult planning good planning? The effects of scenario-based planning on optimistic prediction bias. *Journal of Applied Social Psychology, 42(11)*, 2701-2729. https://doi.org/10.1111/j.1559-1816.2012.00958.x

26. Kahneman, D., & Tversky, A. (1982). Intuitive prediction: Biases and corrective procedures. Judgment Under Uncertainty, 414–421. https://doi.org/10.1017/cb09780511809477.031

27. Sanna, L.J., & Schwarz, N. (2004). Integrating Temporal Biases: The Interplay of Focal Thoughts and Accessibility Experiences. *Psychological Science, 15*(7), 474-481. https://doi.org/10.1111/j.0956-7976.2004.00704.x

28. Scholz, U., Schuz, B., Ziegelmann, J.P., Lippke, S., & Schwarzer, R. (2008). Beyond behavioural intentions: Planning mediates between intentions and physical activity. *British Journal of Health Psychology, 13*(3), 479-494. https://doi.org/10.1348/135910707X216062

29. Gollwitzer, P. M. (1999). Implementation intentions: Strong effects of simple plans. *American Psychologist, 54*(7), 493–503. https://doi.org/10.1037/0003-066X.54.7.493

30. Sniehotta, F.F. (2010). Towards a theory of intentional behaviour change: Plans, planning, and self-regulation. *British Journal of Health Psychology, 14*(2), 261-273. https://doi.org/10.1348/135910708X389042

31. Locke, E. A., & Latham, G. P. (2002). Building a practically useful theory of goal setting and task motivation: A 35-year odyssey. *American Psychologist, 57*(9), 705–717. https://doi.org/10.1037/0003-066X.57.9.705

32. Adriaanse, M.A., de Ridder, D.T.D., & de Wit, J.B.F. (2009). Finding the Critical Cue: Implementation Intentions to Change One's Diet Work Best When Tailored to Personally Relevant Reasons for Unhealthy Eating. *Personality and Social Psychology Bulletin, 35*(1), 60–71. https://doi.org/10.1177/0146167208325612

33. Jiga-Boy, G.M., Clark, A.E., & Semin, G.R. (2010). So Much To Do and So Little Time: Effort and Perceived Temporal Distance. *Psychological Science, 21*(12), 1811-1817. https://doi.org/10.1177/0956797610388043

34. Oettingen, G., & Mayer, D. (2002). The motivating function of thinking about the future: Expectations versus fantasies. *Journal of Personality and Social Psychology, 83*(5), 1198–1212. https://doi.org/10.1037/0022-3514.83.5.1198

35. Jekauc, D. (2015). Enjoyment during exercise mediates the effects of an intervention on exercise adherence. *Psychology, 6*(1), 48–54. https://doi.org/10.4236/psych.2015.61005

36. Weick, M., & Guinote, A. (2010). How long will it take? Power biases time predictions. *Journal of Experimental Social Psychology, 46*(4), 595–604. https://doi.org/10.1016/j.jesp.2010.03.005

37. Foster, G. D., Wadden, T. A., Vogt, R. A., & Brewer, G. (1997). What is a reasonable weight loss? Patients' expectations and evaluations of obesity treatment outcomes. *Journal of Consulting and Clinical Psychology, 65*(1), 79–85. https://doi.org/10.1037/0022-006X.65.1.79

38. Wadden, T. A., Womble, L. G., Sarwer, D. B., Berkowitz, R. I., Clark, V. L., & Foster, G. D. (2003). Great Expectations: "I'm Losing 25% of My Weight No Matter What You Say". *Journal of Consulting and Clinical Psychology, 71*(6), 1084–1089. https://doi.org/10.1037/0022-006X.71.6.1084

39. Foster, G.D., Wadden, T.A., Phelan, S., Sarwer, D.B., & Sanderson, R.S. (2001). Obese patients' perceptions of treatment outcomes and the factors that influence them. *Archives of Internal Medicine, 161*(17), 2133-2139. https://doi.org/10.1001/archinte.161.17.2133

40. Haidt, J. (2021). *The Happiness Hypothesis: Ten Ways to Find Happiness and Meaning in Life* (p. 84). First Edition. Random House Business.

41. Ordonez, L.D., Schweitzer, M.E., Galinsky, A.D., & Bazerman, M. (2009). Goals Gone Wild: The Systematic Side Effects of Over-Prescribing Goal Setting. *Academy of Management Perspectives (23)*. https://doi.org/10.2139/ssrn.1332071

42. Locke, E. A., Shaw, K. N., Saari, L. M., & Latham, G. P. (1981). Goal setting and task performance: 1969–1980. *Psychological Bulletin, 90*(1), 125–152. https://doi.org/10.1037/0033-2909.90.1.125

43. Adams, S. (2013). *How To Fail At Everything And Still Win Big* (p. 30). Portfolio Penguin.

44. Prochaska, J. O., DiClemente, C. C., & Norcross, J. C. (1992). In search of how people change: Applications to addictive behaviors. *American Psychologist, 47*(9), 1102–1114. https://doi.org/10.1037/0003-066X.47.9.1102

45. Trottier, K., Polivy, J., Herman, C.P. (2009). Effects of Resolving to Change One's Own Behavior: Expectations vs Experience. *Behavior Therapy, 40*(2), 164-170. https://doi.org/10.1016/j.beth.2008.05.004

46. Polivy, J., & Herman, C. P. (2002). If at first you don't succeed: False hopes of self-change. *American Psychologist, 57*(9), 677–689. https://doi.org/10.1037/0003-066X.57.9.677

47. Locke, E. A., & Latham, G. P. (2015). Breaking the rules: A historical overview of goal-setting theory. In A. J. Elliot (Ed.), *Advances in motivation science* (Vol. 2, pp. 99–126). Waltham, MA: Academic Press.

48. Latham, G. P., & Locke, E. A. (2006). Enhancing the benefits and overcoming the pitfalls of goal setting. *Organizational Dynamics, 35*(4), 332–340. https://doi.org/10.1016/j.orgdyn.2006.08.008

49. Morris, N. (2019, May). Fitness app users are 'trying to cheat step counters' with this simple hack. *Metro.* https://metro.co.uk/2019/05/16/fitness-app-users-trying-cheat-step-counters-simple-hack-9570167/

50. Camerer, C., Babcock, L., Loewenstein, G., & Thaler, R. (1997). Labor Supply of New York City Cabdrivers: One Day at a Time. *The Quarterly Journal of Economics, 112*(2). https://doi.org/10.1162/003355397555244

51. Moskowitz, G. B. (2012). "The representation and regulation of goals," in *Goal-Directed Behavior*, eds H. Aarts and A. J. Elliot (New York, NY: Psychology Press), 1–47.

52. Sitkin, S. B., See, K. E., Miller, C. C., Lawless, M. W., & Carton, A. M. (2011). The paradox of stretch goals: Organizations in pursuit of the seemingly impossible. *The Academy of Management Review, 36*(3), 544–566. https://doi.org/10.5465/AMR.2011.61031811

53. Lawless, R, (2018, January). A loop eternal: welcome to the Big Dog Backyard Ultra. *The Guardian.* https://www.theguardian.com/lifeandstyle/the-running-blog/2018/jan/30/a-loop-eternal-welcome-to-the-big-dog-backyard-ultra

54. Ulmer, H.V. (1996). Concept of an extracellular regulation of muscular metabolic rate during heavy exercise in humans by psychophysiological feedback. *Experienta, 52*(5), 416-420. https://doi.org/10.1007/BF01919309

55. Poulimeneas, D., Anastasiou, C.A., Kokkinos, A., Panagiotakos, D., & Yannayoulia, M. (2021). Motives for weight loss and weight loss maintenance: results from the MedWeight study. *Journal of Human Nutrition and Dietetics, 34*(3). 504-510. https://doi.org/10.1111/jhn.12856

56. Kingston, K., & Wilson, K. (2008). The application of goal setting in sport. In S.Mellalieu & S. Hanton (Eds.), *Advances in applied sport psychology* (pp. 85–133). London: Routledge.

57. Weinberg, R. S. (2013). Goal setting in sport and exercise: Research and practical applications. *Revista da Educação Física, 24*(2), 171–179. https://doi.org/10.4025/reveducfis.v24.2.17524

58. Nicholls, J. G. (1984). Achievement motivation: Conceptions of ability, subjective experience, task choice, and performance. *Psychological Review, 91*(3), 328–346. https://doi.org/10.1037/0033-295X.91.3.328

59. Kruglanski, A.W., & Szumowska, E. (2020). Habitual Behavior Is Goal-Driven. *Perspectives on Psychological Science, 15*(5). 1256-1271. https://doi.org/10.1177/1745691620917676

60. McEwan, D., Harden, S. M., Zumbo, B. D., Sylvester, B. D., Kaulius, M., Ruissen, G. R., Dowd, A. J., & Beauchamp, M. R. (2016). The effectiveness of multi-component goal setting interventions for changing physical activity behaviour: A systematic review and meta-analysis. *Health Psychology Review, 10*(1), 67–88. https://doi.org/10.1080/17437199.2015.1104258

61. Höchli, B., Brügger, A., & Messner, C. (2018). How focusing on superordinate goals motivates broad, long-term goal pursuit: A theoretical perspective. *Frontiers in Psychology, 9,* Article 1879. https://doi.org/10.3389/fpsyg.2018.01879

62. Chatzisarantis, N.L.D., Hagger, M.S., & Wang, J.C.K (2010). Evaluating the effects of implementation intention and self-concordance on behaviour. *British Journal of Psychology, 101*(4), 705-718. https://doi.org/10.1348/000712609X481796

63. Kaftan, O.J., & Freund, A. M. (2018). *The Way is the Goal: The Role of Goal Focus for Successful Goal Pursuit and Subjective Well-Being.* In: Diener, E; Oishi, S; Tay, L. *Handbook of well-being.* Salt Lake City, UT: DEF Publishers. https://doi.org/10.5167/uzh-147437

64. Freund, A. M., Hennecke, M., & Mustafić, M. (2012). On gains and losses, means and ends: Goal orientation and goal focus across adulthood. In R. M. Ryan (Ed.), *The Oxford handbook of human motivation* (pp. 280–300). Oxford University Press.

65. Freund, A. M., & Hennecke, M. (2012). Changing eating behaviour vs. losing weight: The role of goal focus for weight loss in overweight women. *Psychology & Health, 27*(Suppl 2), 25–42. https://doi.org/10.1080/08870446.2011.570867

66. Bailey, R.B. (2019). Goal Setting and Action Planning for Health Behaviour Change. *American Journal of Lifestyle Medicine, 13*(6). 615-618. https://doi.org/10.1177/1559827617729634

67. Swann, C., Rosenbaum, S., Lawrence, A., Vella, S. A., McEwan, D., & Ekkekakis, P. (2021). Updating goal-setting theory in physical activity promotion: A critical conceptual review. *Health Psychology Review, 15*(1), 34–50. https://doi.org/10.1080/17437199.2019.1706616

68. Simons, D. J., & Chabris, C. F. (1999). Gorillas in our midst: Sustained inattentional blindness for dynamic events. *Perception, 28*(9), 1059–1074. https://doi.org/10.1068/p2952

69. Poulimeneas, D., Anastasiou, C.A., Kokkinos, A., Panagiotakos, D., & Yannayoulia, M. (2021). Motives for weight loss and weight loss maintenance: results from the MedWeight study. *Journal of Human Nutrition and Dietetics, 34*(3). 504-510. https://doi.org/10.1111/jhn.12856

70. Amir, O., & Ariely, D. (2008). Resting on laurels: The effects of discrete progress markers as subgoals on task performance and preferences. *Journal of Experimental Psychology: Learning, Memory, and Cognition, 34*(5), 1158–1171. https://doi.org/10.1037/a0012857

71. Nunes, J. C., & Drèze, X. (2006). The endowed progress effect: How artificial advancement increases effort. *Journal of Consumer Research, 32*(4), 504–512. https://doi.org/10.1086/500480

72. Schweitzer, M. E., Ordóñez, L., & Douma, B. (2004). Goal Setting as a Motivator of Unethical Behavior. *Academy of Management Journal, 47*(3), 422–432. https://doi.org/10.2307/20159591

Chapter 4

1. Dottle, R. (2020, December 16). 'The Queen's Gambit' Chess Boom Moves Online. *Bloomberg.* https://www.bloomberg.com/graphics/2020-chess-boom/

2. NPD Group. (2020, November 25). Sales Spikes for Chess Books and Sets Follow Debut of "Queen's Gambit". https://www.npd.com/news/press-releases/2020/sales-spikes-for-chess-books-and-sets-follow-debut-of-queens-gambit/

REFERENCES

3. Akosubo, T. (2020, December 31). 'It took me 30 years to make Queen's Gambit – Allan Scott.' *EE Live*. https://www.eelive.ng/it-took-me-30-years-to-make-queens-gambit-allan-scott/

4. NASA. (n.d.) *Space Shuttle Columbia and Her Crew*. Retrieved February 28, 2022, from https://www.nasa.gov/columbia/home/index.html

5. The Harvard Gazette. (2008, June 5). *Text of J.K. Rowling's speech*. https://news.harvard.edu/gazette/story/2008/06/text-of-j-k-rowling-speech/

6. Goodman, N. (2012, November 5). James Dyson on Using Failure to Drive Success. *Entrepreneur Europe*. https://www.entrepreneur.com/article/224855

7. Timko, C. A., & Perone, J. (2005). Rigid and flexible control of eating behavior in a college population. *Eating Behaviors, 6*(2), 119–125. https://doi.org/10.1016/j.eatbeh.2004.09.002

8. Byrne, S.M., Cooper, Z., & Fairburn, C.G. (2004). Psychological predictors of weight regain in obesity. *Behaviour Research and Therapy, 42*(11), 1341-1356. https://doi.org/10.1016/j.brat.2003.09.004

9. McLean, J.A., Barr, S.I., & Prior J.C. (2001). Cognitive dietary restraint is associated with higher urinary cortisol excretion in healthy premenopausal women. *The American Journal of Clinical Nutrition, 73*(1). 7-12. https://doi.org/10.1093/ajcn/73.1.7

10. Stewart, T. M., Williamson, D. A., & White, M. A. (2002). Rigid vs. flexible dieting: Association with eating disorder symptoms in nonobese women. *Appetite, 38*(1), 39–44. https://doi.org/10.1006/appe.2001.0445

11. Wang, D.M., Hagger, M.S., & Chatzisarantis, N. (2020). Ironic Effects of Thought Suppression: A Meta-Analysis. *Perspectives on Psychological Science, 15*(3), 778-793. https://doi.org/10.1177/1745691619898795

12. Wegner, D.M., Zanakos, S. (1994). Chronic Thought Suppression. *Journal of Personality, 62*(4), 615-640. https://doi.org/10.1111/j.1467-6494.1994.tb00311.x

13. Barnes, R.D., Masheb, R.M., White, M.A., & Grilo, C.M. (2013). Examining The Relationship between Food Thought Suppression and Binge Eating Disorder. *Comprehensive Psychiatry, 54*(7), 1077-1081. http://dx.doi.org/10.1016/j.comppsych.2013.04.017

14. Wegner, D.M., Broome, A., & Blumberg, S.J. (1997). Ironic Effects of Trying to Relax Under Stress. *Behaviour Research and Therapy, 35*(1), 11-21. https://doi.org/10.1016/S0005-7967(96)00078-2

15. Anderer, J. (2020, January 15). Food Fads: The Average Adult Will Try 126 Different Diets During Their Life! *Study Finds*. https://www.studyfinds.org/food-fads-the-average-adult-will-try-126-different-diets-during-their-life/

16. van Koningsbruggen, G. M., Stroebe, W., & Aarts, H. (2013). Successful restrained eating and trait impulsiveness. *Appetite, 60*, 81–84. https://doi.org/10.1016/j.appet.2012.09.016

17. Stoeber, J., & Childs, J. H. (2010). The assessment of self-oriented and socially prescribed perfectionism: Subscales make a difference. *Journal of Personality Assessment, 92*(6), 577–585. https://doi.org/10.1080/00223891.2010.513306

18. Fedewa, B. A., Burns, L. R., & Gomez, A. A. (2005). Positive and negative perfectionism and the shame/guilt distinction: Adaptive and maladaptive characteristics. *Personality and Individual Differences, 38*(7), 1609–1619. https://doi.org/10.1016/j.paid.2004.09.026

19. Sherry, S. B., & Hall, P. A. (2009). The perfectionism model of binge eating: Tests of an integrative model. *Journal of Personality and Social Psychology, 96*(3), 690–709. https://doi.org/10.1037/a0014528

20. Wade, T.D., & Tiggemann, M. (2013). The role of perfectionism in body dissatisfaction. *Journal of Eating Disorders, 1*(2), https://doi.org/10.1186/2050-2974-1-2

21. Hillis, J. (2020). *Lean and Strong: Eating Skills, Psychology, and Workouts* (p. 24). On Target Publications.

22. Polivy, J., & Herman, C. P. (1985). Dieting and binging: A causal analysis. *American Psychologist, 40*(2), 193–201. https://doi.org/10.1037/0003-066X.40.2.193

23. McGonigal, K. (2013). *The Willpower Instinct: How Self-Control Works, Why It Matters, And What You Can Do To Get More Of It* (p. 144-145). Avery Publishing Group.

24. Herman, C. P., & Mack, D. (1975). Restrained and unrestrained eating. *Journal of Personality, 43*(4), 647–660. https://doi.org/10.1111/j.1467-6494.1975.tb00727.x

25. Tiggemann, M. (2000). Dieting and Cognitive Style: The Role of Current and Past Dieting Behaviour and Cognitions. *Journal of Health Psychology, 5*(1), 17-24. https://doi.org/10.1177/135910530000500106

26. Ali, A. (2011, March 4). The Magnifying Glass Effect. *Physiqonomics*. https://physiqonomics.com/magnifying-glass-effect/

27. Iyengar, S. S., & Lepper, M. R. (2000). When choice is demotivating: Can one desire too much of a good thing? *Journal of Personality and Social Psychology, 79*(6), 995–1006. https://doi.org/10.1037/0022-3514.79.6.995

28. Lally, P., van Jaarsveld, C. H. M., Potts, H. W. W., & Wardle, J. (2010). How are habits formed: Modelling habit formation in the real world. *European Journal of Social Psychology, 40*(6), 998–1009. https://doi.org/10.1002/ejsp.674

29. Orvidas, K.J. (2019). *Mindsets: Implications for Healthy Cognitions and Behaviors.* (Doctoral Dissertation, North Carolina State University). http://www.lib.ncsu.edu/resolver/1840.20/37108

30. Seligman, M. E., & Maier, S. F. (1967). Failure to escape traumatic shock. *Journal of Experimental Psychology, 74*(1), 1–9. https://doi.org/10.1037/h0024514

31. Dweck, C. S., & Reppucci, N. D. (1973). Learned helplessness and reinforcement responsibility in children. *Journal of Personality and Social Psychology, 25*(1), 109–116. https://doi.org/10.1037/h0034248

32. Carmody, T. P., Brunner, R. L., & St Jeor, S. T. (1995). Dietary helplessness and disinhibition in weight cyclers and maintainers. *International Journal of Eating Disorders, 18*(3), 247–256. https://doi.org/10.1002/1098-108X(199511)18:3<247::AID-EAT2260180306>3.0.CO;2-W

33. Dweck, C. S. (1999). *Self-theories: Their role in motivation, personality, and development.* Psychology Press

34. Snyder, C. R., & Higgins, R. L. (1988). Excuses: Their effective role in the negotiation of reality. *Psychological Bulletin, 104*(1), 23–35. https://doi.org/10.1037/0033-2909.104.1.23

35. Bandura, A., Barbaranelli, C., Caprara, G. V., & Pastorelli, C. (1996). Mechanisms of moral disengagement in the exercise of moral agency. *Journal of Personality and Social Psychology, 71*(2), 364–374. https://doi.org/10.1037/0022-3514.71.2.364

36. Sachdeva, S., Iliev, R., Medin, D. L. (2009). Sinning saints and saintly sinners: The paradox of moral self-regulation. *Psychological Science.* 20(4) 523-528. https://doi.org/10.1111/j.1467-9280.2009.02326.x

37. Khan, U., & Dhar, R. (2006). Licensing Effect in Consumer Choice. *Journal of Marketing Research, 43*(2), 259–266. https://doi.org/10.1509/jmkr.43.2.259

38. Fishbach, A., & Dhar, R. (2005). Goals as excuses or guides: The liberating effect of perceived goal progress on choice. *Journal of Consumer Research, 32*(3), 370–377. https://doi.org/10.1086/497548

39. Burnette, J.L., & Finkel, E.J. (2012). Buffering against weight gain following dieting setbacks: An implicit theory intervention. *Journal of Experimental Social Psychology, 48*(3), 721-725. https://doi.org/10.1016/j.jesp.2011.12.020

40. Ulen, C.G., Huizinga, M.M., Beech, B., & Elasy, T.A. (2008). Weight Regain Prevention. *Clinical Diabetes 26*(3). 100–113. https://doi.org/10.2337/diaclin.26.3.100

41. Stoeber, J., & Janssen, DP. (2011). Perfectionism and coping with daily failures: positive reframing helps achieve satisfaction at the end of the day. *Anxiety, Stress, & Coping, 24*(5), 477-497. https://doi.org/10.1080/10615806.2011.562977

42. Optimize By Heroic. (n.d.) *The Equanimity Game.* Retrieved March 8, 2022, from https://www.heroic.us/optimize/plus-one/the-equanimity-game

43. Bobinet, K. (2015). *Well Designed Life: 10 Lessons In Brain Science & Design Thinking for a Mindful, Healthy, & Purposeful Life* (pp. 302-309). engagedIN Press.

44. Markets Insider (2020, January 21). *Neuroscience-based Fresh Tri Proves "Iterative Mindset;" Drives Habit Formation and Weight Loss.* https://markets.businessinsider.com/news/stocks/neuroscience-based-fresh-tri-proves-iterative-mindset-drives-habit-formation-and-weight-loss-1028831081

45. Benzinga. (2020, November 13). *Fresh Tri App Offers New Way to Measure Habit-Changing Progress.* https://www.benzinga.com/pressreleases/20/11/n18355543/fresh-tri-app-offers-new-way-to-measure-habit-change-progress

46. Forman, E.M., & Butryn, M.L. (2016). *Effective Weight Loss: An Acceptance-Based Behavioral Approach, Clinical Guide (Treatments That Work* (pp. 75-77). Oxford University Press.

47. Assaz, D. A., Roche, B., Kanter, J. W., & Oshiro, C. K. B. (2018). Cognitive defusion in acceptance and commitment therapy: What are the basic processes of change? *The Psychological Record, 68*(4), 405–418. https://doi.org/10.1007/s40732-017-0254-z

48. Erskine, J.A.K., & Georgiou, G. (2010). Effects of thought suppression on eating behaviour in restrained and non-restrained eaters. *Appetite, 54*(3), 499-503. https://doi.org/10.1016/j.appet.2010.02.001

49. Forman, E.M., Hoffman, K.L., Juarascio, A.S., Butryn, M.L., & Herbert J.D. (2013). Comparison of acceptance-based and standard cognitive-based coping strategies for craving sweets in overweight and obese women. *Eating Behaviors, 14*(1), 64-68. https://doi.org/10.1016/j.eatbeh.2012.10.016

50. Barnes, R. D., Masheb, R. M., White, M. A., & Grilo, C. M. (2013). Examining the relationship between food thought suppression and binge eating disorder. *Comprehensive psychiatry, 54*(7), 1077–1081. https://doi.org/10.1016/j.comppsych.2013.04.017

51. Forman, E.M., & Butryn, M.L. (2016). *Effective Weight Loss: An Acceptance-Based Behavioral Approach, Clinical Guide (Treatments That Work* (pp. 80-83). Oxford University Press.

REFERENCES

52. Forman, E.M., Butryn, M.L., Manasse, S.M., Crosby, R.D., Goldstein S.P., Wyckoff, E.P., & Thomas, J.G. (2016). Acceptance-based versus standard behavioural treatment for obesity: Results from the mind your health randomized controlled trial. *Obesity, 24*(10), 2050-2056. https://doi.org/10.1002/oby.21601

53. Edgley, R. (2020). *The Art of Resilience: Strategies for an Unbreakable Mind and Body.* HarperCollins.

54. BBC News (2018, November 18). *Ross Edgley sets record for round Great Britain swim.* https://www.bbc.co.uk/news/uk-46088884

55. Fletcher, D., & Sarkar, M. (2013). Psychological resilience: A review and critique of definitions, concepts, and theory. *European Psychologist, 18*(1), 12–23. https://doi.org/10.1027/1016-9040/a000124

56. Werner, E. E. (1993). Risk, resilience, and recovery: Perspectives from the Kauai Longitudinal Study. *Development and Psychopathology, 5*(4), 503–515. https://doi.org/10.1017/S095457940000612X

57. Jim Collins (n.d.). *The Stockdale Paradox.* Retrieved February 28, 2022, from https://www.jimcollins.com/concepts/Stockdale-Concept.html

58. James, L.K., & Till, S.J. (2016). Potential Mechanisms for IgG4 Inhibition of Immediate Hypersensitivity Reactions. *Current Allergy and Asthma Reports, 16*(23). https://doi.org/10.1007/s11882-016-0600-2

59. Davidson, K., & Prkachin, K. (1997). Optimism and unrealistic optimism have an interacting impact on health-promoting behavior and knowledge changes. *Personality and Social Psychology Bulletin, 23*(6), 617–625. https://doi.org/10.1177/0146167297236005

60. Tugade, M. M., & Fredrickson, B. L. (2004). Resilient individuals use positive emotions to bounce back from negative emotional experiences. *Journal of personality and social psychology, 86*(2), 320–333. https://doi.org/10.1037/0022-3514.86.2.320

61. Wagnild, G. M., & Young, H. M. (1993). Development and psychometric evaluation of the Resilience Scale. *Journal of Nursing Measurement, 1*(2), 165–178.

62. Teo, A. R., Choi, H., & Valenstein, M. (2013). Social relationships and depression: ten-year follow-up from a nationally representative study. *PloS one, 8*(4), e62396. https://doi.org/10.1371/journal.pone.0062396

63. Heatherton, T. F., & Nichols, P. A. (1994). Personal accounts of successful versus failed attempts at life change. *Personality and Social Psychology Bulletin, 20*(6), 664–675. https://doi.org/10.1177/0146167294206005

64. Duckworth, A. L., Peterson, C., Matthews, M. D., & Kelly, D. R. (2007). Grit: Perseverance and passion for long-term goals. *Journal of Personality and Social Psychology, 92*(6), 1087–1101. https://doi.org/10.1037/0022-3514.92.6.1087

65. Duckworth, A. L. (2017). *Grit: Why passion and resilience are the secrets to success.* Vermilion.

66. Reed, J., Pitschet, B.L., & Cutton D.M. (2012). Grit, conscientiousness, and the transtheoretical model of change for exercise behavior. *Journal of Health Psychology, 18*(5), 612-619. https://doi.org/10.1177/1359105312451866

Chapter 5

1. Khan Academy. (n.d.). *Frank Lloyd Wright, Fallingwater.* Retrieved December 21, 2021, from https://www.khanacademy.org/humanities/ap-art-history/later-europe-and-americas/modernity-ap/a/frank-lloyd-wright-fallingwater

2. Smithsonian Magazine Staff. (2008, January). 28 Places To See Before You Die. *Smithsonian Magazine.* https://www.smithsonianmag.com/travel/28-places-to-see-before-you-diethe-taj-mahal-grand-canyon-and-more-10804769/

3. Procrastination And Science. (n.d.) *Famous Procrastinators.* Retrieved December 21, 2010, from https://procrastinus.com/procrastination/famous-procrastinators/

4. Steel, Piers, Ph.D. (2012, February 3). Da Vinci, Copernicus and the Astronomical Procrastination of. *Psychology Today.* https://www.psychologytoday.com/gb/blog/the-procrastination-equation/201202/da-vinci-copernicus-and-the-astronomical-procrastination

5. Procastination.com. (n.d.). *What Is Procrastination?* Retrieved December 21, 2021, from https://procrastination.com/what-is-procrastination

6. Clear, James. (n.d.). *Procrastination: A Scientific Guide on How to Stop Procrastinating.* Retrieved December 21, 2021, from https://jamesclear.com/procrastination

7. Rahami, S., Hall, N., & Pychyl, T. A. (2016). Attributions of Responsibility and Blame for Procrastination Behavior. *Frontiers in Psychology, 7*, Article 1179. https://doi.org/10.3389/fpsyg.2016.01179

8. Flett, A. L., Haghbin, M., & Pychyl, T. A. (2016). Procrastination and depression from a cognitive perspective: An exploration of the associations among procrastinatory automatic thoughts, rumination, and mindfulness. *Journal of Rational-Emotive & Cognitive-Behavior Therapy, 34*(3), 169–186. https://doi.org/10.1007/s10942-016-0235-1

9. Sirois, F.M. (2015). Is procrastination a vulnerability factor for hypertension and cardiovascular disease? Testing an extension of the procrastination-health model. *Journal of Behavioral Medicine, 38(3),* 578-89. https://doi.org/10.1007/s10865-015-9629-2

10. Gustavson, D. E., Miyake, A., Hewitt, J. K., & Friedman, N. P. (2014). Genetic Relations Among Procrastination, Impulsivity, and Goal-Management Ability: Implications for the Evolutionary Origin of Procrastination. *Psychological Science, 25(6),* 1178-1188. https://doi.org/10.1177/0956797614526260

11. Ferrari, J. R. (1991). Compulsive procrastination: Some self-reported characteristics. *Psychological Reports, 68*(2), 455–458. https://doi.org/10.2466/PR0.68.2.455-458

12. Tice, D. M., & Bratslavsky, E. (2000). Giving in to feel good: The place of emotion regulation in the context of general self-control. *Psychological Inquiry, 11*(3), 149–159. https://doi.org/10.1207/S15327965PLI1103_03

13. Flett, G. L., Stainton, M., Hewitt, P. L., Sherry, S. B., & Lay, C. (2012). Procrastination automatic thoughts as a personality construct: An analysis of the Procrastinatory Cognitions Inventory. *Journal of Rational-Emotive & Cognitive-Behavior Therapy, 30*(4), 223–236. https://doi.org/10.1007/s10942-012-0150-z

14. Sirois, F.M., & Pychyl, T. A. (2016). Procrastination, Emotion Regulation, and Well-Being. In Sirois, F.M., & Pychyl, T. A. *Procrastination, Health, and Well-Being* (pp. 163-188). Elsevier. https://doi.org/10.1016/B978-0-12-802862-9.00008-6

15. Sirois, F.M., & Pychyl, T. A. (2013). Procrastination and the Priority of Short-Term Mood Regulation: Consequences for Future Self. *Social and Personality Psychology Compass, 7*(2), 115-127. https://doi.org/10.1111/spc3.12011

16. Sirois, F. M. (2004). Procrastination and intentions to perform health behaviors: The role of self-efficacy and the consideration of future consequences. *Personality and Individual Differences, 37*(1), 115–128. https://doi.org/10.1016/j.paid.2003.08.005

17. Bisin, A., & Hyndman, K. (2020). Present-bias, procrastination and deadlines in a field experiment. *Games and Economic Behavior, 119,* 339–357. https://doi.org/10.1016/j.geb.2019.11.010

18. Myrick, J. G. (2015). Emotion regulation, procrastination, and watching cat videos online: Who watches internet cats, why, and to what effect? *Computers in Human Behavior, 52,* 168–176. https://doi.org/10.1016/j.chb.2015.06.001

19. Kidd, C., Palmeria, H., & Aslin, R.N. (2013). Rational snacking: young children's decision-making on the marshmallow task is moderated by beliefs about environmental reliability. *Cognition, 126*(1), 109-14. https://doi.org/10.1016/j.cognition.2012.08.004

20. Hershfield, H.E. (2011). Future self-continuity: how conceptions of the future self transform intertemporal choice. *Annals of the New York Academy of Sciences, 1235*(1), 30-43. https://doi.org/10.1111/j.1749-6632.2011.06201.x

21. Klassen, R.M., Krawchuk, L.L., Rajani, S. (2008). Academic procrastination of undergraduates: Low self-efficacy to self-regulate predicts higher levels of procrastination. *Contemporary Educational Psychology, 33*(4), 915-931. https://doi.org/10.1016/j.cedpsych.2007.07.001

22. Sirois, F. M., Melia-Gordon, M. L., & Pychyl, T. A. (2003). "I'll look after my health, later": An investigation of procrastination and health. *Personality and Individual Differences, 35*(5), 1167–1184. https://doi.org/10.1016/S0191-8869(02)00326-4

23. Berardi, John, Ph.D. Why the "pause-button mentality" is ruining your health and fitness. *Precision Nutrition.* Retrieved December 21, 2021, from https://www.precisionnutrition.com/pause-button-mentality

24. Alexander, E.S., & Onwuegbuzie, A.J. (2007). Academic procrastination and the role of hope as a coping strategy. *Personality and Individual Differences, 42*(7), 1301-1310. https://doi.org/10.1016/j.paid.2006.10.008

25. Zhang, Y., Dong, S., Fang, W., Chai, X., Mei, J., & Fan, X. (2018). Self-efficacy for self-regulation and fear of failure as mediators between self-esteem and academic procrastination among undergraduates in health professions. *Advances in Health Sciences Education, 23*(2), 817-830. https://doi.org/10.1007/s10459-018-9832-3

26. Buehler, R., Griffin, D., & Ross, M. (2002). Inside the planning fallacy: The causes and consequences of optimistic time predictions. In T. Gilovich, D. Griffin, & D. Kahneman (Eds.), *Heuristics and biases: The psychology of intuitive judgment* (pp. 250–270). Cambridge University Press. https://doi.org/10.1017/CBO9780511808098.016

27. Green, L., Myerson, J., & Mcfadden, E. (1997). Rate of temporal discounting decreases with amount of reward. *Memory & Cognition, 25*(5), 715-723. https://doi.org/10.3758/BF03211314

28. Albelwi, T. A., Rogers, R. D., & Kubis, H.-P. (2019). Exercise as a reward: Self-paced exercise perception and delay discounting in comparison with food and money. *Physiology & Behavior, 199,* 333–342. https://doi.org/10.1016/j.physbeh.2018.12.004

29. Steel, P. (2007). The nature of procrastination: A meta-analytic and theoretical review of quintessential self-regulatory failure. *Psychological Bulletin, 133*(1), 65–94. https://doi.org/10.1037/0033-2909.133.1.65

30. Solomon, L. J., & Rothblum, E. D. (1984). Academic procrastination: Frequency and cognitive-behavioral correlates. *Journal of Counseling Psychology, 31*(4), 503–509. https://doi.org/10.1037/0022-0167.31.4.503

31. Schwartz, B. (2005, July). *The paradox of choice* [Video]. TED Conferences. https://www.ted.com/talks/barry_schwartz_the_paradox_of_choice?language=en#t-470586

32. Redelmeier, D. A., & Shafir, E. (1995). Medical decision making in situations that offer multiple alternatives. *JAMA: Journal of the American Medical Association, 273*(4), 302–305. https://doi.org/10.1001/jama.273.4.302

33. Ferrari, J. R., & Pychyl, T. A. (2007). Regulating speed, accuracy and judgments by indecisives: Effects of frequent choices on self-regulation depletion. *Personality and Individual Differences, 42*(4), 777–787. https://doi.org/10.1016/j.paid.2006.09.001

34. Danziger, S., Levav, J., & Avnaim-Posso, L. (2011). Extraneous factors in judicial decisions. *Proceedings of the National Academy of Sciences of the United States of America, 108*(17), 6889-6892. https://doi.org/10.1073/pnas.1018033108

35. Malouff, J. M., & Schutte, N. S. (2019). The efficacy of interventions aimed at reducing procrastination: A meta-analysis of randomized controlled trials. *Journal of Counseling & Development, 97*(2), 117–127. https://doi.org/10.1002/jcad.12243

36. Murru, E.C., & Martin Ginis K.A. (2010). Imagining the possibilities: the effects of a possible selves intervention on self-regulatory efficacy and exercise behavior. *Journal of Sport and Exercise Psychology, 32*(40), 537-534. https://doi.org/10.1123/jsep.32.4.537

37. Wohl, M.J.A., Pychyl, T. A., & Bennett S.H. (2010). I forgive myself, now I can study: How self-forgiveness for procrastinating can reduce future procrastination. *Personality and Individual Differences, 48*(7), 803-808. https://doi.org/10.1016/j.paid.2010.01.029

38. Zhang, S., Becker, B., Chen, Q., & Feng, T. (2018). Insufficient task-outcome association promotes task procrastination through a decrease in hippocampal-striatal interaction. *Human Brain Mapping, 40*(2), 597-607. https://doi.org/10.1002/hbm.24397

39. Krause, K., & Freund, A. M. (2014). How to beat procrastination: The role of goal focus. *European Psychologist, 19*(2), 132–144. https://doi.org/10.1027/1016-9040/a000153

40. Wessel, J., Bradley, G. L., & Hood, M. (2021). A low-intensity, high-frequency intervention to reduce procrastination. *Applied Psychology: An International Review, 70*(4), 1669–1690. https://doi.org/10.1111/apps.12293

41. Clear, James. (n.d.). *If You Commit To Nothing, You'll Be Distracted By Everything.* Retrieved December 21, 2021, from https://jamesclear.com/mental-toughness-marathon-monks

42. Read, D., & Loewenstein, G. (1999). Enduring pain for money: Decisions based on the perception and memory of pain. *Journal of Behavioral Decision Making, 12*(1), 1-17. https://doi.org/10.1002/(SICI)1099-0771(199903)12:1<1::AID-BDM310>3.0.CO;2-V

43. Kang, M.J., & Camerer, C.F. (2013). fMRI evidence of a hot-cold empathy gap in hypothetical and real aversive choices. *Frontiers in Neuroscience, 7*:104. https://doi.org/10.3389/fnins.2013.00104

44. Roeckelein, J. (1998). *Dictionary of Theories, Laws, and Concepts in Psychology.* Greenwood.

Chapter 6

1. This Morning. (2018, October). *The Boy Who Knocked On Doors To Land His Dream Job.* YouTube. https://www.youtube.com/watch?v=jlsKOhwQE3g

2. Loveridge-Green. (2018, October 9). Teenager from council estate wins top finance job after searching for 'richest area in London' and door-knocking for career advice. *The Independent.* https://www.independent.co.uk/news/uk/home-news/london-richest-area-door-knocking-top-finance-job-council-estate-reggie-nelson-gloucester-road-a8573986.html

3. Bandura, A. (1989). Regulation of cognitive processes through perceived self-efficacy. *Developmental Psychology, 25*(5), 729–735. https://doi.org/10.1037/0012-1649.25.5.729

4. Kirk, S.F.L., Penney, T.L., & McHugh, T-L., F. (2010). Characterizing the obesogenic environment: the state of the evidence with directions for future research. *Obesity Reviews, 11*(2), 109-117. https://doi.org/10.1111/j.1467-789X.2009.00611.x

5. 46. Forman, E.M., & Butryn, M.L. (2016). *Effective Weight Loss: An Acceptance-Based Behavioral Approach, Clinical Guide (Treatments That Work* (pp. 37-40). Oxford University Press.

6. Shim, S., Crum, A.J., Galinksy, A. (2016). *The Grace of Control: How A Can-Control Mindset Increases Well-Being, Health, and Performance.* Unpublished manuscript.

7. Weems, C. F., & Silverman, W. K. (2006). An integrative model of control: Implications for understanding emotion regulation and dysregulation in childhood anxiety. *Journal of Affective Disorders, 91*(2-3), 113–124. https://doi.org/10.1016/j.jad.2006.01.009

8. Rotter, J. B. (1966). Generalized expectancies for internal versus external control of reinforcement. *Psychological Monographs: General and Applied, 80*(1), 1–28. https://doi.org/10.1037/h0092976

9. Ferris, T. (Host). (2016, January 13). Eric Weinstein on Challenging "Reality," Working with Peter Thiel, and Destroying Education to Save It (131). In *The Tim Ferris Show.* https://podcasts.apple.com/gb/podcast/131-eric-weinstein-on-challenging-reality-working-with/id863897795?i=1000360610817

10. Bandura, A. (1982). Self-efficacy mechanism in human agency. *American Psychologist, 37*(2), 122–147. https://doi.org/10.1037/0003-066X.37.2.122

11. Langer, E. J., & Rodin, J. (1976). The effects of choice and enhanced personal responsibility for the aged: A field experiment in an institutional setting. *Journal of Personality and Social Psychology, 34*(2), 191–198. https://doi.org/10.1037/0022-3514.34.2.191

12. Ranchor, A.V., Wardle, J., Steptoe, A., Henselmans, I., Ormel, J. & Sanderman R. (2010). The adaptive role oof perceived control before and after cancer diagnosis: A prospective study. *Social Science & Medicine, 70*(11), 1825-1831. https://doi.org/10.1016/j.socscimed.2009.10.069

13. Mirowsky, J., & Ross, C.E. (2007). Life Course Trajectories of Perceived Control and Their Relationship to Education. *American Journal of Sociology, 112*(5), 1339-1382. https://doi.org/10.1086/511800

14. Maier, S. F., & Seligman, M. E. (2016). Learned helplessness at fifty: Insights from neuroscience. *Psychological review, 123*(4), 349–367. https://doi.org/10.1037/rev0000033

15. Bryant, F.B. (1989). A Four-Factor Model of Perceived Control: Avoiding, Coping, Obtaining, and Savoring. *Journal of Personality, 57*(4), 773-797. https://doi.org/10.1111/j.1467-6494.1989.tb00494.x

16. Rothbaum, F., Weisz, J. R., & Snyder, S. S. (1982). Changing the world and changing the self: A two-process model of perceived control. *Journal of Personality and Social Psychology, 42*(1), 5–37. https://doi.org/10.1037/0022-3514.42.1.5

17. Scheier, M. F., Carver, C. S., & Bridges, M. W. (1994). Distinguishing optimism from neuroticism (and trait anxiety, self-mastery, and self-esteem): A reevaluation of the Life Orientation Test. *Journal of Personality and Social Psychology, 67*(6), 1063–1078. https://doi.org/10.1037/0022-3514.67.6.1063

18. Taylor, S. E. (2009). *Health psychology* (7th ed.). McGraw-Hill.

19. Seligman, M. E. P. (1975). *Helplessness: On depression, development, and death.* W H Freeman/Times Books/ Henry Holt & Co.

20. Kidwell, B., & Jewell, R. D. (2010). The motivational impact of perceived control on behavioral intentions. *Journal of Applied Social Psychology, 40*(9), 2407–2433. https://doi.org/10.1111/j.1559-1816.2010.00664.x

21. Robinson, S. A., & Lachman, M. E. (2018). Perceived control and cognition in adulthood: The mediating role of physical activity. *Psychology and aging, 33*(5), 769–781. https://doi.org/10.1037/pag0000273

22. Keltner, D., Gruenfeld, D. H., & Anderson, C. (2003). Power, approach, and inhibition. *Psychological Review, 110*(2), 265–284. https://doi.org/10.1037/0033-295X.110.2.265

23. Thompson, S. C. (1999). Illusions of control: How we overestimate our personal influence. *Current Directions in Psychological Science, 8*(6), 187–190. https://doi.org/10.1111/1467-8721.00044

24. Fenton-O'Creevy, M., Nicholson, N., Soane, E., & Willman, P. (2003). Trading on illusions: Unrealistic perceptions of control and trading performance. *Journal of Occupational and Organizational Psychology, 76*(1), 53-68. https://doi.org/10.1348/096317903321208880

25. Ford, B. Q., Lam, P., John, O. P., & Mauss, I. B. (2018). The psychological health benefits of accepting negative emotions and thoughts: Laboratory, diary, and longitudinal evidence. *Journal of Personality and Social Psychology, 115*(6), 1075–1092. https://doi.org/10.1037/pspp0000157

26. Daily Stoic. (n.d.). *What Is Stoicism? A Definition & 9 Stoic Exercises To Get You Started.* Retrieved March 15, 2022, from https://dailystoic.com/what-is-stoicism-a-definition-3-stoic-exercises-to-get-you-started/#the-dichotomy-of-control

27. Forman, E.M., Manasse, S.M., Butryn, M.L., Crosby, R.D., Dallal, D.H., & Crochiere, R.J. (2019). Long-Term Follow-up of the Mind Your Health Project: Acceptance-Based versus Standard Behavioral Treatment for Obesity. *Obesity, 27*(4), 565-571. https://doi.org/10.1002/oby.22412

28. Holiday, R. (2015). *The Obstacle is the Way* (pp. 144-150). Profile Books.

29. National Archives. (n.d.). *444 Days: Selected Records Concerning the Iran Hostage Crisis 1979-1981.* Retrieved March 15, 2022, from https://www.archives.gov/research/foreign-policy/iran-hostage-crisis

30. Tavris, C., & Aronson, E. (2007). *Mistakes Were Made (But Not By Me): Why We Justify Foolish Beliefs, Bad Decisions, and Hurtful Acts* (pp. 242-246). Houghton Mifflin.

31. Chun, S. (2015, July 16). Six things you didn't know about the Iran hostage crisis. *CNN.* https://edition.cnn.com/2014/10/27/world/ac-six-things-you-didnt-know-about-the-iran-hostage-crisis/index.html

32. Segal, J. (1987). *Winning Life's Toughest Battles.* Random House Publishing Group.

33. Hayes, S.C. (2004). Acceptance and commitment therapy, relational frame theory, and the third wave of behavioral and cognitive therapies. *Behavior Therapy, 35*(4), 639-665. https://doi.org/10.1016/S0005-7894(04)80013-3

34. Lidksy, I. (2017). *Eyes Wide Open: Overcoming Obstacles and Recognizing Opportunities In A World That Can't See Clearly.* Tarcher/Putnam.

35. Portland Psychotherapy. (n.d.). *Willingness in difficult times: Holding the cactus gently.* Retrieved March 15, 2022, from https://portlandpsychotherapy.com/2011/06/willingness-difficult-times-holding-cactus-gently/

36. Singh, N.N., Lancioni, G.E., Karazsia, B.T., Myers, R.E., Kim, E., Chan, J., Jackman, M.M., McPherson, C.L., & Janson, M. (2019). Surfing the Urge: An informal mindfulness practice for the self-management of aggression by adolescents with autism spectrum disorder. *Journal of Contextual Behavioral Science, 12.* 170-177. https://doi.org/10.1016/j.jcbs.2018.10.003

37. Bowen, S., & Marlatt, A. (2009). Surfing the urge: Brief mindfulness-based intervention for college student smokers. *Psychology of Addictive Behaviors, 23*(4), 666–671. https://doi.org/10.1037/a0017127

38. Clark, D. M., Ball, S., & Pape, D. (1991). An experimental investigation of thought suppression. *Behaviour Research and Therapy, 29*(3), 253–257. https://doi.org/10.1016/0005-7967(91)90115-J

39. Ostafin, B. D., & Marlatt, G. A. (2008). Surfing the urge: Experiential acceptance moderates the relation between automatic alcohol motivation and hazardous drinking. *Journal of Social and Clinical Psychology, 27*(4), 404–418. https://doi.org/10.1521/jscp.2008.27.4.404

40. Gardner, F. L., & Moore, Z. E. (2007). *The psychology of enhancing human performance: The Mindfulness-Acceptance-Commitment (MAC) approach.* Springer Publishing Co.

41. Harris, R. (2009). *Act Made Simple: An Easy-To-Read Primer on Acceptance and Commitment Therapy.* New Harbinger Publications.

42. Ciarrochi, J., & Robb, H. (2005). Letting a little nonverbal air into the room: Insights from acceptance and commitment therapy: Part 2: Applications. *Journal of Rational-Emotive & Cognitive-Behavior Therapy, 23*(2), 107–130. https://doi.org/10.1007/s10942-005-0006-x

43. Hatzigeorgidadis, A., Zourbanos, N., Galanis, E., & Theodorakis, Y. (2011). Self-Talk and Sports Performance: A Meta-Analysis. *Perspectives on Psychological Science, 6*(4), 348-356. https://doi.org/10.1177/1745691611413136

44. Kendall, P. C., & Treadwell, K. R. H. (2007). The role of self-statements as a mediator in treatment for youth with anxiety disorders. *Journal of Consulting and Clinical Psychology, 75*(3), 380–389. https://doi.org/10.1037/0022-006X.75.3.380

45. Cousins, S.O'B., & Gilis, M.M. (2005). "Just do it… before you talk yourself out of it": the self-talk of adults thinking about physical activity. *Psychology of Sport & Exercise, 6*(3), 313-334. https://doi.org/10.1016/j.psychsport.2004.03.001

46. Hope, D.A., Burns, J.A., Hayes, S.A., Herbert, J.D., & Warner, M.D. (2010). Automatic Thoughts and Cognitive Restructuring in Cognitive Behavioral Group Therapy for Social Anxiety Disorder. *Cognitive Therapy and Research, 34*(1), 1-12. https://doi.org/10.1007/s10608-007-9147-9

47. Hartmann-Boyce, J., Nourse, R., Boylan, A. M., Jebb, S. A., & Aveyard, P. (2018). Experiences of Reframing during Self-Directed Weight Loss and Weight Loss Maintenance: Systematic Review of Qualitative Studies. *Applied psychology. Health and well-being, 10*(2), 309–329. https://doi.org/10.1111/aphw.12132

48. Frank, J. (2011). *Successful Weight Minding: A Phenomenological Study Of Long-Term Weight Loss And Maintenance.* (Doctoral Dissertation, Alliant International University).

49. Jaska, C.M. (2011). *The experience of maintaining substantial weight loss: a transcendental phenomenological investigation.* (Doctoral Dissertation, Michigan School of Professional Psychology).

50. Turnwald, B. P., Jurafsky, D., Conner, A., & Crum, A. J. (2017). Reading between the menu lines: Are restaurants' descriptions of "healthy" foods unappealing? *Health Psychology, 36*(11), 1034–1037. https://doi.org/10.1037/hea0000501

51. Bacon, L., Keim, N. L., Van Loan, M. D., Derricote, M., Gale, B., Kazaks, A., & Stern, J. S. (2002). Evaluating a "non-diet' wellness intervention for improvement of metabolic fitness, psychological well-being and eating and activity behaviors. *International Journal of Obesity, 26*(6), 854–865. https://doi.org/10.1038/sj.ijo.0802012

52. Turnwald, B. P., Boles, D. Z., & Crum, A. J. (2017). Association Between Indulgent Descriptions and Vegetable Consumption: Twisted Carrots and Dynamite Beets. *JAMA internal medicine, 177*(8), 1216–1218. https://doi.org/10.1001/jamainternmed.2017.1637

Chapter 7

1. BBC Teach. (n.d.) *The Crow and the Peacock.* Retrieved March 22, 2022, from https://www.bbc.co.uk/teach/school-radio/audio-stories-the-crow-and-the-peacock/zk3fhbk

2. Polivy, J. (2017). What's that you're eating? Social comparison and eating behavior. *Journal of Eating Disorders, 5*(18). https://doi.org/10.1186/s40337-017-0148-0

3. Shakya, H.B., Christakis, N.A., & Fowler, J.H. (2015). Self-comparisons as motivators for healthy behavior. *Obesity, 23*(12), 2477-2484. https://doi.org/10.1002/oby.21201

4. Vartanian, L.R. (2015). Impression management and food intake. Current directions in research. *Appetite, 86,* 74-80. https://doi.org/10.1016/j.appet.2014.08.021

REFERENCES

5. Gilbert, P., Price, J., & Allan, S. (1995). Social comparison, social attractiveness, and evolution: How might they be related? *New Ideas in Psychology, 13*(2), 149-165. https://doi.org/10.1016/0732-118X(95)00002-X

6. Festinger, L. (1954). A Theory of Social Comparison Processes. *Human Relations, 7*(2), 117-140. https://doi.org/10.1177/001872675400700202

7. Wills, T. A. (1981). Downward comparison principles in social psychology. *Psychological Bulletin, 90*(2), 245–271. https://doi.org/10.1037/0033-2909.90.2.245

8. Gibbons, F. X. (1986). Social comparison and depression: Company's effect on misery. *Journal of Personality and Social Psychology, 51*(1), 140–148. https://doi.org/10.1037/0022-3514.51.1.140

9. Wood, J. V., Taylor, S. E., & Lichtman, R. R. (1985). Social comparison in adjustment to breast cancer. *Journal of Personality and Social Psychology, 49*(5), 1169–1183. https://doi.org/10.1037/0022-3514.49.5.1169

10. Pemberton, M., & Sedikides, C. (2001). When do individuals help close others improve? The role of information diagnosticity. *Journal of Personality and Social Psychology, 81*(2), 234–246. https://doi.org/10.1037/0022-3514.81.2.234

11. Plante, T. G., Madden, M., Mann, S., Lee, G., Hardesty, A., Gable, N., Terry, A. & Kaplow, G. (2010). Effects of Perceived Fitness Level of Exercise Partner on Intensity of Exertion. Journal of Social Sciences, 6(1), 50-54. https://doi.org/10.3844/jssp.2010.50.54

12. Collins, R. L. (1996). For better or worse: The impact of upward social comparison on self-evaluations. *Psychological Bulletin, 119*(1), 51–69. https://doi.org/10.1037/0033-2909.119.1.51

13. Goethals, G. R., & Klein, W. M. P. (2000). Interpreting and inventing social reality: Attributional and constructive elements in social comparison. In J. Suls & L. Wheeler (Eds.), *Handbook of social comparison: Theory and research* (pp. 23–44). Kluwer Academic Publishers. https://doi.org/10.1007/978-1-4615-4237-7_2

14. Thornton, D.A., & Arrowood, A.J. (1966). Self-evaluation, self-enhancement, and the locus of social comparison. *Journal of Experimental Social Psychology, 1*(1), 40-48. https://doi.org/10.1016/0022-1031(66)90064-3

15. Mussweiler, T., Rüter, K., & Epstude, K. (2004). The man who wasn't there: Subliminal social comparison standards influence self-evaluation. *Journal of Experimental Social Psychology, 40*(5), 689-696. https://doi.org/10.1016/j.jesp.2004.01.004

16. Sedikides, C., & Strube, M. J. (1997). Self-evaluation: To thine own self be good, to thine own self be sure, to thine own self be true, and to thine own self be better. In M. P.

Zanna (Ed.), *Advances in experimental social psychology,* Vol. 29, pp. 209–269). Academic Press. https://doi.org/10.1016/S0065-2601(08)60018-0

17. Pennebaker, J.W. (1997). Writing About Emotional Experiences as a Therapeutic Process. *Psychological Science, 8*(3), 162-166. https://doi.org/10.1111/j.1467-9280.1997.tb00403.x

18. Brehm, J. W. (1966). *A theory of psychological reactance.* Academic Press.

19. Collins, R. L. (1996). For better or worse: The impact of upward social comparison on self-evaluations. *Psychological Bulletin, 119*(1), 51–69. https://doi.org/10.1037/0033-2909.119.1.51

20. Taylor, S.E., Neter, E., Wayment, H.A (1995). Self-Evaluation Processes. *Personality and Social Psychology Bulletin, 21*(12), 1278-1287. https://doi.org/10.1177/01461672952112005

21. Swann, W. B., Jr. (2012). Self-verification theory. In P. A. M. Van Lange, A. W. Kruglanski, & E. T. Higgins (Eds.), *Handbook of theories of social psychology* (pp. 23–42). Sage Publications Ltd. https://doi.org/10.4135/9781446249222.n27

22. Morse, S., & Gergen, K. J. (1970). Social comparison, self-consistency, and the concept of self. *Journal of Personality and Social Psychology, 16*(1), 148–156. https://doi.org/10.1037/h0029862

23. Higgins, E. T., Loeb, I., & Moretti, M. (1995). Self-discrepancies and developmental shifts in vulnerability: Life transitions in the regulatory significance of others. In D. Cicchetti & S. L. Toth (Eds.), *Emotion, cognition, and representation* (pp. 191–230). University of Rochester Press.

24. Luttmer, E.F.P. (2005). Neighbors as Negatives: Relative Earnings and Well-Being. *The Quarterly Journal of Economics, 120*(3), 963-1002. https://doi.org/10.1093/qje/120.3.963

25. Wheeler, L., & Miyake, K. (1992). Social comparison in everyday life. *Journal of Personality and Social Psychology, 62*(5), 760–773. https://doi.org/10.1037/0022-3514.62.5.760

26. Aspinwall, L. G., & Taylor, S. E. (1993). Effects of social comparison direction, threat, and self-esteem on affect, self-evaluation, and expected success. *Journal of Personality and Social Psychology, 64*(5), 708–722. https://doi.org/10.1037/0022-3514.64.5.708

27. Chua, T.H.H., & Chang, L. (2016). Follow me and like my beautiful selfies: Singapore teenage girls' engagement in self-presentation and peer comparison on social media. *Computers in Human Behavior, 55*, Part A, 190-197. https://doi.org/10.1016/j.chb.2015.09.011

28. Patrick, H., Neighbors, C., & Knee, C.R. (2004). Appearance-Related Social Comparisons: The Role of Contingent Self-Esteem and Self-Perceptions of Attractiveness. *Personality and Social Psychology Bulletin, 30*(4), 501-514. https://doi.org/10.1177/0146167203261891

29. Datareportal. (n.d.) *Global Social Media Stats.* Retrieved March 22, 2022, from https://datareportal.com/social-media-users

30. Naslund, J.A., Bondre, A., Torous, J., & Aschbrenner, K.A. (2020). Social Media and Mental Health: Benefits, Risks, and Opportunities for Research and Practice. *Journal of Technology in Behavioral Science, 5*, 245-257. https://doi.org/10.1007/s41347-020-00134-x

31. Feinstein, B. A., Hershenberg, R., Bhatia, V., Latack, J. A., Meuwly, N., & Davila, J. (2013). Negative social comparison on Facebook and depressive symptoms: Rumination as a mechanism. *Psychology of Popular Media Culture, 2*(3), 161–170. https://doi.org/10.1037/a0033111

32. de Vries, D. A., & Kühne, R. (2015). Facebook and self-perception: Individual susceptibility to negative social comparison on Facebook. *Personality and Individual Differences, 86*, 217–221. https://doi.org/10.1016/j.paid.2015.05.029

33. Holland, G., & Tiggemann, M. (2016). A systematic review of the impact of the use of social networking sites on body image and disordered eating outcomes. *Body Image, 17*, 100-110. https://doi.org/10.1016/j.bodyim.2016.02.008

34. Chou, H-T., & Edge, N. (2012). "They Are Happier and Having Better Lives than I Am": The Impact of Using Facebook on Perception of Others' Lives. *Cyberpsychology, Behavior, and Social Networking, 15*(2), 117-121. https://doi.org/10.1089/cyber.2011.0324

35. Fardouly, J., & Vartanian, L.R. (2015). Negative comparisons about one's appearance mediate the relationship between Facebook usage and body image concerns. *Body Image, 12*, 82-88. https://doi.org/10.1016/j.bodyim.2014.10.004

36. 36. Fardouly, J., Willburger, B.K., & Vartanian, L.R. (2017). Instagram use and young women's body image concerns and self-objectification: Testing mediational pathways. *New Media & Society, 20*(4), 1380-1395. https://doi.org/10.1177/1461444817694499

37. Warrender, D., &Milne, R. (2020). How use of social media and social comparison affect mental health. *Nursing Times, 116*(3), 56-59.

38. Haferkamp, N., & Krämer, N.C. (2011). Social Comparison 2.0: Examining the Effects of Online Profiles on Social-Networking Sites. *Cyberpsychology, Behavior, and Social Networking, 14*(5), 309-314. https://doi.org/10.1089/cyber.2010.0120

39. Fardouly, J., Willburger, B.K., & Vartanian, L.R. (2017). Instagram use and young women's body image concerns and self-objectification: Testing mediational pathways. *New Media & Society, 20*(4), 1380-1395. https://doi.org/10.1177/1461444817694499

40. Hunt, M.G., Marx, R., Lipson, C., & Young, J. (2018). No More FOMO: Limiting Social Media Decreases Loneliness and Depression. *Journal of Social and Clinical Psychology, 37*(10), 751-768. https://doi.org/10.1521/jscp.2018.37.10.751

41. Lewallen, J., & Behm-Morawitz, E. (2016). Pinterest or Thinterest?: Social Comparison and Body Image on Social Media. *Social Media + Society, 2*(1), https://doi.org/10.1177/2056305116640559

42. Valkenburg, P.M., & Peter, J. (2007). Internet Communication and Its Relation to Well-Being: Identifying Some Underlying Mechanisms. *Media Psychology, 9*(1), 43-58. https://doi.org/10.1080/15213260709336802

43. Cohen, R., Fardouly, J., Newton-John, T., & Slater, A. (2019). #BoPo on Instagram: An experimental investigation of the effects of viewing body positive content on young women's mood and body image. *New Media & Society, 21*(7), 1546-1564. https://doi.org/10.1177/1461444819826530

44. Tiggemann, M., & Anderberg, I. (2019). Social media is not real: The effect of 'Instagram vs reality' images on women's social comparison and body image. *New Media & Society, 22*(12), 2183-2199. https://doi.org/10.1177/1461444819888720

45. Wu, J., & Srite, M. (2015). Benign Envy, Social Media, and Culture. *Digit 2015 Proceedings, 1.* https://aisel.aisnet.org/digit2015/1

46. Coyne, S.M., Rogers, A.A., Zurcher, J.D., Stockdale, L., Booth, M. (2020). Does time spent using social media impact mental health?: An eight year longitudinal study. Computers In Human Behavior, 104, Article 106160. https://doi.org/10.1016/j.chb.2019.106160

47. Weinstein, E. (2018). The social media see-saw: Positive and negative influences on adolescents' affective well-being. *New Media & Society, 20*(10), 3597-3623. https://doi.org/10.1177/1461444818755634

48. Liu, Q-Q., Zhou, Z-K., Yang, X-J., Niu, G-F., Tian, Y., & Fan, C-Y. (2017). Upward social comparison on social network sites and depressive symptoms: A moderated mediation model of self-esteem and optimism. *Personality and Individual Differences, 113,* 223-228. https://doi.org/10.1016/j.paid.2017.03.037

49. Vaterlaus, J.M., Patten, E.V., Roche, C., & Young, J.A. (2015). #Gettinghealthy: The perceived influence of social media on young adult health behaviors. *Computers in Human Behavior, 45,* 151-157. https://doi.org/10.1016/j.chb.2014.12.013

50. Zhang, J., Brackbill, D., Yang, S., & Centola, D. (2015). Efficacy and causal mechanism of an online social media intervention to increase physical activity: Results of a randomized controlled trial. *Preventive Medicine Reports, 2,* 651-657. https://doi.org/10.1016/j.pmedr.2015.08.005

51. van de Ven, N., Zeelenburg, M., & Pieters, R. (2011). Why Envy Outperforms Admiration. *Personality and Social Psychology Bulletin, 37*(6), 784-795. https://doi.org/10.1177/0146167211400421

52. Pavlova, M.K., Lechner, C.M., & Silbereisen, R.K. (2017). Social Comparison in Coping With Occupational Uncertainty: Self-Improvement, Self-Enhancement, and the Regional Context. *Journal of Personality, 86*(2), 320-333. https://doi.org/10.1111/jopy.12317

53. Emmons, R. A., & McCullough, M. E. (2003). Counting blessings versus burdens: An experimental investigation of gratitude and subjective well-being in daily life. *Journal of Personality and Social Psychology, 84*(2), 377–389. https://doi.org/10.1037/0022-3514.84.2.377

54. Medvec, V. H., Madey, S. F., & Gilovich, T. (1995). When less is more: Counterfactual thinking and satisfaction among Olympic medalists. *Journal of Personality and Social Psychology, 69*(4), 603–610. https://doi.org/10.1037/0022-3514.69.4.603

55. Bailis, D. S., & Chipperfield, J. G. (2006). Emotional and self-evaluative effects of social comparison information in later life: How are they moderated by collective self-esteem? *Psychology and Aging, 21*(2), 291–302. https://doi.org/10.1037/0882-7974.21.2.291

56. Smith, R. H. (2000). Assimilative and contrastive emotional reactions to upward and downward social comparisons. In J. Suls & L. Wheeler (Eds.), *Handbook of social comparison: Theory and research* (pp. 173–200). Kluwer Academic Publishers. https://doi.org/10.1007/978-1-4615-4237-7_10

57. Buunk, B. P., Oldersma, F. L., & de Dreu, C. K. W. (2001). Enhancing satisfaction through downward comparison: The role of relational discontent and individual differences in social comparison orientation. *Journal of Experimental Social Psychology, 37*(6), 452–467. https://doi.org/10.1006/jesp.2000.1465

58. Callan, M.J., Kim, H., & Matthews, W.J. (2015). Age differences in social comparison tendency and personal relative deprivation. *Personality and Individual Differences, 87,* 196-199. https://doi.org/10.1016/j.paid.2015.08.003

59. Petersen, J. (2018). *12 Rules For Life: An Antidote to Chaos* (pp. 85-111). Allen Lane.

60. Steele, C. M., & Liu, T. J. (1983). Dissonance processes as self-affirmation. *Journal of Personality and Social Psychology, 45*(1), 5–19. https://doi.org/10.1037/0022-3514.45.1.5

61. Salzberg, S. (2002). *Loving-Kindness* (p. 118). Shambhala.

62. Covington, M. V., & Beery, R. G. (1976). *Self-worth and school learning*. Holt, Rinehart & Winston.

63. Crocker, J. (2002). The Costs of Seeking Self-Esteem. *Journal of Social Issues, 58*(3), 597-615. https://doi.org/10.1111/1540-4560.00279

64. Ram Dass Foundation. (n.d.). *Acknowledging Your Own Beauty*. Retrieved March 22, 2022, from https://www.ramdass.org/acknowledging-your-own-beauty/

Chapter 8

1. Keller, J. (2013, May 13). Internet addiction is just the next evolutionary step. *Salon*. https://www.salon.com/2013/05/31/internet_addiction_is_just_the_next_evolutionary_step_partner/

2. Griffiths, M., & Wood, R. (2001). The psychology of lottery gambling. *International Gambling Studies, 1*(1), 27-45. https://doi.org/10.1080/14459800108732286

3. University of Chicago. (2016). New insights into Americans' perceptions and misperceptions of obesity treatments, and the struggles many face. (Report, October). *American Society for Metabolic & Bariatric Surgery*. https://www.norc.org/PDFs/ASMBS%20Obesity/ASMBS%20NORC%20Obesity%20Poll_Brief%20B%20REV010917.pdf

4. Park, N., Peterson, C., & Seligman, M.E.P. (2006). Character strengths in fifty-four nations and the fifty US states. *The Journal of Positive Psychology, 1*(3), 118-129. https://doi.org/10.1080/17439760600619567

5. Baumeister, R. F., Heatherton, T. F., & Tice, D. M. (1994). *Losing control: How and why people fail at self-regulation*. Academic Press.

6. Mischel, W., Shoda, Y., & Rodriguez, M. L. (1989). Delay of gratification in children. *Science, 244*(4907), 933–938. https://doi.org/10.1126/science.2658056

7. Tangney, J.P., Baumeister, R.F., & Boone, A.L. (2008). High Self-Control Predicts Good Adjustment, Less Pathology, Better Grades, and Interpersonal Success. *Journal of Personality, 72*(2), 271-324. https://doi.org/10.1111/j.0022-3506.2004.00263.x

8. Segerstrom, S. C., Hardy, J. K., Evans, D. R., & Winters, N. F. (2012). Pause and plan: Self-regulation and the heart. In R. A. Wright & G. H. E. Gendolla (Eds.), *How motivation affects cardiovascular response: Mechanisms and applications* (pp. 181–198). American Psychological Association. https://doi.org/10.1037/13090-009

9. Zahn, D., Adams, J., Krohn, J., Wenzel, M., Mann, C.G., Gomille, L.K., Jacobi-Scherbening, V., & Kubiak, T. (2016). Heart rate variability and self-control—A meta-analysis. *Biological Psychology, 115*, 9-26. https://doi.org/10.1016/j.biopsycho.2015.12.007

10. Segerstrom, S.C, & Nes, L.S. (2007). Heart Rate Variability Reflects Self-Regulatory Strength, Effort, and Fatigue. *Psychological Science, 18*(3), 275-281. https://doi.org/10.1111/j.1467-9280.2007.01888.x

11. Lopez, R. B., Chen, P. A., Huckins, J. F., Hofmann, W., Kelley, W. M., & Heatherton, T. F. (2017). A balance of activity in brain control and reward systems predicts self-regulatory outcomes. *Social cognitive and affective neuroscience, 12*(5), 832–838. https://doi.org/10.1093/scan/nsx004

12. Inzlicht, M., Schmeichel, B. J., & Macrae, C. N. (2014). Why self-control seems (but may not be) limited. *Trends in Cognitive Sciences, 18*(3), 127–133. https://doi.org/10.1016/j.tics.2013.12.009

13. Hofmann, W., Friese, M., Strack, F. (2009). Impulse and Self-Control From a Dual-Systems Perspective. *Perspectives on Psychological Science, 4*(2), 162-176. https://doi.org/10.1111/j.1745-6924.2009.01116.x

14. Baumeister, R. F., Bratslavsky, E., Muraven, M., & Tice, D. M. (1998). Ego depletion: Is the active self a limited resource? *Journal of Personality and Social Psychology, 74*(5), 1252–1265. https://doi.org/10.1037/0022-3514.74.5.1252

15. Dorris, D. C., Power, D. A., & Kenefick, E. (2012). Investigating the effects of ego depletion on physical exercise routines of athletes. *Psychology of Sport and Exercise, 13*(2), 118–125. https://doi.org/10.1016/j.psychsport.2011.10.004

16. Duffy, J., & Hall, S. M. (1988). Smoking abstinence, eating style, and food intake. *Journal of Consulting and Clinical Psychology, 56*(3), 417–421. https://doi.org/10.1037/0022-006X.56.3.417

17. Ciarocco, N.J., Echevarria, J., & Lewandowski Jr., G.W. (2012). Hungry for Love: The Influence of Self-Regulation on Infidelity. *The Journal of Social Psychology, 152*(1), 61-74. https://doi.org/10.1080/00224545.2011.555435

18. Gailliot, M.T., & Baumeister, R.F. (2007). The Physiology of Willpower: Linking Blood Glucose to Self-Control. *Personality and Social Psychology Review, 11*(4), 303-327. https://doi.org/10.1177/1088868307303030

19. Noakes, T.D., Peltonen, J.E., & Rusko, H.K. (2001). Evidence that a central governor regulates exercise performance during acute hypoxia and hyperoxia. *Journal of Experimental Biology, 204*(18), 3225-3234. https://doi.org/10.1242/jeb.204.18.3225

20. Baumeister, R.F. (2014). Self-regulation, ego depletion, and inhibition. *Neuropsychologia, 65*, 313-319. https://doi.org/10.1016/j.neuropsychologia.2014.08.012

21. Clarkson, J. J., Otto, A. S., Hassey, R., & Hirt, E. R. (2016). Perceived mental fatigue and self-control. In E. R. Hirt, J. J. Clarkson, & L. Jia (Eds.), *Self-regulation and ego control* (pp. 185–202). Elsevier Academic Press. https://doi.org/10.1016/B978-0-12-801850-7.00010-X

22. Job, V., Dweck, C.S., & Walton, G.M. (2010). Ego Depletion – Is It All In Your Head?: Implicit Theories About Willpower Affect Self-Regulation. *Psychological Science, 21*(11), 1686-1693. https://doi.org/10.1177/0956797610384745

23. Job, V., Walton, G. M., Bernecker, K., & Dweck, C. S. (2013). Beliefs about willpower determine the impact of glucose on self-control. *Proceedings of the National Academy of Sciences of the United States of America, 110*(37), 14837–14842. https://doi.org/10.1073/pnas.1313475110

24. Clarkson, J. J., Hirt, E. R., Jia, L., & Alexander, M. B. (2010). When perception is more than reality: The effects of perceived versus actual resource depletion on self-regulatory behavior. *Journal of Personality and Social Psychology, 98*(1), 29–46. https://doi.org/10.1037/a0017539

25. Kurzban, R. (2010). Does the Brain Consume Additional Glucose during Self-Control Tasks? *Evolutionary Psychology, 8*(2), 244-259. https://doi.org/10.1177/147470491000800208

26. Lange, F., Seer, C., Rapior, M., Rose, J., & Eggert, F. (2014). Turn It All You Want: Still No Effect of Sugar Consumption on Ego Depletion. *Journal of European Psychology Students, 5*(3), 1–8. http://doi.org/10.5334/jeps.cc

27. Job, V., Walton, G. M., Bernecker, K., & Dweck, C. S. (2015). Implicit theories about willpower predict self-regulation and grades in everyday life. *Journal of Personality and Social Psychology, 108*(4), 637–647. https://doi.org/10.1037/pspp0000014

28. Henselmans, M. (2021). The Science of Self-Control: 53 Tips to stick to your diet, be more productive, and excel in life (p. 41). *Independently published.*

29. Miniter, F. (2012). Ultimate Man's Survival Guide: Rediscovering the Lost Art of Manhood (p. 15). *Regnery Publishing.*

30. Hirt, E.R., Clarkson, J.J., & Jia, L. (2016). Self-Regulation and Ego Control. *Academic Press.*

31. Heckman, B. W., Ditre, J. W., & Brandon, T. H. (2012). The restorative effects of smoking upon self-control resources: A negative reinforcement pathway. *Journal of Abnormal Psychology, 121*(1), 244–249. https://doi.org/10.1037/a0023032

32. Yusainy, C., & Lawrence, C. (2015). Brief mindfulness induction could reduce aggression after depletion. *Consciousness and Cognition, 33*, 125-134. https://doi.org/10.1016/j.concog.2014.12.008

33. Muraven, M., Slessavera, E. (2003). Mechanisms of Self-Control Failure: Motivation and Limited Resources. *Personality and Social Psychology Bulletin, 29*(7), 894-906. https://doi.org/10.1177/0146167203029007008

34. Agrawal, N. & Wen Wan, E. (2009). Regulating Risk or Risking Regulation? Construal Levels and Depletion Effects in the Processing of Health Messages? *Journal of Consumer Research, 36*(3), 448-462. https://doi.org/10.1086/597331

35. Boksem, M.A.S, Meijman, T.F., & Loris, M.M. (2006). Mental fatigue, motivation, and action monitoring. *Biological Psychology, 72*(7), 123-132. https://doi.org/10.1016/j.biopsycho.2005.08.007

36. Werle, C. O. C., Wansink, B., & Payne, C. R. (2015). Is it fun or exercise? The framing of physical activity biases subsequent snacking. *Marketing Letters: A Journal of Research in Marketing, 26*(4), 691–702. https://doi.org/10.1007/s11002-014-9301-6

37. Clarkson, J.J., Hirt, E.R., Chapman, D.A., & Jia, L. (2010). The Impact of Illusory Fatigue on Executive Control: Do Perceptions of Depletion Impair Working Memory Capacity? *Social Psychological and Personality Science, 2*(3), 231-238. https://doi.org/10.1177/1948550610386628

38. Heatherton, T.F., & Wagner, D.D. (2011). Cognitive neuroscience of self-regulation failure. *Trends in Cognitive Sciences, 15*(3), 132-139. https://doi.org/10.1016/j.tics.2010.12.005

39. Herman, C. P., & Polivy, J. (1975). Anxiety, restraint, and eating behavior. *Journal of Abnormal Psychology, 84*(6), 666–672. https://doi.org/10.1037/0021-843X.84.6.666

40. Schmeichel, B. J., & Inzlicht, M. (2013). Incidental and integral effects of emotions on self-control. In M. D. Robinson, E. Watkins, & E. Harmon-Jones (Eds.), *Handbook of cognition and emotion* (pp. 272–290). The Guilford Press.

41. Dreisbach, G., & Fischer, R. (2015). Conflicts as Aversive Signals for Control Adaptation. *Current Directions in Psychological Science, 24*(4), 255-260. https://doi.org/10.1177/0963721415569569

42. Trope, Y., & Pomerantz, E. M. (1998). Resolving conflicts among self-evaluative motives: Positive experiences as a resource for overcoming defensiveness. *Motivation and Emotion, 22*(1), 53–72. https://doi.org/10.1023/A:1023044625309

43. Fedorikhin, A., & Patrick, V. M. (2010). Positive mood and resistance to temptation: The interfering influence of elevated arousal. *Journal of Consumer Research, 37*(4), 698–711. https://doi.org/10.1086/655665

44. Inzlicht, M., Werner, K.M., Briskin, J.L., & Roberts, B.W. (2021). Integrating Models of Self-Regulation. Annual Review of Psychology, 72, 319-345. https://doi.org/10.1146/annurev-psych-061020-105721

45. Vosgerau, J., Scopelliti, I., & Eun Huh, Y. (2019). Exerting Self-Control ≠ Sacrificing Pleasure. *Journal of Consumer Psychology, 30*(1), 181-200. https://doi.org/10.1002/jcpy.1142

46. Magen, E., Kim, B., Dweck, C.S., & McClure, S.M. (2014). Behavioral and neural correlates of increased self-control in the absence of willpower. *Psychological and Cognitive Sciences, 111*(27). https://doi.org/10.1073/pnas.1408991111

47. Muraven, M., Baumeister, R.F., & Tice, D.M. (1999). Longitudinal Improvement of Self-Regulation Through Practice: Building Self-Control Strength Through Repeated Exercise. *The Journal of Social Psychology, 139*(4), 446-457. https://doi.org/10.1080/00224549909598404

48. Inzlicht, M., & Berkman, E. (2015). Six Questions for the Resource Model of Control (and Some Answers). *Social and Personality Psychology Compass, 9*(10), 511-524. https://doi.org/10.1111/spc3.12200

49. Milyavskaya, M., & Inzlicht, M. (2018). Attentional and motivational mechanisms of self-control. In D. de Ridder, M. Adriaanse, & K. Fujita (Eds.), *The Routledge international handbook of self-control in health and well-being* (pp. 11–23). Routledge/Taylor & Francis Group

50. Požgain, I., Požgain, Z., & Degmečić, D. (2014). Placebo And Nocebo Effect: A Mini-Review. *Psychiatria Danubina*, 26(2), 100–1

51. Miller, E. M., Walton, G. M., Dweck, C. S., Job, V., Trzesniewski, K. H., & McClure, S. M. (2012). Theories of willpower affect sustained learning. *PloS One, 7*(6), https://doi.org/10.1371/journal.pone.0038680

52. Bernecker, K., & Job, V. (2015). Beliefs about willpower moderate the effect of previous day demands on next day's expectations and effective goal striving. *Frontiers in Psychology, 6,* Article 1496. https://doi.org/10.3389/fpsyg.2015.01496

53. Tuk, M. A., Zhang, K., & Sweldens, S. (2015). The propagation of self-control: Self-control in one domain simultaneously improves self-control in other domains. *Journal of Experimental Psychology: General, 144*(3), 639–654. https://doi.org/10.1037/xge0000065

REFERENCES

54. Deci, E. L., & Ryan, R. M. (2008). Facilitating optimal motivation and psychological well-being across life's domains. *Canadian Psychology/Psychologie canadienne, 49*(1), 14–23. https://doi.org/10.1037/0708-5591.49.1.14

55. Gjestvang, C., Abrahamsen, F., Strensrud, T., & Haakstad, L.A.H. (2020). Motives and barriers to initiation and sustained exercise adherence in a fitness club setting – A one year follow-up study. *Scandinavian Journal of Medicine & Science in Sports, 30*(9), 1796-1805. https://doi.org/10.1111/sms.13736

56. Deci, E. L., & Ryan, R. M. (2000). The "what" and "why" of goal pursuits: Human needs and the self-determination of behavior. *Psychological Inquiry, 11*(4), 227–268. https://doi.org/10.1207/S15327965PLI1104_01

57. Englert, C., & Bertrams, A. (2015). Autonomy as a protective factor against the detrimental effects of ego depletion on tennis serve accuracy under pressure. *International Journal of Sport and Exercise Psychology, 13*(2), 121–131. https://doi.org/10.1080/1612197X.2014.932828

58. Williams, G. C., Grow, V. M., Freedman, Z. R., Ryan, R. M., & Deci, E. L. (1996). Motivational predictors of weight loss and weight-loss maintenance. *Journal of Personality and Social Psychology, 70*(1), 115–126. https://doi.org/10.1037/0022-3514.70.1.115

59. Milyavskaya, M., Inzlicht, M., Hope, N., & Koestner, R. (2015). Saying "no" to temptation: Want-to motivation improves self-regulation by reducing temptation rather than by increasing self-control. *Journal of Personality and Social Psychology, 109*(4), 677–693. https://doi.org/10.1037/pspp0000045

60. Woolley, K., & Fishbach, A. (2016). For the Fun of It: Harnessing Immediate Rewards to Increase Persistence in Long-Term Goals. *Journal of Consumer Research, 42*(6), 952-966. https://doi.org/10.1093/jcr/ucv098

61. Muraven M. (2008). Autonomous Self-Control is Less Depleting. *Journal of research in personality, 42*(3), 763–770. https://doi.org/10.1016/j.jrp.2007.08.002

62. Laran, J., & Janiszewski, C. (2011). Work or Fun? How Task Construal and Completion Influence Regulatory Behavior. *Journal of Consumer Research, 37*(6), 967-983. https://doi.org/10.1086/656576

63. Berkman, E.T., Hutcherson, C.A., Livingston, J.L., Kahn, L.E., Inzlicht, M. (2017). Self-Control as Value-Based Choice, *Current Directions in Psychological Science, 26*(5), 422-428. https://doi.org/10.1177/0963721417704394

64. Pink, D. (2018). *Drive: The Surprising Truth About What Motivates Us* (p. 146). Canongate Books.

65. Muraven, M., Slessavera, E. (2003). Mechanisms of Self-Control Failure: Motivation and Limited Resources. *Personality and Social Psychology Bulletin, 29*(7), 894-906. https://doi.org/10.1177/0146167203029007008

66. Muraven, M., Collins, R. L., Morsheimer, E. T., Shiffman, S., & Paty, J. A. (2005). The Morning After: Limit Violations and the Self-Regulation of Alcohol Consumption. *Psychology of Addictive Behaviors, 19*(3), 253–262. https://doi.org/10.1037/0893-164X.19.3.253

67. Neff, K. D., & Dahm, K. A. (2015). Self-compassion: What it is, what it does, and how it relates to mindfulness. In B. D. Ostafin, M. D. Robinson, & B. P. Meier (Eds.), *Handbook of mindfulness and self-regulation* (pp. 121–137). Springer Science + Business Media. https://doi.org/10.1007/978-1-4939-2263-5_10

68. Leary, M. R., Tate, E. B., Adams, C. E., Batts Allen, A., & Hancock, J. (2007). Self-compassion and reactions to unpleasant self-relevant events: The implications of treating oneself kindly. *Journal of Personality and Social Psychology, 92*(5), 887–904. https://doi.org/10.1037/0022-3514.92.5.887

69. Adams, C.E, & Leary, M.R. (2007). Promoting Self-Compassionate Attitudes Towards Eating Among Restrictive and Guilty Eaters. *Journal of Social and Clinical Psychology, 26*(10), 1120-1144. https://doi.org/10.1521/jscp.2007.26.10.1120

70. Fain, J. (2011). *The Self-Compassion Diet: A Step-by-Step Program to Lose Weight with Loving-Kindness* (p. 16). Sounds True Inc.

71. Leary, M. R., Tate, E. B., Adams, C. E., Batts Allen, A., & Hancock, J. (2007). Self-compassion and reactions to unpleasant self-relevant events: The implications of treating oneself kindly. *Journal of Personality and Social Psychology, 92*(5), 887–904. https://doi.org/10.1037/0022-3514.92.5.887

72. Meyers, A. W., Stunkard, A. J., & Coll, M. (1980). Food accessibility and food choice: A test of Schachter's externality hypothesis. *Archives of General Psychiatry, 37*(10), 1133–1135. https://doi.org/10.1001/archpsyc.1980.01780230051007

73. Schüz, B., Bower, J., & Ferguson, S. G. (2015). Stimulus control and affect in dietary behaviours. An intensive longitudinal study. *Appetite, 87,* 310–317. https://doi.org/10.1016/j.appet.2015.01.002

74. Lobel, A. (1979). *Frog and toad together.* Harper Collins.

75. Duckworth, A. L., Gendler, T. S., & Gross, J. J. (2016). Situational Strategies for Self-Control. *Perspectives on psychological science: a journal of the Association for Psychological Science, 11*(1), 35–55. https://doi.org/10.1177/1745691615623247

REFERENCES

76. Duckworth, A.L., Gendler, T.S., & Gross, J.J. (2014). Self-Control in School Age Children. *Educational Psychologist, 49*(3), 199-217. https://doi.org/10.1080/00461520.2014.926225

77. Milkman, K. L., Minson, J. A., & Volpp, K. G. (2014). Holding the Hunger Games Hostage at the Gym: An Evaluation of Temptation Bundling. *Management science, 60*(2), 283–299. https://doi.org/10.1287/mnsc.2013.1784

78. Galla, B. M., & Duckworth, A. L. (2015). More than resisting temptation: Beneficial habits mediate the relationship between self-control and positive life outcomes. *Journal of Personality and Social Psychology, 109*(3), 508–525. https://doi.org/10.1037/pspp0000026

79. Wood, W., & Rünger, D. (2016). Psychology of Habit. *Annual Review of Psychology, 67,* 289-314. https://doi.org/10.1146/annurev-psych-122414-033417

80. Lin, P-Y., Wood, W., & Monterosso, J. (2016). Healthy eating habits protect against temptations. *Appetite, 103,* 432-440. https://doi.org/10.1016/j.appet.2015.11.011

81. Carels, R. A., Burmeister, J. M., Koball, A. M., Oehlhof, M. W., Hinman, N., LeRoy, M., Bannon, E., Ashrafioun, L., Storfer-Isser, A., Darby, L. A., & Gumble, A. (2014). A randomized trial comparing two approaches to weight loss: differences in weight loss maintenance. *Journal of Health Psychology, 19*(2), 296–311. https://doi.org/10.1177/1359105312470156

82. Schneider, I.K., Gillebaart, M., & Mattes, A. (2019). Meta-analytic evidence for ambivalence resolution as a key process in effortless self-control. *Journal of Experimental Social Psychology, 85,* Article 103846. https://doi.org/10.1016/j.jesp.2019.103846

83. Milyavskaya, M., & Inzlicht, M. (2017). What's so great about self-control? Examining the importance of effortful self-control and temptation in predicting real-life depletion and goal attainment. *Social Psychological and Personality Science, 8*(6), 603–611. https://doi.org/10.1177/1948550616679237

84. Hofmann, W., Baumeister, R. F., Förster, G., & Vohs, K. D. (2012). Everyday temptations: An experience sampling study of desire, conflict, and self-control. *Journal of Personality and Social Psychology, 102*(6), 1318–1335. https://doi.org/10.1037/a0026545

85. Duckworth, A. L., Gendler, T. S., & Gross, J. J. (2016). Situational Strategies for Self-Control. *Perspectives on psychological science: a journal of the Association for Psychological Science, 11*(1), 35–55. https://doi.org/10.1177/1745691615623247

Printed in Great Britain
by Amazon

28188614R00189